Administrative J

G000090155

Administrative Justice

SOME NECESSARY REFORMS

☙❧

*(Report of the Committee of the JUSTICE–All Souls
Review of Administrative Law in the United Kingdom)*
Chairman: Patrick Neill, QC

OXFORD · CLARENDON PRESS
1988

Oxford University Press, Walton Street, Oxford OX2 6DP

Oxford New York Toronto
Delhi Bombay Calcutta Madras Karachi
Petaling Jaya Singapore Hong Kong Tokyo
Nairobi Dar es Salaam Cape Town
Melbourne Auckland

and associated companies in
Beirut Berlin Ibadan Nicosia

Oxford is a trade mark of Oxford University Press

Published in the United States
by Oxford University Press, New York

British Library Cataloguing in Publication Data
Justice
Administrative justice: some necessary
reforms.
1. Administrative law—Great Britain
I. Title II. All Souls College
344.102'6   KD4879
ISBN 0–19–825587–X
ISBN 0–19–825586–1 (Pbk)

Library of Congress Cataloguing in Publication Data
Data available

Typeset by Joshua Associates Limited, Oxford
Printed and bound
in Great Britain by Biddles Ltd
Guildford and Kings Lynn

Preface

This report is the product of a review of administrative law in the United Kingdom carried out over a number of years by a committee of persons with some practical knowledge of the subject; an account of its proceedings is given in Appendix 2. The range of experience at the disposal of the review was extended through the invaluable help provided by our Scottish Working Group and our Advisory Panel; the names of their members are given on pages vi and vii. I would like to place on record the Committee's gratitude to them all for their assistance.

The wisdom and perception of Sir Otto Kahn-Freund were lost to the Committee by his death soon after we began work. Regrettably also Lord Crowther-Hunt did not live to see the last revision of the report.

In a report of this extent it is hardly to be expected that the Committee would be unanimous on every one of its points, but its approach and its general conclusions enjoy the support of all its members.

It would have been impossible to accomplish, or even to embark on, this review without the generous support of the Leverhulme Trust Fund. Dr Ronald Tress, CBE, then Director of the Trust Fund, took a keen interest in our work. We also acknowledge with gratitude the financial help provided by the numerous benefactors listed on page viii.

An important contribution to the review was provided by those who gave oral evidence, by the respondents to the Discussion Paper issued by the Committee in May 1981, and by those who corresponded with the Committee on other occasions; their names are listed in Appendices 4 and 5.

The readiness of lawyers and administrators in Australia, Canada, Hong Kong, New Zealand, Singapore and the United States to give freely of their time for the discussion of administrative law furnished us with first-hand information on recent developments in those countries.

We gratefully acknowledge the assistance provided for the review by the following persons and organizations as well as by those mentioned in Appendix 3.

Australia

The Administrative Review Council: Mr F. L. Tucker, Chairman; Dr G. D. S. Taylor and Dr J. E. Griffiths, Directors of Research.

The Hon. Sir Nigel Bowen, KBE Chief Judge, Federal Court.

The Rt Hon. Sir Zelman Cowan, AK, GCMG, GCVO, QC.

The Hon. Mr Justice J. D. Davies, President, Administrative Appeals Tribunal.

Sir John Dillon, CMG, Ombudsman, State of Victoria.

The Hon. R. J. Ellicott, QC.

The Hon. Mr Justice M. D. Kirby, CMG, formerly Chairman, Australian Law Reform Commission.

The Hon. Sir Anthony Mason, KBE.

Professor J. E. Richardson, formerly Commonwealth Ombudsman.

Canada

Mr Mario Bouchard, Co-ordinator of the Administrative Law Project of the Law Reform Commission of Canada.

Hong Kong

The Hon. Sir Oswald Cheung, QC, Unofficial Member of the Executive and Legislative Councils.

Netherlands

Dr J. H. van Krefeld.

New Zealand

The Hon. Mr Justice R. I. Barker.

Professor K. J. Keith.

The Hon. Mr Justice Peter Mahon.

Professor D. L. Mathieson.

Professor J. F. Northey.

Mr E. W. Thomas, QC.

Singapore

The Hon. Tan Boon Teik, Attorney-General.

Professor Mrs Tan Boon Teik.

United Kingdom

Sir Cecil Clothier, KCB, QC, formerly Parliamentary Commissioner for Administration.

Commissioners for Complaints, Northern Ireland: Mr Stephen
McGonagle; Mr T. H. Kernohan.

The Commission for Local Administration in England: Dr D. C. M.
Yardley, Chairman; Mr F. P. Cook; Mr Michael Hyde.

The Commission for Local Administration in Wales: Mr D. E. A.
Jones; Mr Hywel F. Jones.

The Commissioner for Local Administration in Scotland: the late
Mr Eric Gillett; Mr Kenneth Brittan, Secretary; Dr Brian
Thomson.

The Commonwealth Secretariat, Legal Division: Mr Jeremy
Pope, Director; Dr A. Sarup.

The Council on Tribunals: Mr J. M. Hawksworth and Mr M. W.
Sayers, Secretaries.

Lord Goodman.

Mr Alexander Hermon.

The Hon. Lord Hunter, VRD.

Master D. R. Thompson, Master of the Crown Office.

Professor Sir William Wade, QC.

United States of America

The Administrative Conference of the United States: Mr Loren
Smith, Chairman; Mr Steven Babcock, Director; Mr Richard
Berg, Secretary and Counsel.

Mr James Sedivy.

Mr Ivan Lawrence, QC, MP rendered special assistance in the
procurement of official publications.

The Committee have at all times been indebted to the Institute of
Advanced Legal Studies and to its successive Directors, Professor
Aubrey Diamond and Sir Jack Jacob, QC for permitting us to hold
our meetings at the Institute's premises.

Essential secretarial services were provided by Mrs Glenys
Brown, Mrs Hazel Cranny, Mrs D. A. Fernandes, Miss Fiona
Harper, Mrs Lorna Symons and Mrs Anne Wall. Messrs Oswald
Hickson, Collier & Co. and Messrs Peter Carter Ruck & Co. kindly
allowed us to use their copying facilities.

In writing this report we have taken account of the main developments up to 31 July 1986 though in certain instances we have
referred expressly to subsequent events. Our recommendations are
given at the end of each chapter.

Patrick Neill

Contents

The Committee

Sir Patrick Neill, QC (Chairman)
Sir John Boynton, MC
Professor A. W. Bradley
The Lord Croham, GCB
The Lord Crowther-Hunt of Eccleshill
Professor Aubrey Diamond
Percy Everett, DSC
Professor S. E. Finer
Professor J. F. Garner
Professor Sir Otto Kahn-Freund
Professor The Lord McGregor of Durris
Sir Lou Sherman, OBE, JP
Paul Sieghart
David Widdicombe, QC (Vice-Chairman)
Professor D. G. T. Williams

R. C. H. Briggs (Secretary)
R. E. Wraith, CBE (assisted with the research)

Sir Otto Kahn-Freund served as a member of the Committee until his death on 16 August 1979, and Lord Crowther-Hunt until his death on 16 February 1987. Paul Sieghart joined the Committee in December 1979 and Sir John Boynton in March 1980. Sir Lou Sherman was prevented by pressure of other commitments from taking an active part in the work of the Committee, and resigned from it in November 1981.

The Scottish Working Group

Professor A. W. Bradley (Convenor)
Professor G. S. Cowie
The Hon. Lord Cullen
R. P. Fraser, CB
Ivor R. Guild, WS
Joseph Mellick, OBE (obiit 24 September 1983)
The Hon. Lord Prosser

The Advisory Panel

Dr J. M. Benn CB
  (formerly Parliamentary Commissioner for Administration and
  Commissioner for Complaints, Northern Ireland)
The Hon. Mr Justice F. G. Brennan
  (a Justice of the High Court of Australia)
The Rt Hon. Sir Robin Cooke
  (President of the Court of Appeal of New Zealand)
The Hon. Mr Justice J. D. Davies
  (lately President, Australian Administrative Appeals Tribunal)
The Lord Devlin
  (a former Lord of Appeal in Ordinary)
Professor David Donnison
  (formerly Chairman of the Supplementary Benefit Commission)
The Hon. Lord Dunpark
  (Senator of the College of Justice in Scotland and Lord of
  Sessions)
Sir John Foster, KBE, QC
  (chairman of JUSTICE, obiit 1 February 1982)
Sir Arnold France, GCB
  (formerly Chairman, Board of Inland Revenue and Permanent
  Secretary, Ministry of Health)
The Hon. Lord Mackenzie Stuart
  (President of the Court of Justice of the European Economic
  Community)
Sir Nicholas Morrison, KCB
  (formerly Chairman, Local Government Boundary Commission
  and Permanent Under-Secretary of State, Scottish Office) (obiit
  7 July 1981)
Sir William Murrie, KCB
  (formerly Permanent Under-Secretary of State for Scotland)

Sir Peter Parker, MVO
  (formerly Chairman, British Rail)
Sir Idwal Pugh, KCB
  (formerly Parliamentary Commissioner for Administration and
  Second Permanent Secretary, Department of the Environment)
Mme Nicole Questiaux
  (Maître des Requettes au Conseil d'Etat)
Baroness Serota
  (formerly Chairman, Commission for Local Administration in
  England and Wales)
The Lord Wilberforce, CMG, OBE
  (a former Lord of Appeal in Ordinary)
The Rt Hon. Sir Harry Woolf
  (a Lord Justice of Appeal)

The Financial Supporters of the Review

Allied-Lyons PLC
Anon
Anon
The Bank of England
BAT Industries PLC
J. Bibby & Sons Ltd.
BICC PLC
The BOC Group
Boots Charitable Trust
BPB Industries PLC
Brooke Bond Group PLC
The British Petroleum Company PLC
Burmah Oil Trading Ltd.
Butterworth Law Publishers Ltd.
Cable & Wireless PLC
Cayzer Irvine & Co. Ltd.
Chubb & Son's Lock & Safe Co. Ltd.
Consolidated Gold Fields PLC
Courtaulds PLC
Currys Group PLC
Czarnikow Holdings Ltd.
Davies & Newman Holdings PLC
The Distillers Company PLC
H. A. S. Djanogly Esq.
Drake & Scull Holdings PLC
Ellis & Everard, PLC
English China Clays PLC
The Esmée Fairbairn Charitable Trust
Esso Exploration & Production UK Ltd.

European Law Centre Ltd.
The Extel Group PLC
Flight Refuelling Ltd.
Freemans of London PLC
Gallaher Ltd.
The General Electric Company PLC
Gerrard & National PLC
The Goldsmiths' Company
Grand Metropolitan PLC
Guest Keen & Nettlefolds PLC
The Guinness Peat Group PLC
A. V. Hammond & Co.
The Hargreaves Group PLC
Harrisons & Crosfield PLC
The Hill Samuel Group PLC
Hoare Govett Ltd.
The House of Fraser PLC
IMI PLC
Imperial Chemical Industries PLC
The Imperial Group PLC
King & Shaxson PLC
The Lord Kissin of Camden
Kleinwort Benson Ltd.
Laporte Industries (Holdings) PLC
Lazard Brothers & Co. Limited
Charles Letts & Company Ltd.
The Leverhulme Trust Fund
The John Lewis Partnership PLC
Lex Service PLC
Linfood Holdings PLC
Lloyds Bank PLC
Y. J. Lovell (Holdings) PLC
Marks & Spencer PLC
Marley PLC
Mobil Services Company Ltd.
National Westminster Bank PLC
Norcros PLC
Phoenix Assurance PLC
The Pilgrim Trust
Pilkington Brothers PLC

Table of Statutes

Table of Statutory Instruments

Table of Cases

1

Introduction

1.1. In 1969 the Law Commission, with the support of the Scottish Law Commission, suggested that a Royal Commission should be established to undertake a comprehensive examination of administrative law. The Government rejected this proposal. Commentators were inclined to be critical of the Government's failure to act on this recommendation and of the official view which was put forward that the time was not ripe for such an undertaking. Instead, the attention of the Law Commissions was directed to procedural reform. The English Commission's work led in 1978 to the introduction of the new method of challenging administrative decision-making—the application for judicial review. This Committee was established in the same year (see further Appendix 2). In our Discussion Paper of April 1981 we said: 'The Review Committee has been set up because no government has been willing to undertake, or to authorise the Law Commission to undertake, a full-scale examination of the existing deficiencies in the administrative law of the United Kingdom.'

1.2. As quickly became apparent after we began work, the change in procedure to which we have referred has transformed the face of administrative law. There has been an enormous increase in the number of cases brought before the courts; judicial and professional attitudes have changed. It seems a far cry from the day when Professor (now Sir William) Wade could write (*Crossroads in Administrative Law—Current Legal Problems*, 1968, at pp. 84–5):

There is an extraordinary reluctance to recognise the subject [sc. administrative law] as a body of general principles, indeed to recognise it as a subject at all. The doctrines which have been carefully laid down in past decisions, and which in any other branch of the law would be regarded as the ABC of the subject, are liable at any moment to be thrown to the winds . . . The cases make up as conspicuous a body of law as it is possible to imagine, and one would suppose that the legal profession would make every effort to systematise it. Yet learned judges are able to say that the law has lost the power to control the executive [Devlin J. in 1956], that there is no such thing in this country as droit administratif [Salmon LJ—1964] and that we do not have a developed system of administrative law [Lord Reid—1963]. There can surely be no branch of the law of comparable importance—if any branch of the law is of comparable importance—where so much law has achieved so little recognition.

1.3. The subject is now recognized and the principles are in the process of becoming systematized. No longer do judges say that the law has lost the power to control the executive. That power is repeatedly exercised. It is difficult to say precisely when the tide turned. *Ridge* v. *Baldwin* in 1963 and *Anisminic* in 1968 can be seen as seminal decisions. But it is really with the introduction of the application for judicial review that the flow of cases began to grow to a torrent. By 1981 there were 533 applications for leave to apply for judicial review of which 376 were granted; in 1984 there were 931 applications of which 693 were granted; and in 1985 the number of applications had by the end of the first week in July exceeded the figure for the whole of 1984. Whereas in 1981 four judges were nominated to hear cases in the Crown Office List, there are now fourteen.

1.4. Naturally this volume of work has led to the development of new legal doctrines. To give but one example, a public authority is now generally required to act in accordance with the legitimate expectations which its previous statements or actions have aroused. So, if a minister promises not to deport illegal immigrants without giving each a hearing, he will be held to his promise; and the same will be true if an undertaking is given to consult with trade unions or other interested parties before reaching a decision.

1.5. Alongside the development of the law has come the widescale recognition of its potential and a willingness to experiment in new fields of activity. We now have interest groups, concerned with environmental, planning, and similar issues, taking their cases to court. The law reports record the enterprise of such bodies as the Child Poverty Action Group, People before Profit, Covent Garden Community Association, and Friends of Shipley Country Park. Public authorities have not stood aside from these developments. Nor have they appeared merely in the role of defendants. It is common now to find authority suing authority and resorting to the law when political arguments have failed. Thus, Bromley Council successfully thwarted the Greater London Council's first foray into a cheap fares policy in public transport. And we can find in Otto Kirchheimer's words a perceptive description applicable today to our modern administrative justice:

Throughout the modern era, whatever the dominant legal system, both governments and private groups have tried to enlist the support of the courts for upholding or shifting the balance of political power. With or without disguise, political issues are brought before the courts; they must be faced and weighed on the scales of law much though the judges may be inclined to evade them.[1]

1.6. Sometimes the judicial inclination to evade may be manifest. If we look back to the famous Stevenage New Town case where the minister's prior public statements were alleged to indicate that he had already determined that a new town would be built at Stevenage, we find the House of Lords rejecting out of hand any suggestion that the minister was so biased as to be incapable of considering fairly the case put forward by the objectors. 'No judicial, or quasi-judicial, duty was imposed on the [minister], and any reference to judicial duty, or bias, is irrelevant in the present case. The [minister's] duties under ... the Act ... are ... purely administrative ... The only question is whether he has complied with the statutory directions to appoint a person to hold the public inquiry, and to consider that person's report.'[2] These views would not be followed today. The rigid division between the categories 'administrative', 'judicial', and 'quasi-judicial' have been abandoned. A minister in the position of the respondent in the *Stevenage* case would be expected to act fairly, due allowance being made for his commitment to a particular policy. On proof of unfair conduct the court would intervene.

1.7. Requests for court intervention in political issues, or as regards matters of policy, are of everyday occurrence. In the course of a week in July 1986 the popular press carried reports of proceedings brought by the Alliance, against the BBC, seeking fair coverage of its views; by St Bartholomew's Hospital, against the University Grants Committee, resisting the closure of its medical school; and by a South-African-born athlete, against the sporting authority which

---

[1] *Political Justice: The Use of Legal Procedure for Political Ends*, 1961, p. 147.
[2] *Franklin* v. *Minister of Town and County Planning* [1948] AC 87, 102 per Lord Thankerton delivering the unanimous opinion of the House.

had imposed a last-minute ban on her participation in the Commonwealth Games.

1.8. It is only now, after the system of judicial review has been operating for close on a decade, that it seems sensible to take stock and to see what deficiencies persist in the way decisions are arrived at by ministers, departments, and public authorities, and in the procedural and substantive law available to the citizen seeking redress. The decade has also been an active one for tribunals, ombudsmen, and inquiries. It is now possible to identify a number of problems for which solutions must be found.

1.9. Looking back over the period of thirty years before our Committee was set up, it is clear that important initiatives by the legislature ameliorated the lot of the citizen in his struggle with officialdom. In 1947, the Crown Proceedings Act largely assimilated the position of the Crown to that of an ordinary defendant in civil proceedings. In 1954, the special statutory limitation period of one year, which protected public authorities against claims for breach of duty, was abolished. In 1958, the Tribunals and Inquiries Act was enacted (in accordance with recommendations in the Franks Report) establishing the Council on Tribunals and providing (*inter alia*) that tribunals should give reasoned decisions if asked to do so. In 1967, the office of ombudsman ('Parliamentary Commissioner for Administration') was created. In 1969 the Commission for Complaints in Northern Ireland was established. In 1974 (for Scotland 1975), Local Ombudsmen were created. Then in 1977 came the new Order 53 of the Rules of the Supreme Court (subsequently confirmed by the Supreme Court Act, 1981) providing the new weapon—the application for judicial review. Comparable procedural reforms were implemented in Scotland and Northern Ireland in 1985. Against this background the law was able to develop in the way we have described.

1.10. Our Terms of Reference are set out in Appendix 1. As may be seen, they are of extraordinary width; there is scarcely any aspect of administrative law that would not fall within their purview. For purely practical reasons we have decided in composing this report to concentrate on those areas where we have specific reforms to advocate. The subjects which we tackle are discussed in detail and at considerable length. Our task would have been impossible, and this report would have been inordinately bulky, if we had succumbed to the temptation to analyse every matter which attracted our interest—

for example, public interest immunity (formerly Crown privilege), government contracts, delegated legislation, and freedom of information. The reader who seeks enlightenment on these topics in this Report will be disappointed.

1.11. The underlying philosophy which we have adopted in preparing this Report can be judged by six themes which run through the following chapters and may be expressed in summary form as follows:

(*a*) the need to prevent grievances;
(*b*) the need for openness in decision-making;
(*c*) the ease of access to remedies;
(*d*) the adequacy of remedies;
(*e*) the need to keep the law up to date;
(*f*) the need for public information.

We expand on these below.

The need to prevent grievance

1.12. Although our Terms of Reference start by pointing us in the direction of 'effective redress of grievances suffered', we think that it is of paramount importance to minimize the number of occasions when there is any grievance to redress. To this end chapter 2 advocates the adoption of principles of good administration, backed by more specific departmental codes. Thus, in the planning field effective appeal procedures are essential if appellants and objectors are to feel that their case has been fairly considered.

The need for openness in decision-making

1.13. Decisions should be clear and intelligible. Administrators should be required on demand to give reasons for their decisions and to state the facts on which such decisions are based. A rule to this effect will serve the purpose already mentioned—the prevention of grievance. This is because the discipline of having to give a properly articulated decision reduces the chance of an irrational or prejudiced decision. Furthermore, a reasoned decision can be understood and, if thought to be wrong, challenged. We devote chapter 3 to this topic.

Remedies should be freely available

1.14. We are opposed to artificial barriers which make it difficult for a person to avail himself of a needed remedy. Acting on this principle we are against the requirement in Order 53 that the leave of the court must be obtained by the applicant for judicial review. We present the argument for this view in chapter 6. On the same principle we advocate the abolition of the rule which requires that the fiat of the Attorney General must be obtained before an action to declare or enforce a public right can be brought (chapter 8). In the same way we think that it is wrong to require a complainant to route his complaint to the Parliamentary Commissioner for Adminstration ('the PCA') through his MP and his complaint against the local authority through a councillor (chapter 5). In each case he should be able to complain direct.

Adequacy of remedies

1.15. It is not much to the point to have a streamlined procedure for getting to court if the remedies which the judge can award are inadequate. In this regard the outstanding gap in the available remedies is the fact that damages cannot be awarded for loss caused by a public authority through wrongful conduct not amounting to a recognized tort (chapter 11). In the ombudsman field, it is essential that the remedies recommended by the Local Ombudsmen should be complied with (chapter 5).

The need to keep the law up to date

1.16. There is a danger that rigidity and ossification will take over. As administrative law is now such an important part of the law, we think that a careful watch needs to be kept over all the institutions to ensure that they fulfil their tasks promptly and efficiently. Hence in chapter 4 we advocate the creation of an Administrative Review Commission.

The need for public information and access

1.17. More should be done to inform the public of avenues of redress. The grounds on which judicial review can be sought should be codified in a statute (though in a form which leaves room for the growth of the law to continue). The decisions of the ombudsmen should be digested and published in book form. The operation of the legal aid scheme should be extended to cover appearances before more tribunals.

2

The Formulation of Principles of Good Administration

SUMMARY OF ARGUMENT. Good administration is more to be desired than remedies for bad administration. A clear and authoritative statement of the principles that ought to be followed by administrators should be drawn up. The United Kingdom has already participated in the preparation of two such complementary sets of principles through the Council of Europe and the work of its Committee of Ministers, but no action on them has been taken domestically. In 1971 a JUSTICE Committee produced a draft legislative Statement of the Principles of Good Administration. There is some relevant American experience, contained in the Recommendations of the Administrative Conference of the United States. The ombudsmen have exposed in their reports the most common cases in which administrators err. There is thus plenty of source material on which to draw in formulating an up-to-date set of principles. Some countries (such as Australia and Barbados) have enacted statements of the grounds on which administrative decisions can be challenged in the courts. Such statements are to some extent the obverse of principles of good administration. The broad general principles which we advocate should, wherever practical and convenient, be backed up by more specific codes for the conduct of business. These should be prepared within departments. Care must be taken to avoid rigidity. Sensitivity and flexibility are essential to good administration. The principles which we have in mind could best be written by the ombudsmen. They should not be enacted by legislation. We anticipate that the courts could take note of them in appropriate cases.

Good Administration

2.1. The committee's Terms of Reference direct attention to methods for securing effective redress of grievances. One of the specific topics, however, which is listed for consideration is 'whether the administrative agencies should be required to observe a code of administrative practice, and if so whether any, and what, remedy or redress should be provided for a breach of such code'.

2.2. As prevention is better than cure, so good administration is better than remedies for bad administration. The practical question which has first to be addressed is whether a code (or codes) of good administrative practice could play a useful role in helping to reduce the number of occasions upon which grievances arise. This involves a prior question, which is whether it is feasible to formulate satisfactory principles of good administration. In fact, significant attempts have already been made to achieve such formulations, so we propose to begin by considering them. In addition, there is now in the reports of the ombudsmen an invaluable source of information as to the commonest examples of maladministration in central and local government. We will also refer to what is, to some extent, the obverse of any attempted formulation of principles of good administration, namely, a statement of the grounds on which a court will set aside an administrative decision. Two legislatures have enacted such statements. Naturally, these statements do not cover the whole range of deficient performance which for one reason or another deserves to be classified as bad administration, but they go part of the way by setting out the main heads under which the law will treat the absence of due administrative process as so marked as to lead to the striking down of an offending decision.

Committee of Ministers of the Council of Europe—a Resolution and a Recommendation

2.3. Through the Council of Europe the United Kingdom has participated in a process which has led to two complementary formulations of minimum standards of good administrative practice. One of the principal tasks given to the Council of Europe by its Statute is the protection of the individual's fundamental rights and freedoms. This remit includes protecting the citizen with regard to the procedural aspects of administrative decision-making which affect him. The Committee of Ministers has taken a particular interest in this topic since 1970. The first step was a comparative law project which involved the study of the administrative law of the member states (including that of the United Kingdom) to find out what common principles existed for the protection of the individual against the administration. This study resulted in a report published in 1975 entitled *An Analytical Survey of the Rights of the Individual in the Administrative Procedure and his Remedies against Administrative Acts.*

Resolution (77) 31

2.4. With the benefit of this Survey the Committee of Ministers was able to take the next step, which was the adoption on 28th September 1977 of Resolution (77) 31 entitled *On the Protection of the Individual in relation to the Acts of Administrative Authorities*. This Resolution recommended that the governments of member states should be guided in their law and administrative practice by the five principles set out in the Annex to the Resolution. The text of the Annex is reproduced in Appendix 6a to this Report. The Annex was supported by an explanatory memorandum.

2.5. The five principles in the Annex as thus explained may be summarized as follows:

1. *Right to be heard*. A person concerned with an administrative act which is likely to affect directly and adversely his rights, liberties, or interests should have a right to be heard. He should be informed of this right and be given the opportunity to put forward facts and arguments and (where appropriate) evidence. All this should be taken into account by the administrative authority before deciding.

2. *Access to information*. A person concerned, in order effectively to exercise his right to be heard, should on request be given access, by appropriate means, to the relevant factors on which the administrative act is intended to be based and before the act is taken.

3. *Assistance and representation*. It should be possible for a person concerned to be assisted or represented in the administrative process.

4. *Statement of reasons*. Where an administrative act is of such a nature as adversely to affect the rights, liberties, or interests of the person concerned, it is essential (particularly in view of a possible appeal) that it should be reasoned. The reasons may be given at the time when the act is taken or, upon request, subsequently.

5. *Indication of remedies*. Where an administrative act in written form adversely affects the rights, liberties, or interests of the person concerned, it should indicate the normal remedies against it (including the applicable time-limits).

2.6. The use of the term 'the person concerned' in these principles is designed to make it clear that they apply both to natural and legal persons. The second introductory paragraph of the Annex recognizes that, in the implementation of the principles, account must be taken of the requirements of good and efficient administration, the interests of third parties, and major public interests. Particular circumstances may justify the modification or exclusion of one or more principles. Nevertheless, every endeavour should be made, in conformity with the fundamental aim of the Resolution, to achieve 'the highest possible degree of fairness'.

2.7. The Resolution deliberately abstained from indicating what sanction should be attached to a failure to comply with the principles. The legal systems of the member states differed in this respect and the matter was left to be dealt with by domestic rules.

Recommendation No. R(80)2

2.8. The Committee of Ministers decided to deal next with the principles which should control the exercise of discretionary power. On 11 March 1980, after a further comparative law study had been completed, the Committee adopted Recommendation No. R(80)2 entitled *Concerning the Exercise of Discretionary Powers by Administrative Authorities*. This takes the form of a recommendation to the governments of member states that they should be guided in their law and administrative practice by the principles annexed to the Recommendation. The principles are to be understood as complementing those already expressed in Resolution (77) 31. The text is reproduced in Appendix 6b to this Report. An explanatory memorandum approved by the European Committee on Legal Cooperation under the Statute of Europe accompanies the principles.

2.9. The Appendix to the Recommendation which contains the principles is divided into four parts. The first part deals with scope and definitions. The other parts, which consist of eleven principles, are divided into: Basic Principles (Principles 1 to 6), Procedure (Principles 7 and 8), and Control (Principles 9 to 11). The eleven principles, as further explained in the explanatory memorandum, may be summarized as follows (we have adopted the headings used in the explanatory memorandum).

1. *Purpose of the discretionary power*. An administrative authority must use a power exclusively for the purpose for which it is conferred. Legislation should make clear the purpose for which a power is to be used.

2. *Objectivity and impartiality*. Relevant factors must be taken into account in reaching a decision and irrelevant factors must be

disregarded. The term 'factor' includes the legal basis for a decision. The administrative authority should endeavour to acquaint itself with all material information.

3. *Equality before the law*. Like cases must be treated in like manner and discrimination must be avoided.

4. *Proportionality*. An appropriate balance must be maintained between the adverse effects which an administrative authority's decision may have on the rights, liberties, or interests of the person concerned and the purpose which the authority is seeking to pursue.

5. *Reasonable time*. Decisions must be taken by administrative authorities within a reasonable time. What constitutes a reasonable time varies with the circumstances, such as the complexity of the matter at stake, its urgency, and the number of persons involved. Speed is highly desirable where the grant of an authorization or licence is in issue and where the administrative authority, by taking some step, creates uncertainty as regards the scope of the rights, liberties, or interests of persons affected. Delay can cause considerable practical difficulties and may constitute a hidden form of arbitrariness.

6. *Application of guidelines*. General administrative guidelines (such as circulars, codes of practice, office memoranda, and other administrative measures of an internal nature) must be applied in a consistent manner, but, at the same time, account must be taken of the particular circumstances of each case.

7. *Publicity of guidelines*. General administrative guidelines which govern the exercise of a discretionary power must

(a) be made public, and
(b) be communicated to the person concerned at his request.

The request may be made before or after the decision is taken.

8. *Departure from a guideline*. Where an administrative authority departs from a general administrative guideline in such a manner as to affect adversely the rights, liberties, or interests of a person concerned, he should be given the reasons for the decision (either together with the decision or, upon request, subsequently).

9. *Nature of control*. By recourse to a court or other independent body it must be possible to control the legality of an act taken in the exercise of a discretionary power. This principle does not exclude the possibilities (a) that the act is subject to preliminary control by an administrative authority empowered to decide both on legality

and on the merits or (*b*) that the control by the court or other independent body extends to the merits as well as to legality. The commentary recognizes that the limits of the concepts 'legality' and 'merits' are not always 'precise and clear'.

10. *Abstention on the part of an administrative authority.* Where no time-limit is laid down by law for taking a decision in the exercise of a discretionary power, the authority's failure to decide within a reasonable time should be subject to control by a competent authority. (Obviously this principle is closely linked with Principle 5 above.)

11. *Powers of the control body to obtain information.* The court or other independent body, which controls the exercise of a discretionary power, must have such powers of obtaining information as are necessary for the exercise of its functions. In particular it must have access to the information on the basis of which the administrative authority took its decision. This principle does not exclude those systems where only the parties to a case and, notably, the administrative authority are allowed to produce the relevant elements, provided always that the control body has power to order certain elements to be produced.

2.10. As was the case with the earlier Resolution, the term 'person concerned' covers both natural and legal persons. It is again expressly recognized in Part I of Recommendation No. R(80)2 that, in implementing the recommended principles, account must be taken of the requirements of good and efficient administration, the interests of third parties, and major public interests. Those requirements or interests may justify the modification or exclusion of one or more principles either in particular cases or in specific areas of public administration. Every endeavour should, nevertheless, be made 'to observe the spirit' of the Recommendation.

The JUSTICE Report *Administration under Law*

2.11. Some years before the Committee of Ministers of the Council of Europe enunciated the principles which we have discussed above, a committee of JUSTICE, under the chairmanship of the late Keith Goodfellow QC, had been considering the impact of the administrative process on the lives and affairs of citizens. That committee, in its proposals for reform, attached great importance to the encouragement of good administration. In the committee's report *Administration under Law*, published in 1971, it was recommended that Parliament should enact a Statement of the Principles of Good Administration which would serve as 'a framework for all government departments, local authorities, statutory undertakers and nationalised industries' (Report, p. 36, Recommendation (1)). A draft of such a statement was appended to the report and is reproduced as Appendix 7 to this Report. Attention to the JUSTICE proposals was drawn again in a letter published in *The Times* on 29 March 1976 from the late Sir John Foster QC, the Chairman of JUSTICE.

2.12. We can briefly summarize the ten principles which are contained in the JUSTICE draft. For ease of reference we have supplied headings which do not appear in the original.

1. *Prior notification: right to be heard.* Before deciding, the authority must take all reasonable steps to give notice of its intentions to all persons who will be particularly and materially affected. Such persons must be given a reasonable opportunity to make representations.

2. *No decision to be retrospective.* No decision should have retrospective effect unless its object is to relieve particular hardship resulting from an earlier decision.

3. *Ascertaining the material facts.* The authority, before deciding, must take all reasonable steps to ascertain the material facts.

4. *Duty of authority to supply material information.* Subject to Principle 8 below, an authority should promptly comply with a reasonable request for information relating to the discharge of its duties or the exercise of its powers.

5. *Duty to decide within two months in the case of a statutory duty.* Upon receiving a written request to make a decision in pursuance of a statutory duty to decide, where no time-limit is prescribed, the authority must make a decision within two months. This time may be extended by agreement or where exceptional circumstances make it impracticable to reach a decision within that period. Particulars of such circumstances must be notified. The decision must in such cases be made as soon as possible.

6. *Duty to decide within a reasonable time in the case of a statutory power or discretion.* Upon receiving a written request to make a decision in pursuance of a statutory power or discretion, the authority must make a decision within a reasonable time.

7. *Statement of reasons.* Subject to Principle 8 below, an

authority should, upon request, give a written statement of the reasons justifying its decision.

8. *Exceptions to the duties to supply material information and to give reasons.* Compliance with Principles 4 and 7 above may be excused on the grounds of (*a*) prejudice to national security, (*b*) two months' delay in making the relevant request, or (*c*) in the case of a request for reasons, if the request is made by a person not particularly and materially affected by the decision and the giving of a statement of reasons would be contrary to the interests of any person so affected.

9. *Notification of decision.* The authority must take steps to ensure that its decisions are made known to persons likely to be affected.

10. *Compliance with statutory counterpart of matters referred to in these principles.* Compliance with an express statutory provision in respect of a matter referred to in these principles should *pro tanto* be deemed to be compliance therewith.

2.13. The JUSTICE committee further proposed that in respect of any decision taken in breach of the Principles of Good Administration, a right of action in the High Court should accrue in favour of a person particularly and materially affected by it, in the absence of a right of appeal to a specialist tribunal or an inferior court (Report, p. 28, paragraph 63).

2.14. The JUSTICE principles are similar in many respects to the principles adopted by the Committee of Ministers of the Council of Europe. In some aspects the JUSTICE principles go wider than anything adopted by the Committee of Ministers. For example, JUSTICE Principles 4, 7, and 8(c) envisage that information should be supplied and reasons should be given both to persons particularly and materially affected and to persons not so affected. Indeed the JUSTICE Report expressly advocates the sort of access to information that we would today tend to provide for by Freedom of Information legislation (see the JUSTICE Report at pp. 21–2, paragraphs 45 and 46).

2.15. On the other hand, the Committee of Ministers' principles include additional points which are not formulated as principles in the JUSTICE list. See Resolution (77) 31, Principle 3 (paragraph 2.5 above) and Recommendation No. R(80)2, Principles 1, 2 (in part), 3, 4, 6, and 7 (paragraph 2.9 above). Principle 8 in the Recommendation is only a specific example of the more general obligation to give reasons. What requires justification in that particular case is the departure from the guideline. Principles 9 and 11 in the Recommendation refer rather to the opportunities to challenge legality in the courts than to the decision-making process within the administration. The same may be said of Principle 10 in the Recommendation to the extent that it goes beyond what is implicit in Principle 5. We would not envisage that any Principles of Good Administration that may hereafter be adopted in the United Kingdom to assist the process of administration and to limit the occasions upon which grievances might arise would include matters such as are contained in Principles 9, 10, and 11 in the Recommendation.

Recommendations of the Administrative Conference of the United States

2.16. In chapter 4 below the work of the Administrative Conference of the United States is considered in more detail. Here it will suffice to state that it is an advisory body which was established in 1968 under a statute enacted in 1964. Its purposes are to identify causes of inefficiency, delay, and unfairness in administrative proceedings affecting private rights and to recommend improvements to the President, the agencies, the Congress, and the courts. It has about ninety members, over half of whom come from the federal agencies and government, the remaining members being practising lawyers, academics, and other specialists in federal administrative procedure. One of the functions of the Administrative Conference is to make recommendations as to the practice and procedure to be followed by those who regulate and adjudicate in administrative matters. At federal level in the United States it is largely the federal administrative agencies which do this (for example, bodies like the Interstate Commerce Commission, the Federal Trade Commission, the Civil Aeronautics Board, and the Securities and Exchange Commission) though some government departments are also directly involved in administering schemes in fields such as social security and housing. Since its first plenary session in 1968 the Administrative Conference has produced a considerable number of recommendations relevant to agency practice and procedure. It publishes all of them in its series entitled *Recommendations and Reports.* In effect these are formulations of recommended good administrative practice. The recommendations generally differ from the statements of principle which we have so far been discussing in that they tend to be more specific and more detailed. Some are directed at particular agencies, but for the most part they are drawn in general terms. Simply by way of illustration we give the titles of six such recommendations of general application (with the official recommendation number in brackets after each title, the first number indicating the year of adoption):

> Representation of the poor in agency rule-making of direct consequence to them (No. 68–5).
> Articulation of agency policies (No. 71–3).
> Public participation in administrative hearings (No. 71–6).
> Procedures for resolution of environmental issues in licensing proceedings (No. 73–6).
> Time-limits on agency actions (No. 78–3).
> Improvements in the administration of the Government in the Sunshine Act (No. 84–3).

The text of recommendations deemed to be of continuing interest is to be found in the US Code of Federal Regulations, General Provisions, Title 1, Chapter III, Part 305. (A revised edition appears annually. The recommendations adopted at Plenary Sessions of the Conference—normally held in June and December every year—are published in the Federal Register.)

2.17. Two quotations must suffice to indicate the nature of these recommendations. The first is taken from Recommendation No. 71–3 on the articulation of agency policies:

Agency policies which affect the public should be articulated and made known to the public to the greatest extent feasible. To this end, each agency which takes actions affecting substantial public or private interests, whether after hearings or through informal action, should, as far as is feasible in the circumstances, state the standards that will guide its determination in various types of agency action, either through published decisions, general rules or policy statements other than rules.

(The Conference returned to this topic in 1983 in a statement published in 48 Federal Register 31181.) The passage which we have quoted may be compared with principle 7 in the Council of Ministers' Recommendation No. R(80)2 set out in paragraph 2.9 above.

2.18. Our second quotation is taken from the recommendation dealing with time-limits on agency actions (No. 78–3). The problem of excessive delay in reaching administrative decisions seems to be a

universal problem in the modern state. Certainly America is no
exception. Section 6(1) of the original Administrative Procedure
Act, 1946 (now codified as section 555(b) of Title 5 USC) required
each agency to conclude any matter presented to it 'with reasonable
dispatch', and section 10(e)(A) (now section 706(1) of Title 5)
authorized a reviewing court to 'compel agency action unlawfully
withheld or unreasonably delayed'. In practice, however, courts
were reluctant to exercise this power. The concept of unreasonable
delay proved an elusive one and agencies successfully pleaded
limited resources with which to cover many competing claims for
official attention. Congress attempted to find a solution by setting
statutory time-limits for particular decisions. This policy has only
been partially successful. Sometimes the time-limits could only be
complied with by failing to accord to an interested party a right to a
full and fair hearing; in other cases compliance would have con-
flicted with the demands of sound decision-making. To help to
resolve these difficulties the Administrative Conference adopted
Recommendation No. 78–3. The general thrust of this recommendation is to the effect that statutory time-limits are undesirable
and that dispatch is a matter best dealt with by internal action within
the agencies. Paragraph 3 of the Recommendation provides as
follows:

Whether or not required to do so by statute, each agency should adopt time
limits or guidelines for the prompt disposition of its adjudicatory and rule-
making actions, either by announcing schedules for particular agency
proceedings or by adopting regulations that contain general timetables for
dealing with categories of the agency's proceedings.

A comparison may here be made with Principle 5 (reasonable time)
in the Council of Ministers' Recommendation No. R(80)2 (see
paragraph 2.9 above) and with Principles 5 and 6 in the JUSTICE list
(paragraph 2.1 above).

Maladministration (whether or not causing injustice): the work of the ombudsmen

2.19. The ombudsman system has now been in operation in the
United Kingdom for a number of years. The function of the ombudsmen is to investigate allegations that injustice has been caused by
maladministration. All the ombudsmen publish annual reports
giving details of cases in which maladministration has (or, as the case

may be, has not) been found to have occurred (with or without resulting injustice). In addition they have between them written a very large number of separate reports on individual cases. This material constitutes a mine of information about unsatisfactory administration. Some of the PCA's case-law was analysed and distilled by Gregory and Hutchesson in their book *The Parliamentary Ombudsman* published in 1975 (especially chapters 8 and 9, pp. 279–360). Simply by way of example we cite the topic headings listed on p. 281. '1. Assorted mistakes, errors and oversights; 2. Failing to impart information or provide adequate explanations; 3. Giving inaccurate information and misleading advice; 4. Misapplication of departmental rules and instructions; 5. Peremptory or inconsiderate behaviour on the part of officials; 6. Unjustifiable delay.' Later the authors state (p. 309): 'But by far the commonest procedural defect identified by the Commissioner in connection with discretionary decisions has been a failure to take account of all the circumstances relating to the case in question.' Our reading of the reports of the ombudsmen published since 1975 leads us to think that this comment still has validity. In addition to straightforward cases of incompetence we would single out from these reports, as very common instances of maladministration, unjustifiable delay and misleading advice.

Statutory statements of the grounds on which a court will set aside an administrative decision

2.20. As we pointed out in paragraph 2.2 above, statements of the grounds on which administrative decisions may be struck down by the courts are to some extent the obverse of the Principles of Good Administration which we have been considering. In Australia the Federal Parliament has enacted a list of the grounds on which judicial review of an administrative decision may be sought (Administrative Decisions (Judicial Review) Act, 1977, as amended in 1978 and 1980, section 5—reproduced in Appendix 8 to this Report). A similar, but not identical, list is to be found in section 4 of the Administrative Justice Act, 1980 of Barbados (Appendix 9 to this Report). This Act was drafted by Professor Sir William Wade QC. The grounds of review contained in section 5(1) of the Australian Act may be expressed in the following abbreviated form:

(*a*) breach of the rules of natural justice;
(*b*) breach of mandatory procedural requirements;

(c) lack of jurisdiction;
(d) absence of statutory authority;
(e) improper exercise of statutory power;
(f) error of law;
(g) decision induced by fraud;
(h) absence of evidence;
(i) decision otherwise contrary to law.

Section 5(2) of the Act expands on (e) in the above list by stating that improper exercise of a power is to be construed as including a reference to the following (again stated here in abbreviated form):

(a) taking an irrelevant consideration into account;
(b) failing to take a relevant consideration into account;
(c) exercising a power for a non-statutory purpose;
(d) exercising a power in bad faith;
(e) acting at the direction of another person;
(f) applying a rule or policy without regard to the merits of a particular case;
(g) unreasonable exercise of power;
(h) producing an uncertain result;
(i) any other exercise of a power in a way that constitutes abuse of the power.

The problem of excessive delay in making a decision is met by a provision to the effect that judicial review can be sought on the ground of unreasonable delay where there is a duty to decide. This remedy is available both where no time-limit is prescribed for the making of the decision (section 7(1)) and where the prescribed time-limit has expired (section 7(2)). The Act in addition confers on a person who is entitled to apply for judicial review the right to obtain a statement of the reasons for the challenged decision (section 13(1)). (The text of these sections is in Appendix 8.)

2.21. It is obvious from even a cursory reading of the grounds of attack set out in paragraph 2.20 above that very many of them could be established only by proving a breach of one of the principles of good administrative practice adopted by the Committee of Ministers (and set out in paragraphs 2.5 and 2.9 above).

The views of those who commented on our Discussion Paper

2.22. Several correspondents urged the need for the publication of principles of good administration. The argument generally deployed was that such principles would be useful to administrators and would help to reduce the number of cases in which grievances arose. Two correspondents referred specifically to the principles agreed by the Commitee of Ministers of the Council of Europe and noted that the United Kingdom appeared to have taken no action to implement the recommendations.

2.23. In particular the Law Society told us that it had taken up with the Lord Chancellor's Department early in 1979 the implications of the adoption of Resolution (77) 31. It had suggested that it was impossible to take the view that UK law in its existing state fully complied with the principles of the Resolution and it inquired as to what action was to be taken. The reply of the Department was not encouraging. The government's view at the time was that the Resolution was of limited value and that it was not worth wasting time and money on elaborating it. Recently, it seems that there has been a change of attitude, for the Council on Tribunals reported in their Annual Report for 1984–5 (at paragraph 2.11) that they had been asked by the Lord Chancellor's Department 'to contribute to monitoring how far the principles of Resolution (77) 31 of the Council of Europe have been observed'. The Council reported that they were able to give examples from the tribunal field. No indication as to the nature of these examples is given in their report.

2.24. An interesting difference of approach emerged from the replies made to our Discussion Paper respectively by the Parliamentary Ombudsman and by the Local Ombudsmen for England. The Local Ombudsmen supported the introduction, on a voluntary (non-statutory) basis, of a code of principles of good administration. The Parliamentary Ombudsman, then Sir Cecil Clothier QC, was opposed to a code, fearing that if the principles were anything more than pious generalizations, they could be a cause of undesirable bureaucratic rigidity. Codes could become the enemy of that sensitivity and flexibility which were essential to good administration. While we understand this anxiety, we think that the dangers can be averted by drawing up the principles in such a way as to make it clear that every case has to be dealt with on its merits and by stressing that circumstances may necessitate deviations from the normal rules.

Our Conclusions

2.25. We think that it would be highly desirable to build up the work of the Committee of Ministers of the Council of Europe, which we have described earlier in this chapter, and to endeavour to produce an updated and comprehensive set of Principles of Good Administration to which the public would have access and which could be communicated to all administrators. We bear in mind that the Committee of Ministers put forward its Resolution and Recommendation as guides to the member states in their law *and administrative practice* (emphasis supplied). Accordingly, subject to two exceptions explained in paragraph 2.26 below, we do not think it would be appropriate to set out the principles in the form of legislation, though no doubt the courts would take note of the principles. A failure (without good cause) to comply with a principle might in some cases be a ground for judicial review. In our view, the person who, if he could be persuaded to undertake the task, is best equipped to formulate and publish such principles and the person whose efforts in this field would have the greatest authority is the holder of the office of Parliamentary Ombudsman. He would, no doubt, work in consultation with and be assisted by the Local Ombudsmen and the Northern Ireland PCA and Commissioner for Complaints. If the Parliamentary Ombudsman declines the task, the Local Ombudsmen and the Commissioner could perhaps be persuaded to do it on their own. In any event this exercise should be under the oversight of the Administrative Review Commission which we propose in chapter 4. The starting point for the reformulation is the work of the Committee of Ministers enshrined in the Resolution and Recommendation. This work needs to be supplemented by reference to the proposals of the JUSTICE Committee (paragraphs 2.11 and 2.12 above) and by reference to the practical experience of the ombudsmen themselves. To take but one example, in view of the frequency of complaints about misleading advice by officials, there is room for one or more principles dealing specifically with this topic. In formulating the principles the ombudsmen could also usefully have in mind the grounds on which an administrative decision can be challenged in law (see paragraphs 2.20 and 2.21 above).

2.26. We have said that in general the Principles of Good Administration should be on a non-statutory basis. There are, however, two topics referred to in the Council of Ministers' recommendations which, in our view, need the backing of legislation. These are the duty to give reasons (which forms the subject matter of chapter 3 below) and the provision of a remedy where there is unreasonable or excessive delay (as to which see chapter 11, paragraphs 11.34 and 11.83 below).

2.27. The principles would necessarily be expressed in general terms. Inevitably they would be open to the charge of generality and vagueness. So we also propose that, wherever practical and convenient, they should be backed up by sharper and more specific departmental rules. These should be drawn up within departments and should give directions as to how the work of the department or particular aspects of it should be handled and, in appropriate cases, should set out timetables. Copies of such departmental rules should be publicly available. Such departmental advice could also include guidance as to matters which have in the past been the subject of public complaint or ombudsman investigation. An example of such guidance is the circular issued by the Department of the Environment in Northern Ireland to its divisional planning officers drawing attention to deficiencies in the workings of the planning control process and indicating where improvement could be effected. (See the Annual Report for 1983 of the Northern Ireland PCA, Appendix II). Many efficient departments already have in-house rules and codes of practice. It is, however, very apparent from the reports of the Parliamentary Ombudsman and the Local Ombudsmen that by no means all departments do. In the preparation of these departmental rules special care must be taken to ensure that there is room for flexibility to accommodate special cases.

2.28. The advantage of inviting the ombudsmen to take a lead in the way we have advocated is that a formulation of principles drawn up by them could be revised and expanded in the light of experience without any of the delay attendant upon the enactment of amending legislation. One function of the Administrative Review Commission (the creation of which we recommend in chapter 4 below) would be to act as a reviewer and critic of the practical operation of the principles and departmental codes. It would be for that Commission to draw attention to gaps and to propose to the ombudsmen and to departments amendments which appeared to be necessary in the general principles and in the departmental codes. The Commission could, for example, urge a department to adopt rules and practices to ensure the prompt and efficient discharge of particular classes of business.

CHAPTER 2. RECOMMENDATIONS

1. An up-to-date set of Principles of Good Administration should be drawn up and published. Copies should be made available to all administrators (paragraph 2.25).
2. The principles should be drawn up using as a basis the Council of Europe's Committee of Ministers' Resolution (77) 31 and Recommendation No. R (80)2 (paragraphs 2.4–2.10 and 2.25).
3. This basis should be supplemented by reference to other sources including (a) the JUSTICE Report *Administration under Law* and (b) the ombudsmen's reports dealing with maladministration. Account should also be taken of the grounds on which the courts will strike down decisions (paragraphs 2.11–2.15, 2.19–2.21, and 2.25).
4. The principles should not have the force of law or be embodied in a statute, save in two respects (paragraphs 2.25 and 2.26).
5. The best person to draw them up (and amend them as required) would be the Parliamentary Commissioner for Administration. If he is unwilling to do this the Local Ombudsmen and the Northern Ireland PCA and Commissioner for Complaints might undertake the task (paragraphs 2.25 and 2.28).
6. Wherever practical and convenient, the principles should be supplemented by sharper and more specific departmental rules or codes of practice drawn up by departments directing how work is to be handled and, in appropriate cases, setting out timetables. Copies of these rules and codes of practice should be publicly available (paragraph 2.27).
7. One function of an Administrative Review Commission (see the Recommendations in chapter 4 below) would be to scrutinize and review the practical operation of the principles and the departmental codes of practice, to draw attention to gaps (including the absence of any relevant rules or prescribed practices), and to propose amendments (paragraph 2.28).
8. Rigidity should be avoided. The principles and any departmental rules or codes of practice should be drafted in such a way as to emphasize the importance of flexibility (paragraphs 2.24 and 2.27, last sentence).

3

The Duty to Give Reasons

SUMMARY OF ARGUMENT. Those who exercise administrative authority should be ready to give an account of what they do. When they make decisions which affect individuals they should justify and explain their actions. The attainment in practice of these desirable aims is impeded by the fact that there is no general rule of law that reasons must be given for administrative decisions. Statute has altered the position in relation to most tribunal decisions. The change also applies to most inquiries. Nevertheless the absence of a general duty to give reasons is a serious gap in the law. Reasons are needed:

(a) to improve the quality of decision-making;
(b) to satisfy the citizen's desire for just and fair treatment;
(c) to enable him to decide whether the decision is open to challenge.

We believe in the concept of the 'citizens's right to be fully informed' and we think that in the interests of more open government the time has come to follow the lead taken in other countries and to introduce into the law a general duty to give reasons for administrative decisions. While in theory this might be achieved by the development of the common law by the judges, so many opportunities have been missed and there is such a weight of judicial decisions denying the existence of the duty that we believe it is necessary for the legislature to intervene. A statutory formulation should follow the Australian example and enable the citizen to request a written statement which sets out the findings on material questions of fact, refers to the evidence or other material on which those findings are based, and gives the reasons for the decision. We recognize that the general duty would have to be subject to exceptions.

Introduction

3.1. In the last chapter we showed how one of the five principles of good administration recommended by the Committee of Ministers of the Council of Europe required a statement of reasons to be given for an administrative decision affecting rights, liberties, or interests (chapter 2, paragraph 2.5, Principle 4). While, in general, it is our view that the formulation of the principles of good administration which we advocate in chapter 2 should be put on a non-statutory basis (paragraph 2.25), we think that the duty to give reasons is of such fundamental importance that an exception must be made and that this principle ought to be imposed in the form of an enforceable legal duty. The enactment of such a duty is necessary because the common law has generally failed to deal adequately with the problem.

3.2. The discussion in this chapter is arranged in the following manner:

Part I. The position at common law. The absence of a general duty to give reasons. Judicial attempts to grapple with the problem created by silence.

Part II. Statutory intervention in relation to tribunal decisions and decisions given after Ministerial inquiries. The Tribunals and Inquiries Acts 1958 and 1971.

Part III. Reasons in other legal systems.

USA
Canada
Australia
Israel
France
European Community law.

Part IV. Our conclusions.

PART I

THE POSITION AT COMMON LAW

THE ABSENCE OF A GENERAL DUTY TO GIVE REASONS

Possible options for a reviewing court

3.3. When a reviewing court is confronted by a decision of an administrative authority for which no reasons are given the court could in theory adopt one of the following courses of action:

(*a*) it might order the decision-maker to state his reasons;

(*b*) it might try to infer the reasons (if there is any documentary or other material available that permits this exercise to be carried out);

(c) it might presume that a decision for which no reasons have been given is arbitrary or otherwise unsupportable; or

(d) it might simply admit defeat and confess its inability to review the unreasoned decision.

In general the courts of the United Kingdom have adopted route (d). The bold course of (a) has hardly ever been followed. In recent years examples of (b) and (c) have begun to appear. Other jurisdictions have encountered similar difficulties and it has been felt necessary for the legislature to intervene.

The Donoughmore Committee's view

3.4. As a matter of principle it seems scarcely possible to doubt that a person ought to know why a decision has gone against him. This is as true for administrative decisions as it is for judicial decisions. In 1932 the Donoughmore Committee on Ministers' Powers (Cmd. 4060) stated: 'Any party affected by a decision should be informed of the reasons on which the decision is based . . . in the form of a reasoned document . . . (which) should state the conclusions as to the facts and to any points of law which have emerged' (Report p. 100). The Committee regarded this as a canon of judicial conduct implicit in the rule of law, the observance of which was 'demanded by our national sense of justice' (p. 76). It also referred to the right to reasons as 'the third principle of natural justice' (p. 80).

The existing law

3.5. Yet, fifty years after the Donoughmore Committee Report, Professor Sir William Wade QC stated the law as follows: 'It has never been a principle of natural justice that reasons should be given for decisions. Since there is no such rule even in the courts of law themselves, it has not been thought suitable to create one for administrative bodies.' (*Administrative Law*, 5th edn. (1982), p. 486.) Similar statements of the law are given by de Smith (*Judicial Review of Administrative Action*, 4th edn. (1980), p. 148) and Craig (*Administrative Law* (1983), p. 278).

3.6. Lord Denning once suggested that the law draws a distinction between two categories of case. If a man seeks a privilege to which he has no particular claim, such as an appointment to a post, he can be refused the privilege without being given any reason. If, on the other hand, an existing property right is affected, or if a man is being deprived of his livelihood, or if indeed any right or interest or legitimate expectation is being taken or denied, as the case may be, then the man is entitled to be told the reasons and to be given the chance of being heard. For, said Lord Denning, 'the giving of reasons is one of the fundamentals of good administration' (*Breen* v. *Amalgamated Engineering Union* [1971] 2 QB 175, 191). It will be seen that, according to this way of putting the matter, the entitlement to reasons is directly linked to the right to be heard. In practice what commonly happens is that a right to be heard or to make written representations is accorded by the decision-maker, but the decision is thereafter announced without any indication of the reasons for it. At that point English law generally fails to insist upon the giving of reasons. Nor does the law of Scotland (for which see *Stair Memorial Encyclopaedia*, *The Laws of Scotland* (1987), vol. 1, pp. 129–133).

Cases illustrating the general rule

3.7. The Minister of Health was held entitled to reject a claim for superannuation benefit, exercising his powers under section 35 of the Local Government Superannuation Act 1937, without giving any reason to the applicant (*Wilkinson* v. *Barking Corporation* [1948] 1 KB 721, 728 per Scott LJ). In *Davies* v. *Price* [1958] 1 WLR 434, 440 Parker LJ said of an Agricultural Land Tribunal (the decision of which can determine whether or not a tenant is turned out of his farm): 'The tribunal, though bound to give a written decision, are not bound to state their reasons, or indeed any reasons.' (Shortly afterwards the law was changed. Agricultural Land Tribunals were included among the statutory tribunals required by the Tribunals and Inquiries Act 1958 to give reasons for their decisions.)

3.8. An alien can be refused an extension of his permission to stay in the United Kingdom without being given a reason (*Schmidt* v. *Secretary of State for Home Affairs* [1969] 2 Ch. 149, 171, 173). The Gaming Board did not have to give reasons for refusing the proprietors of Crockfords a certificate under the Gaming Act 1968 (*R.* v. *Gaming Board for Great Britain*, ex parte *Benaim and Khaida* [1970] 2 QB 417). The certificate, if granted, would have signified the consent of the Gaming Board to the applicants seeking a gaming licence for the premises. The relief sought was certiorari to quash the unreasoned decision of the Gaming Board, mandamus to compel the Board to give the applicants sufficient information to enable them to answer the case against them, and mandamus to reconsider the application in the light of further representation. All forms of relief were refused.

3.9. *Cannock Chase District Council* v. *Kelly* [1978] 1 WLR 1 decided that a local authority, exercising its Housing Act 1957 powers to give a tenant notice to quit, did not have to state its reasons either when issuing the notice or in court proceedings in which it claimed possession. The position has since altered by legislation.

3.10. In *Payne* v. *Lord Harris* [1981] 1 WLR 754 it was held that a prisoner was not entitled to know the reasons why parole had been refused. Although this decision was in part influenced by the fact that elsewhere in the statutory scheme there was an express obligation to give reasons to a person recalled to prison from parole, the Court of Appeal went on to hold that the duty to act fairly (or observe natural justice) did not impose on the Parole Board any obligation to explain a refusal of parole. In another case affecting prisoners, Lord Diplock, giving the judgment of the House of Lords, pointed out that Boards of Visitors of prisons, who have power to decide on forfeiture of remission of sentence, are not subject to the statutory duty, now imposed on most tribunals, to give reasons for their decisions (*O'Reilly* v. *Mackman* [1983] 2 AC 237, 277).

3.11. In *R.* v. *Social Security Commissioner*, ex parte *Sewell* (*The Times*, 2 January and 2 February 1985) a Social Security Commissioner, although invited by Woolf J. (as he then was) to give limited reasons explaining why he had refused the applicant leave to appeal from a decision of a national insurance tribunal, declined to comply with the judge's request holding that he was bound by principle if not by authority to give no reasons. When the matter came before him the second time, the judge said the case demonstrated the possibility of injustice when leave was refused without reasons. The Commissioner, although not bound to give reasons, was entitled to do so. The judge quashed the refusal to grant leave. This approach was, however, overturned by the Court of Appeal in *R.* v. *Social Security Commissioner*, ex parte *Connolly* (*The Times* 3 January 1986) where it was pointed out that, as regards the particular decision rendered by the Commissioner (refusing leave to appeal), the applicable statutory regulations (The Tribunals and Inquiries (Social Security Commissioners) Order, 1980, SI 1980/1637, rule 2) specifically exempted Social Security Commissioners from the statutory duty (imposed by Section 12(1) of the Tribunals and Inquiries Act, 1971) to give reasons and it would be unconstitutional for the court to override that statutory dispensation. It was further stated that there was no basic requirement of natural justice that reasons should always be given when a discretion such as this was exercised. Reference was made to the views of the House of Lords in *Antaios Compania Naviera SA* v. *Salen Rederierna AB* [1985] AC 191, 205–6 where, in the field of commercial arbitration, their Lordships instructed High Court judges that they should not normally give reasons for the grant or refusal (under the Arbitration Act, 1979, section 1(3)(b)) of leave to appeal to the High Court from an arbitral award. In the opinion of the Court of Appeal a judge 'should not confront commissioners with the embarrassing choice of either complying with the court's wishes and waiving the exemption Parliament had given them, or declining the invitation and running the risk of apparent discourtesy to the court'. (In fact the relevant exemption was granted not by Parliament but by the Lord Chancellor and the Lord Advocate, who together issued the statutory instrument.)

3.12. In cases referred to above the decision-maker who was held to have no duty to give reasons was a minister, a local authority, or a statutory board or tribunal. Megarry V.-C. in *McInnes* v. *Onslow-Fane* [1978] 1 WLR 1520 adopted the same approach in holding that the British Boxing Board of Control, an unincorporated body established to regulate the sport of boxing, was not bound to give reasons when refusing an application for a manager's licence. 'I think it is clear', he said (p. 1551), 'that there is no general obligation to give reasons for a decision'.

The historical origin of the rule

3.13. It is at first sight difficult to understand why a judicial attitude developed which favoured secrecy by decision-makers and enabled public authorities and tribunals (in the absence of a mandatory statutory requirement) to conceal their reasoning and findings of fact from the parties affected and from the court. The problem is not made any easier when it is recalled that historically in England the Court of King's Bench had for centuries prided itself on the breadth of its supervisory power over inferior adjudicators. In Scotland a comparable plenary jurisdiction devolved upon the Court of Session as the successor to the Privy Council in Scotland (Kames, *Law Tracts*, 5th edn., p. 228). In England the prerogative writs of certiorari, mandamus, and prohibition were forged into powerful instruments enabling the Court of King's Bench to control excesses of jurisdiction and to compel compliance with the law. Thus in 1700 we find Holt CJ saying in *Groenwelt* v. *Burwell* 1 Salk. 144, 145: 'It is a consequence of every inferior jurisdiction of record, that their proceedings be removable into this Court, to inspect the Record to see whether they keep themselves within the limits of their jurisdiction.'

3.14. Yet it was also Holt CJ who said in a poor law (settlement) case (a passage made familiar to modern lawyers through the erudite judgment of Lord Goddard CJ in the Divisional Court, *R.* v. *Northumberland Compensation Appeal Tribunal*, ex parte *Shaw* [1951] 1 KB 711, 721): 'Where the justices of the peace give a special reason for their settlement, and the conclusion which they make in point of law will not warrant the premises, there we will rectify their judgment; but if they had given no reason at all, then we would not have travelled into the fact.' (*Parish of Riceslip* v. *Parish of Henden* (1698) 5 Mod. 416, 417.)

3.15. When an issue arose as to whether the justices of the peace or any inferior tribunal had acted within its jurisdiction, evidence was admissible to supplement the record and to show what had actually taken place, but this course was not permitted if the object was to try to establish that the legal reasoning of the decision was faulty or that the facts did not warrant the conclusion. In the latter case the court confined itself to an examination of the record transmitted and would not admit extrinsic evidence (*Baldwin & Francis Ltd.* v. *Patents Appeal Tribunal* [1959] AC 663). Nor would it require the justices or tribunal to furnish a statement of reasons.

3.16. It seems that the Court of King's Bench was content to leave the matter in the hands of the justices, in this sense: if the justices felt the case to be one of difficulty they could either consult the court or set out their reasons in the decision itself (thereby creating what was known as 'a speaking order') which would enable the matter to be resolved by the court. The parties could not, however, force the justices to take this course.

3.17. The foregoing explanation is put forward on the basis of what was said in two late nineteenth-century cases. In *R.* v. *Chantrell* (1875) LR 10 QB 589, Field J. (delivering the judgment of himself and Blackburn J.) said:

The question whether a case was one of difficulty or not, fit to be reserved for the Court, was to be determined by the sessions and not by the parties. But if they found it one of difficulty, and stated a case for the opinion of the Court, then it became necessary that a certiorari should issue to bring that case before the Court, that being the only mode by which the order would be brought into the Court having jurisdiction to quash or confirm it.

The history of the matter was again discussed three years later in the House of Lords in *Overseers of the Poor of Walsall* v. *LNWR* (1878) 4 App. Cas. 30, 44, where Lord Penzance said:

Of course until the Court of Quarter Sessions set out some facts upon the face of their orders, the Court of Queen's Bench could not interfere with them except upon matters of form; but whenever they did set out facts, and it is shewn that, I may say for centuries, the practice was to set them out whenever the justices at sessions had doubts, the Court of Queen's Bench dealt with the facts as they appeared upon the face of the order, pronounced the order sufficient or insufficient, and quashed it if the Court saw reason to do so.

3.18. The legislature took advantage of the settled rule that it was not possible to quash for error of law if the record was laconic, merely stated the result, gave no reasons and set out no evidence. In the field of criminal law Jervis's Acts (the first was passed in 1848) provided for a standard form of conviction which omitted any statement of the evidence. In Lord Sumner's memorable words (*R.* v. *Nat Bell Liquors Ltd.* [1922] 2 AC 128, 159) this statutory provision 'did not stint the jurisdiction of the Queen's Bench, or alter the actual law of certiorari. What it did was to disarm its exercise. The effect was not to make that which had been error, error no longer, but to remove nearly all opportunity for its detection. The face of the record 'spoke' no longer: it was the inscrutable face of a sphinx.'

3.19. In recent years in civil matters some relaxation of the rule may be detected in a tendency towards a benevolent extension of what constitutes 'the record'. Affidavits filed in certiorari proceedings (*R.* v. *Southampton Justices*, ex parte *Green* [1976] QB 11, 22), a subsequent letter from the tribunal explaining its decision (*R.* v. *Supplementary Benefits Commission*, ex parte *Singer* [1973] 1 WLR 713) and a transcript of an oral judgment (*R.* v. *Knightsbridge Crown Court*, ex parte *International Sporting Club Ltd.* [1982] QB 304) have all been treated as part of the record, thereby enabling the court to review a decision.

3.20. Nevertheless the fundamental deficiency in this system of legal control lies in the fact that the decision-maker can restrict what goes into the record, but it is the contents of the record which determine whether it is possible to ascertain (and hence to challenge) the reasons for the decision.

Dissatisfaction with the operation of the general rule

3.21. Notwithstanding the strength and generality of the proposition that there is no duty to give reasons for a decision, it is possible to point to cases in which courts have been seriously troubled by the absence of reasons and have criticized the silence of the decision-makers and done their best to achieve justice. The judicial criticisms of silence have taken various forms. Sometimes the language of a particular statute has enabled a court to say that the absence of reasons made it impossible to tell whether the decision-maker had acted within his jurisdiction. On other occasions silence has been said to render illusory the opportunity for appeal or for review. The courts have shown themselves disinclined to presume in favour of a silent decision-maker that facts existed which would support the decision. It has even been said (in cases where there was a statutory right of appeal) that the absence of reasons is, without more, an error of law which vitiates a decision. Finally, the court will sometimes go to considerable trouble to ferret out reasons which could have been (but were not) stated explicitly.

Reasons insisted upon in order to demonstrate that the decision was within jurisdiction and to check arbitrariness

3.22. An example of the jurisdictional approach is to be found in the judgment of Mellor J. in *R. v. Sykes* (1875) 1 QB 52. A statute provided that a liquor licence could only be refused by justices on one of four grounds specified in the statute. If the justices refused under one of the heads covered by the fourth ground they were bound to state in writing 'the grounds of their decision'. The justices refused a licence and declined to state on which ground they acted. The court granted a mandamus requiring the justices to hear and determine the case according to law. Mellor J. said (pp. 53–4):

The justices may not be obliged to state the reasons which have induced them to refuse the licence on one of the four grounds named in the section; but at all events, they ought to state on which of the grounds it was that they refused the licence, in order to justify their decision, and show that they were acting within their jurisdiction. They refused to state on which ground they refused the licence; and they still, by their silence, refuse to do so. Until they have declared the ground of their refusal they have not heard and determined the application according to the law . . .

3.23. Quain J., who concurred in the result, put the matter somewhat differently. He referred to the possibility of arbitrariness and the deprivation of the right to the written statement required by statute. He said (p. 54):

The justices, by refusing a licence *sub silentio*, and refusing to state on which of the grounds they acted, might practically evade the enactment altogether, and refuse licences arbitrarily and on other grounds than the four mentioned in the section. They cannot be said to have 'heard and determined' the application until they have stated on which ground their refusal was based; especially as, if their refusal proceeded on the fourth ground, the justices are bound to specify to the applicant in writing the grounds of their decision; and this right he would practically be deprived of if the justices were at liberty to refuse the licence without saying on which of the four grounds it was refused.

3.24. The *Sykes* decision was followed in subsequent cases. In *R.* v. *Thomas* [1892] 1 QB 426 a beerhouse licence had been refused to an applicant on one of the statutory grounds. Another applicant then sought a licence in respect of the same premises. The justices dismissed the application without giving any reason. The court held that the justices were obliged to state the ground of the decision and a mandamus was issued. It was further held that mandamus could not be resisted on the ground that there was a right of appeal from the justices to quarter sessions. As no reason had been given the applicant would not know against what to appeal.

3.25. In a subsequent House of Lords case (Ex parte *Gorman* [1894] AC 23, 28) Lord Herschell LC spoke somewhat sceptically about the proposition, derivable from the *Sykes* case, that the justices do not 'hear and determine' such a case until they state the ground of their decision. He evidently thought that if they heard the case and refused a licence they might well be regarded as having heard and determined it. But he did not criticize the earlier cases in so far as they decided that the proper course for the justices was to state the ground of their decision.

Failure to give reasons may render illusory a right of appeal

3.26. In *Minister of National Revenue* v. *Wright's Canadian Ropes Ltd.* [1947] AC 109 the Privy Council laid great stress on the fact that the statute there in question gave a right of appeal from the minister's decision. Under section 6(2) of the (Canadian) Income War Tax Act the minister was given power to 'disallow any expense which he in his discretion may determine to be in excess of what is reasonable or normal for the business carried on by the taxpayer'. The minister had, without giving any reason, disallowed certain commission payments made by the taxpayer in the course of conducting its business. The Privy Council pointed out that the legislature must have intended the statutory right of appeal to be an effective right. It had further to be assumed that the power of disallowance given to the minister could not be exercised in an arbitrary manner. Delivering the opinion of the Privy Council Lord Greene MR said (p. 123):

Their Lordships find nothing in the language of the Act or in the general law which would compel the Minister to state his reasons for taking action under section 6(2). But this does not necessarily mean that the Minister by keeping silence can defeat the taxpayer's appeal. To hold otherwise would mean that the Minister could in every case, or, at least, the great majority of cases, render the right of appeal given by the statute completely nugatory. The court is, in their Lordships' opinion, always entitled to examine the facts which are shown by evidence to have been before the Minister when he made his determination. If those facts are in the opinion of the court insufficient in law to support it, the determination cannot stand. In such a case the determination can only have been an arbitrary one.

Faced with silence the court may decline to infer the existence of facts or reasons which would justify the decision

3.27. On the facts proved in evidence in *Minister of National Revenue* v. *Wright's Canadian Ropes Ltd.* (above) there was no material which could have justified the disallowance by the minister. Counsel for the minister, therefore, invited the Privy Council to assume in the minister's favour that there may have been other facts before the minister (in particular in a report made by the Inspector of Taxes which was never disclosed in the legal proceedings) which entitled the minister to decide as he did. The Privy Council firmly refused to make a favourable assumption in favour of a minister who had not condescended to state the additional material facts or to prove them. The proper inference to be drawn was that the minister had nothing before him which influenced his decision except the documents which the court had. For, as Lord Greene pointed out (p. 125):

If he had in fact had such material it would, in their Lordships' opinion, have been impossible to suppose that he would not have informed the respondents of at least the substance of it when the matter was originally brought before him so as to give the respondents a fair opportunity of meeting the case against them. The contrary supposition would involve that the appellant had come to a decision adverse to the respondents on material of which, so far as he knew, the respondents were completely ignorant, and knowledge of which he deliberately withheld from them.

The *Padfield* case—whether a minister by keeping silent can render his decision unreviewable

3.28. *Padfield* v. *Minister of Agriculture, Fisheries and Food* [1968] AC 997 is an important decision of the House of Lords rejecting an argument on behalf of the Crown that an unfettered discretion had been conferred on the minister by the words 'if the Minister in any case so directs'. The House of Lords scrutinized the reasons which the minister had given for not taking the action contemplated in the relevant statute and held that all his reasons were bad ones. In the present context what is of interest is the attitude of the House of Lords to the suggestion that if the minister had kept silent the exercise of his discretion would have been unreviewable.

3.29. The House of Lords overturned the decision of the Court of Appeal. Lord Denning MR had dissented in that court and had dealt with the argument that the minister need give no reasons by saying ([1968] AC at pp. 1006-7): 'If the Minister is to deny the complainant a hearing—and a remedy—he should at least have good reasons for his refusal: and if asked, he should give them. If he does not do so, the court may infer that he has no good reason.'

3.30. In the House of Lords Lord Reid agreed with this approach. In his opinion it was not true to say that a decision could not be questioned if no reasons were given for it. If it was the minister's duty not to act so as to frustrate the policy and objects of the Act, and if it were to appear from all the circumstances of the case that that had been the effect of the minister's refusal, then the court would be entitled to act ([1968] AC at pp. 1032-3). Lord Pearce put the matter as follows (p. 1053):

I do not regard a Minister's failure or refusal to give any reasons as a sufficient exclusion of the court's surveillance. If all the *prima facie* reasons seem to point in favour of his taking a certain course to carry out the intentions of Parliament in respect of a power which it has given him in that regard, and he gives no reason whatever for taking a contrary course, the court may infer that he has no good reason and that he is not using the power given by Parliament to carry out its intentions.

There is also a passage in the speech of Lord Upjohn to the same effect (p. 1061).

Seeking out the minister's reasons

3.31. A New Zealand case, which followed the *Padfield* approach, affords a good example of a court striving to ascertain the reasons for a minister's decision by looking at antecedent documents, such as departmental advice tendered to the minister, in order to try to deduce the reasons which motivated his decision. In *Fiordland Venison Ltd.* v. *Minister of Agriculture and Fisheries* [1978] 2 NZLR 341 the minister refused the applicant a game-packing house licence without giving any reason. The applicable regulations were written in such a way that the minister had no discretion but was bound to issue a licence if satisfied of five specified matters. It was conceded before the court that the minister was satisfied as to four of them. The Court of Appeal of New Zealand carefully scrutinized the evidence to try to infer why the minister was not satisfied as to the fifth matter. He could have filed an affidavit explaining his decision but he did not do so. The Court of Appeal said that a report containing departmental advice was 'the most important clue' to his thought processes (p. 348). From that and other material the judges were able to infer that his reasons were bad and that he should have been satisfied of the fifth matter if he had directed himself correctly. A declaration was granted that the applicant was entitled to a licence. Significantly the court expressed its agreement with the views of the New Zealand Public and Administrative Law Reform Committee (12th Report, 1978, paragraph 51) that in the normal course those affected by administrative decisions are entitled to an explanation (p. 346).

The theory that the absence of reasons may constitute an error

3.32. The short-lived National Industrial Relations Court, when considering appeals from industrial tribunals, held that the tribunals were bound to explain how they reached their conclusions.

3.33. In *Norton Tool Co. Ltd.* v. *Tewson* [1972] ICR 501, 505 the President of the Court, Sir John Donaldson, said:

If an appellant is to succeed, he must satisfy this court that the tribunal has erred in principle. But it is a corollary of the discretion conferred upon the tribunals that it is their duty to set out their reasoning in sufficient detail to show the principles upon which they have proceeded. A similar obligation lies upon this court, when sitting as a court of first instance from which appeal lies to the Court of Appeal on questions of law alone. Were it otherwise, the parties would in effect be deprived of their right of appeal on questions of law. No great elaboration is required and the task should not constitute a burden. Indeed, the need to give reasons may well assist in the process of properly making the discretionary assessment of damages. In the present case the tribunal has not made entirely clear the principles upon which it has acted and to that extent has erred in law.

3.34. In another case, *Alexander Machinery (Dudley) Ltd.* v. *Crabtree* [1974] ICR 120, 122, Sir John Donaldson repeated his view that it was wrong for an industrial tribunal simply to state the total compensation to be awarded without showing how the figure was arrived at. He said: 'The basis of this proposition is that in the absence of reasons it is impossible to determine whether or not there has been an error of law. Failure to give reasons therefore amounts to a denial of justice and is itself an error of law.' (It should be noted, however, that the High Court of Australia has recently treated these two decisions by Sir John Donaldson as if they were cases to which a statutory duty to give reasons applied: *Public Service Board of New South Wales* v. *Osmond* (1986) 63 ALR 559, per Gibbs CJ.)

3.35. More recently the Court of Appeal was not prepared to endorse the general proposition contained in the last sentence of the quotation. The Court of Appeal took the view that in any particular case the parties were entitled to be told by the tribunal, either from what was expressly or inferentially stated in the decision, to what point it had addressed its mind and upon what basis of fact the conclusion had been reached. Sometimes the answer on both points might be obvious without any need for elaboration (*R.* v. *Immigration Appeal Tribunal, ex parte Khan* [1983] QB 790, 794). The court accepted that a good test to apply to the reasons given by a tribunal was this: is the tribunal providing both parties with the materials which will enable them to know that the tribunal has made no error of law in reaching its findings of fact?

3.36. For our part we think that the failure to give reasons can amount to a denial of justice. Silence may sometimes make it impossible to deduce the true reasons. All chance of review or appeal from the decision is blocked. We are, however, less convinced by the theory that the failure to give reasons itself amounts to an error of law.

PART II

STATUTORY INTERVENTION

THE TRIBUNALS AND INQUIRIES ACTS, 1958 AND 1971
The Franks Committee

3.37. The Franks Committee was appointed in 1955 to review the way in which tribunals performed their functions. The Committee was also asked to consider ministerial inquiries. In its influential report *Administrative Tribunals and Enquiries* (Cmnd. 218), published in July 1957, the Committee had this to say about the need for tribunals to give reasons for their decisions (p. 24, paragraph 98):

Almost all witnesses have advocated the giving of reasoned decisions by tribunals. We are convinced that if tribunal proceedings are to be fair to the citizen reasons should be given to the fullest practicable extent. A decision is apt to be better if the reasons for it have to be set out in writing because the reasons are then more likely to have been properly thought out. Further, a reasoned decision is essential in order that, where there is a right of appeal, the applicant can assess whether he has good grounds of appeal and know the case he will have to meet if he decides to appeal.

The report recognized that in the simpler cases the tribunal might not be able to do more than to say that it preferred the evidence of one side's witnesses, or that, in its expert opinion, the rent of certain premises should be £x. 'But generally fuller reasons for decisions can be given.' This analysis of the problem led the Committee to its Recommendation (22) in these terms: 'Decisions of tribunals should be reasoned and as full as possible.'

3.38. The Committee also recommended that tribunal decisions should be put into writing and should include (as well as the reasons) a statement of the findings of fact by the tribunal. 'The giving of oral decisions on the spot in appropriate cases is to be commended, but they should always be confirmed in writing' (Report, p. 24, paragraph 99, and Recommendation (23)).

3.39. The Committee adopted the same approach in relation to reports made by inspectors following a planning inquiry. Such reports, in addition to giving the inspectors' findings of fact and inferences based thereon, should contain 'the reasoning from those facts, including the application to the particular case of any considerations of policy, and should normally conclude with recommendations for the Minister's action' (Report, p. 71, paragraph 328, and Recommendation (80)). The Committee came down decisively in favour of publication of inspectors' reports and rejected the arguments for secrecy. Inspectors' reports should accompany the minister's letter of decision (Report, pp. 71-3, paragraphs 329-44, and Recommendation (81)).

3.40. The minister's letter of decision should set out in full his findings and inferences of fact and the reasons for the decision (Recommendation (84)). On reasons the Committee said (Report, pp. 75-6, paragraph 351):

It is not sufficient for a deciding Minister merely to assure the recipients of his letter that he has considered the evidence at the enquiry and the (confidential) report of the inspector. It is a fundamental requirement of fair play that the parties concerned in one of these procedures should know at the end of the day why the particular decision has been taken. Where no reasons are given the individual may be forgiven for concluding that he has been the victim of arbitrary decision. The giving of full reasons is also important to enable those concerned to satisfy themselves that the prescribed procedure has been followed and to decide whether they wish to challenge the Minister's decision in the courts or elsewhere. Moreover, as we have already said in relation to tribunal decisions, a decision is apt to be better if the reasons for it have to be set out in writing because the reasons are then more likely to have been properly thought out.

Tribunals and Inquiries Acts, 1958 and 1971

3.41. The year after the publication of the Franks Committee's Report, Parliament enacted the Tribunals and Inquiries Act, 1958 (since re-enacted in a consolidating Act of 1971). The tribunals listed in the First Schedule to the Act (in the updated list) now include nearly all significant tribunals. Section 12 of the Act imposes a duty on them to furnish a statement (written or oral) of the reasons for the decision. The duty only arises if a request for reasons is made on or before the giving or notification of the decision.

3.42. Reasons can be refused or curtailed on grounds of national security and the tribunal can refuse to give reasons to a person not primarily concerned with the decision if it is of the opinion that to furnish them would be contrary to the interests of any person primarily concerned (section 12(2) of the 1971 Act). (A cross-reference may be made here to Principle 8 in the JUSTICE Principles of Good Administration summmarized in paragraph 2.12 above.)

3.43. The statement of reasons is to be taken to form part of the decision and to be incorporated in the record (section (12(5)). The significance of this provision is that it opens up the possibility of applying for certiorari if an error of law appears in the statement of reasons, that is on the face of the record (compare paragraphs 3.15 and 3.19 above). Error of law includes, of course, not merely mistakes as to statute or common law, but such aspects of the decision-making process as ignoring relevant factors or taking into consideration irrelevant factors.

3.44. It may be noted that the statutory provision requiring the giving of reasons is less stringent than that recommended by the Franks Committee in three respects:

(a) the duty only arises if a request for reasons is made (though, in practice, procedural rules made separately for each tribunal by statutory instrument have since imposed an unqualified duty in most cases);

(b) reasons may be given orally and do not have to be confirmed in writing;

(c) there is no requirement for the reasons to be accompanied by a statement of the findings of fact of the tribunal.

3.45. The statutory obligation to give reasons is also imposed on a minister when notifying any decision taken by him after a statutory inquiry held by him or on his behalf (section (12(1)(b) of the 1971 Act). The like duty was made to apply in a case where the person concerned had the right to require the holding of a statutory inquiry. This covers the case where an individual waives the right to a formal inquiry.

3.46. In the planning field the statutory obligations to give reasons (imposed by the Tribunals and Inquiries Acts of 1958 and 1971 and by such statutory rules as the Town and Country Planning (Inquiries Procedure) Rules, 1974, SI 1974 No. 419, r.12(1)) have been amplified by administrative practice. Thus, the inspector's report is in comprehensive form and is always disclosed in addition to the decision letter. Where the written representation procedure is followed (that is, where there is no inquiry) reasons are given as a matter of good administrative practice. This is done whether or not a request for reasons is made.

3.47. Quite apart from the Tribunals and Inquiries Act provision, there are now many other statutory rules and regulations which impose on decision-makers a duty to give reasons. Examples can readily be given from detailed rules of procedure laid down for particular tribunals and in the field of town and country planning and housing legislation. We have already referred in the context of social security legislation a rare example of a tribunal being expressly relieved of an obligation to give reasons (see paragraph 3.11 above). The Council on Tribunal's observation on this seems apt:

We did not consider that steps to relieve [the pressure of workload on the Commissioners] should result in applicants being deprived of the reasons for decisions made against them; without that knowledge recourse to judicial review would be made more difficult. (*Annual Report*, 1985–6, paragraph 4.66.)

The Council also point to the value of decisions of the Social Security Commissioners as precedents. We share the Council's views on both points.

The standard of reasons required

3.48. Whatever the precise statutory language the courts appear generally to follow the lead taken by Megaw J. (as he then was), construing section 12(1) of the Tribunals and Inquiries Act, 1958 in *Re Poyser and Mills Arbitration* [1964] 2 QB 467, 478 and to require 'proper', 'adequate', and 'intelligible' reasons to be given. He said:

... Parliament having provided that reasons shall be given, in my view that must clearly be read as meaning that proper, adequate, reasons must be given; the reasons that are set out must be reasons which will not only be intelligible, but which deal with the substantial points that have been raised ... I do not say that any minor or trivial error, or failure to give reasons in relation to every particular point that has been raised at the hearing, would be sufficient ground for invoking the jurisdiction of this court. I think there must be something substantially wrong or inadequate in the reasons that are given in order to enable the jurisdiction of this court to be invoked.

3.49. In *Edwin H. Bradley &Sons Ltd.* v. *Secretary of State for the Environment* [1982] JPL 43 Glidewell J. (as he then was) added a rider to the words of Megaw J. when he said that reasons can be briefly stated. The House of Lords have recently adopted with approval the guidance given by Megaw J. and the gloss added by Glidewell J. (*Westminster City Council* v. *Great Portland Estates* [1985] AC 661, 673, per Lord Scarman).

3.50. Another relevant statement is that of Lord Denning (also considering section 12(1) of the 1958 Act) in *Iveagh* v. *Minister of Housing and Local Government* [1964] 1 QB 395, 410: 'The whole purpose of the enactment is to enable the parties and the courts to see what matters he [sc. the minister] has taken into consideration and what view he has reached on the points of fact and law which arise. If he does not deal with the points that arise, he fails in his duties: and the court can order him to make good the omission.'

3.51. Cases in which the court has criticized ambiguous or incoherent reasons include *Givaudan* v. *Minister of Housing* [1966] 3 All ER 696 and *French Kier Developments* v. *Secretary of State for the Environment* [1977] 1 All ER 296. In the *Givaudan* case Megaw J. quashed the minister's decision (rejecting an appeal from an inspector) because the reasons given in his letter were either unclear or wrong. Similarly, in *French Kier* the Secretary of State's decision was quashed by Willis J. The reasons (if any) given in the minister's letter were, said the judge, 'so vague, inadequate and unintelligible as to leave anyone reading the letter quite unable to understand why ... the inspector's recommendation was rejected' (p. 304g).

3.52. On the other hand cases can be cited in which the court appears to have given its approval to a perfunctory statement of reasons. Thus, in *Elliott* v. *London Borough of Southwark* [1976] 2 All ER 781 the local authority refused the plaintiffs' request to make a 'rehabilitation order' in respect of their houses under a statutory provision (Housing Act, 1974, section 114) which gave effect to a new policy of permitting restoration as an alternative to the demolition of old houses. The houses in question were currently subject to a compulsory purchase order which had been made (and confirmed after a public inquiry in which the plaintiffs had participated) in order to implement a clearance order covering a development area. If the plaintiffs had succeeded in their request for a rehabilitation order the compulsory purchase order would have ceased to have effect. The statute required the Council to give reasons for refusing the rehabilitation order. The Council's letter said simply that it had 'resolved to refuse the application for the reason that the properties should be demolished and the sites used for the erection of new housing accommodation'. It seems to us that there is force in the criticism that, in the circumstances, this language stated a conclusion without attempting to justify it. Such a terse statement gave no indication of what matters the Council had taken into account. The Court of Appeal met this attack by saying that there was 'no evidence' that the Council (which followed an 'elaborate committee procedure') had failed to consider all relevant factors or had taken into account irrelevant factors (pp. 789b, 790j, and 791c–d). The retort to this is that the object of reasons is to provide evidence of what matters have (and have not) been considered. As Russell LJ said during the argument in the *Iveagh* case ([1964] 1 QB at p. 405): 'But the purpose of requiring the Minister to give reasons for his decision under the Tribunals and Inquiries Act, 1958, is to enable anyone interested to see whether there is in law a fault in his process of reasoning, so that they may attack the decision.' The Council's letter signally failed to perform this function. The same might be said of the immigration officer's statement in *R*. v. *Secretary of State for the Home Department*, ex parte *Swati* [1986] 1 All ER 717.

Effect of failure to give any reasons or any adequate reasons

3.53. The authorities are in some disarray as to the effect of a failure to comply with a statutory duty to give reasons. There is general agreement that mandamus can be issued to compel the provision of proper reasons. It is also clear that if the reasons given disclose an error of law the decision can be quashed (*Lavender and Son Ltd.* v. *Minister of Housing and Local Government* [1970] 3 All ER 871). We have already cited the view of Sir John Donaldson (now Master of the Rolls) that a failure to give reasons is an error of law and we have noted the reluctance of the Court of Appeal to accept this statement in an unqualified form (paragraphs 3.33–3.35 above). Where a statutory requirement exists the judgment of Megaw J. in *Re Poyser and Mills Arbitration* (paragraph 3.48 above) is authority for saying that incomplete and insufficient reasons demonstrate an error of law. On the other hand, where a planning authority failed to carry out its statutory duty to give reasons for the grant of a conditional planning permission, that failure was held not to render the condition void; furthermore, an enforcement notice alleging non-compliance with the condition was valid (*Brayhead*

(*Ascot*) *Ltd.* v. *Berkshire County Council* [1964] 2 QB 303).

3.54. In *Re Allen and Matthews' Arbitration* [1971] 2 QB 518, which arose out of the award of an arbitrator under the Agricultural Holdings Act, 1948, it was necessary to invite the court to look at affidavit evidence in order to show that the arbitrator had failed to deal with one of the tenant's arguments. (The arbitrator had merely said that in the light of his knowledge and experience and having inspected the holding and comparable holdings he had determined the rent on the statutory basis.) Mocatta J. held that he was not permitted to consider the affidavits because there was a long-standing rule of law to the effect that an arbitrator's award could only be set aside for error of law appearing on the face of the award. Affidavits could not be used so as to create an error in an award which was good on its face. This case is thus clearly distinguishable from *Re Poyser and Mills Arbitration* above.

3.55. A leading authority is the decision of the Divisional Court (Lord Parker CJ, Cooke and Bridge JJ.) in *Mountview Court Properties* v. *Devlin* (1970) 21 P&CR 689. There, a rent assessment committee had failed to provide adequate reasons. It was not a case like *Re Poyser and Mills Arbitration* (above) where it was possible to infer from what was said that there had been an error of law. It was held that a failure to give reasons is not *per se* a ground for allowing an appeal (where a statutory right of appeal from a tribunal decision is accorded) and that it was up to the appellant to demonstrate that the decision of the rent assessment committee was vitiated by the fact that it had been reached by an erroneous process of legal reasoning (see especially per Bridge J. at pp. 695–6 of the report).

3.56. Woolf J. held in *Crake* v. *Supplementary Benefits Commission* [1982] 1 All ER 498 that he was bound by the *Mountview* decision, although he recognized that in the years since it was decided the approach of courts had changed and that they were now much more ready than they used to be to infer an error of law from inadequate reasons (p. 570j). The judge was confronted by reasons given by a Supplementary Benefits Appeal Tribunal which he regarded as inadequate and falling far short of the standard required by section 12(1) of the Tribunals and Inquiries Act, 1971, and indeed by the tribunal's own procedural rules. Nevertheless, by looking at material outside the reasons, in particular at the tribunal's notes of what had taken place at the hearing, the judge was able to conclude that the tribunal had reached the correct result.

3.57. In *United Kingdom Association of Professional Engineers* v. *ACAS* [1981] AC 424 a question arose as to section 12(4) of the Employment Protection Act, 1975 which required ACAS to make a written report with findings and the reasons for and against making a recommendation for recognition. The House of Lords held, reversing the Court of Appeal, that provided a report by ACAS showed that there had been a full examination of the issue referred and that its conclusion was reasonable in the context of the findings included in the report, ACAS had a wide discretion as to what findings to make and as to what reasons to give.

Commentary on the authorities dealing with a statutory duty to give reasons

3.58. It seems to us that a statutory obligation which is confined to a requirement to produce a statement of 'the reasons' for a decision does not go far enough. This restricted formula allows a tribunal or other decision-maker to produce a document which passes the scrutiny of the court but which fails to reveal what findings were made or how the material issues of fact and law were resolved. This conclusion seems justified on the basis of the *Elliott* case (paragraph 3.52 above) and *Re Allen and Matthews' Arbitration* (paragraph 3.54 above). A statutory obligation to set out 'findings' in addition to reasons, as in the *ACAS* case (paragraph 3.57), is a more stringent requirement. As we demonstrate in Part III below, some legislatures have required both reasons and findings in creating the statutory duty.

3.59. So long as the statutory requirement is restricted to 'reasons', we believe that tribunals and decision-makers ought to interpret the obligation broadly so as to further the intention of the legislature. This clearly is so that parties should know the real basis upon which the decision was given. The court should be ready to assist by ordering further and better reasons to be given. It is unsatisfactory if the court is asked to do this many months after the decision. What is needed is a two-stage procedure: (*a*) a person receiving a statement of reasons supplied pursuant to a statutory duty should be entitled to apply to the tribunal or decision-maker for supplementary reasons, either in general terms (if the first statement of reasons is alleged to be manifestly defective) or dealing with specific points (as where the decision-maker has given no indication of how a particular point has been resolved); (*b*) if dissatisfied with the response, the person aggrieved should be entitled to apply to the court for an order. Both procedures would be ineffective unless implemented rapidly. Short time-limits could, therefore, be imposed. As Woolf J. pointed out in *Crake* v. *Supplementary Benefits Commission* [1982] 1 All ER 498, 508d some tribunals are informal bodies which are difficult to reconvene (he was thinking in particular of Supplementary Benefits Appeal Tribunals) and which may, when reconvened, have little recollection of the particular case.

PART III

REASONS IN OTHER LEGAL SYSTEMS

The United States

Generally

3.60. In the USA the general policy has been to require the administrative agencies at both federal and state level to give reasons for their decisions and to articulate the findings upon which such decisions are based.

State statutes

3.61. State statutes commonly require that administrative decisions be supported by 'findings of fact' or 'a statement of reasons for the decision' or 'a determination of each issue of fact or law necessary to the decision' or 'written findings of fact and conclusions of law' or 'a separate statement of the ultimate conclusions upon each contested issue of fact'. The Revised Model State Administrative Procedure Act, formulated by the National Conference of Commissioners on Uniform State Laws, requires (section 12) each decision in a contested case to contain separately 'findings of fact and conclusions of law' and further requires that the findings of fact 'shall be accompanied by a concise and explicit statement of the underlying facts supporting the findings' (*Administrative Law, Cases and Comment*, Gellhorn, Byse and Strauss, 7th edn. (1979), pp. 350–1).

Federal statutes

3.62. Federal statutes creating federal administrative agencies generally follow the same pattern. For example, the Communications Act of 1935, which established the Federal Communications Commission and empowered it to deal with such matters as the licensing of radio stations, required the Commission, within thirty days of rendering a challenged decision, to file 'a full statement in writing of the facts and grounds for its decision as found and given by it' (section 402(c)). It was further provided that the reviewing court should be limited to questions of law, and that findings of fact by the Commission, if supported by substantial evidence, were to be conclusive evidence unless clearly appearing to be arbitrary or capricious (section 402(e)).

3.63. In 1946 a federal statute of general application was enacted. The Administrative Procedure Act, 1946, introduced a comprehensive code covering the actions of administrative agencies in the fields of both informal rule-making and adjudication in contested matters. The relevant provision which dealt with the process of adjudication in so-called 'on-the-record proceedings' (as contrasted with the adoption of informal rules) was section 8(b) of the Act. This is now (subject to some drafting changes) section 557(c) of Title 5 of the United States Code (1982 edition). This provision begins by conferring a right on parties to submit to the administrative agency, at the stage at which it is formulating its decision or recommendation, proposed findings and conclusions, or exceptions to earlier tentative decisions of the agency or decisions by subordinate employees. There then follow these words:

The record shall show the ruling on each finding, conclusion or exception presented. All decisions, including initial, recommended, and tentative decisions, are a part of the record and shall include a statement of—

(*a*) findings and conclusions, and the reasons or basis therefor, on all the material issues of fact, law or discretion presented on the record, and
(*b*) the appropriate rule, order, sanction, relief, or denial thereof.

3.64. Of particular significance in the provision quoted above are the following:

(*a*) there must be an agency 'record' which has to include all the evidence, all the submissions, the adjudication, and the order;
(*b*) the adjudication must satisfy the threefold requirement of stating 'findings', 'conclusions', and 'reasons' (or the basis for the decision);
(*c*) these findings, conclusions, and reasons must deal with all the material issues of fact, law, and discretion presented.

3.65. The Administrative Procedure Act has been broadly construed to apply not merely to adjudications required by statute to be determined on the record after the opportunity for an agency hearing but to hearings read into statutes as 'necessitated by the Constitution' (*Wong Yang Sung* v. *McGrath* 339 US 33, 50 (1950)). The Act has been viewed as remedial legislation the purpose of which should be effected 'where the evils it was aimed at appear' (id.).

The strict attitude of the United States courts in requiring compliance with the obligations to state findings and to give reasons

3.66. The attitude of the courts in reviewing decisions of administrative agencies has been to require the agencies to spell out clearly the basis upon which they have proceeded. The essential findings of fact and the process of reasoning must be laid bare. Mere statements of the ultimate conclusion which simply 'track' or 'parrot' the statutory language will not suffice (*USV Pharmaceutical Corporation* v. *Secretary of Health etc. and the Commissioner of Food and Drugs* 466 F. 2d 455, 461–2 (DC Cir. 1972). For, as was said by the court in *Citizens Bank of Weirton* v. *West Virginia Board of Banking and Financial Institutions* 233 SE 2d 719, 727 (1977):

Whenever an agency may be permitted to state its findings of fact in bare statutory language, the decision may be rendered by a clerk or secretary who has been given the agency's ultimate conclusion, i.e. in this case 'application granted', and assigned the task of filling in the appropriate form. This is not the rational thought process contemplated by the [state] Administrative Procedures Act.

3.67. The necessity for adequate fact finding was well described by the US Court of Appeals in a judgment given by Judge Stephens in *Saginaw Broadcasting Co.* v. *Federal Communications Commission* 96 F. 2d 554, 559 (DC Cir.), cert. denied 305 US 613 (1938):

The requirement that courts, and commissions acting in a quasi-judicial capacity, shall make findings of fact, is a means provided by Congress for guaranteeing that cases shall be decided according to the evidence and the law, rather than arbitrarily or from extra-legal considerations; and findings of fact serve the additional purpose, where provisions for review are made, of apprising the parties and the reviewing tribunal of the factual basis of the action of the court or commission, so that the parties and the reviewing tribunal may determine whether the case has been decided upon the evidence and the law or, on the contrary, upon arbitrary or extra-legal considerations. When a decision is accompanied by findings of fact, the reviewing court can decide whether the decision reached by the court or commission follows as a matter of law from the facts stated as its basis, and also whether the facts so stated have any substantial support in the evidence. In the absence of findings of fact the reviewing tribunal can determine neither of these things. The requirement of findings is thus far from a technicality. On the contrary, it is to insure against Star Chamber methods, to make certain that justice shall be administered according to facts and law. This is fully as important in respect of commissions as it is in respect of courts.

3.68. The parties and the reviewing court should not be left in a position of uncertainty as to precisely what the administrative body actually decided. In *United States* v. *Chicago etc. Rly Co.* 294 US 499, 510–11 (1935) Mr Justice Cardozo in reversing an order of the Interstate Commerce Commission on the ground of inadequate fact-finding said:

The difficulty is that it has not said so with the simplicity and clearness through which a halting impression ripens into reasonable certitude. In the end we are left to spell out, to argue, to choose between conflicting inferences. Something more precise is requisite in the quasi-jurisdictional findings of an administrative agency ... We must know what a decision means before the duty becomes ours to say whether it is right or wrong.

3.69. The same imperative was expressed by Frankfurter J. in a memorable phrase: 'The administrative process will best be vindicated by clarity in its exercise' (*Phelps Dodge Corporation* v. *National Labor Relations Board* 313 US 177, 197 (1941)). And, in another case, the same learned judge pointed out that 'the courts cannot exercise their duty to review unless they are advised of the considerations underlying the action under review ... the orderly functioning of the process of review requires that the grounds upon which the administrative agency acted be clearly disclosed and adequately sustained.' (*Securities and Exchange Commission* v. *Chenery Corporation* 318 US 80, 94–5 (1941).)

3.70. So in *Schaffer Transportation Commission* v. *USA and Interstate Commerce Commission* 355 US 83 (1957) the Supreme Court (Frankfurter J. dissenting) set aside an order of the Interstate Commerce Commission on the ground that the order did not demonstrate that the Commission had directed its mind to material evidence and to the relevant part of Congress's controlling National Transportation Policy.

Canada

Traditionally no general duty to give reasons has been recognized in Canadian law

3.71. At common law, until recently, the traditional view prevailed that administrators were not bound to give reasons for their decisions. This view was unequivocally expounded by Thorson P. in the Exchequer Court of Canada in *Pure Spring Co. Ltd.* v. *Minister of National Revenue* [1947] 1 DLR 501, 534: 'The weight of authority is overwhelming that an administrative officer need not, unless he chooses to do so, give reasons for the exercise of such [sc. a statutory] discretion.'

3.72. To the like effect is the judgment of Pratte J. in the Federal Court of Appeal of Canada in *Canadian Arsenals Ltd.* v. *Canada Labour Relations Board* [1979] 2 FC 393, 399–400: 'In the absence of legislative enactments to the contrary, courts of law are not required to give reasons for their decisions. The same rule applies to administrative or quasi-judicial bodies. The mere fact that an administrative body is subject to the supervisory power of the Federal Court of Appeal does not have the effect of placing that body under an obligation to give reasons for its decisions.'

3.73. In *Proulx* v. *Public Service Staff Relations Board* [1978] 2 FC 133, 141 Jackett CJ said that a failure to give reasons was not a breach of natural justice, though the absence of reasons might be a ground for concluding that unfair procedures had been followed in arriving at the decision. (This suggestion is an echo of Lord Greene's dictum in *Minister of National Revenue* v. *Wright's Canadian Ropes Ltd.* [1947] AC 109, 125 cited at paragraph 3.27 above.) In *Re Stoangi and Law Society of Upper Canada* (No. 2) (1979) 100 DLR (3d) 639, 649–50 it was accepted (by the Divisional Court of the High Court of Justice in Ontario) that there was no duty imposed on a tribunal at common law to give reasons for its decision.

Desirability of reasons stressed

3.74. There are, however, indications that some judges are beginning to look at the matter differently. In the *Proulx* case mentioned above Jackett CJ emphasized the desirability of reasons. In his view their primary function was to make decisions more acceptable by convincing the parties (particularly the unsuccessful party) that the matter had been dealt with in an unbiased judicial manner. In *NW Utilities* v. *City of Edmonton* [1979] 1 SCR 684, 705–6 Estey J., in delivering the judgment of the Supreme Court of Canada, said:

The law reports are replete with cases affirming the desirability if not the legal obligation at common law of giving reasons for decisions . . . This obligation is a salutary one. It reduces to a considerable degree the chances of arbitrary or capricious decisions, reinforces public confidence in the judgment and fairness of administrative tribunals, and affords parties to administrative proceedings an opportunity to assess the question of appeal and if taken, the opportunity in the reviewing or appellate tribunal of a full hearing which may well be denied where the basis of the decision has not been disclosed. This is not to say, however, that absent a requirement by statute or regulation a disposition by an administrative tribunal would be reviewable solely by reason of a failure to disclose its reasons for such disposition.

The failure to give reasons may defeat the right to make representations or to appeal and hence may involve a breach of natural justice

3.75. In *Re Basu and Bettschen* (1976) 59 DLR (3d) 392 it was held, on a line of reasoning similar to that contained in the quotation from the *Minister of National Revenue* case cited in paragraph 3.26 above, that the failure to give reasons deprived the appellant of the opportunity to make effective representations. The appellant was a doctor whose hospital appointment was not renewed. No reason was given. The relevant by-laws provided that there could be a subsequent 'hearing' at which the doctor could appear. Hall JA said (p. 400) that the statutory requirement for there to be a hearing meant that 'at the very least the board will hear what the applicant has to say about its reasons for not reappointing her. In denying this essential information to the applicant, the board has not demonstrated the objectivity and fair play essential. There has therefore been a denial of natural justice.'

3.76. In two cases in 1982 the Court of Appeal of Nova Scotia adopted and applied the views of Sir John Donaldson in *Norton Tool Co. Ltd.* v. *Tewson* [1972] ICR 501, 505 (cited in paragraph 3.33 above).

3.77. The facts in *Re RDR Construction and Rent Review Commission* (1982) 139 DLR (3d) 168 were that a residential tenancy officer gave no reason for his decision increasing the rent payable by the tenant. When the case went on review to the Rent

Review Commission the Commission declined to disclose to the tenant the record of the proceedings below. In particular the tenant did not know on what cost information from the landlord the residential tenancy officer had acted. The Court of Appeal held that it was a breach of natural justice not to disclose the relevant material to the tenant. In order to present his case on review the tenant needed to know the reasons underlying the officer's decision.

3.78. In *Re Yarmouth Housing Ltd. and Rent Review Commission* (1983) 139 DLR (3d) 544 the Court of Appeal went one step further and held that the Commission itself was bound to give reasons. In such reasons the Commission should not confine itself merely to a recital of the information placed before it and its conclusions, but it had a duty to set out why it rejected the information and evidence produced by the applicant. MacKeighan CJNS said (p. 555): 'The applicant is entitled to know on what grounds his appeal has been rejected and where, in the opinion of the commissioner, he has gone wrong.'

3.79. It remains to be seen whether the views of the Court of Appeal of Nova Scotia commend themselves to Canadian courts generally. If so, the giving of reasons will move from being a desideratum (as the Supreme Court thought—see paragraph 3.74 above) into the sphere of legal duty.

Ontario statute imposes duty on tribunals to give reasons on request

3.80. As regards tribunals, the Province of Ontario has followed the same path as the United Kingdom. In 1968 the McRuer Commission on Civil Rights recommended that a statutory duty should be imposed on tribunals to give reasons if requested (Report No. 1, Vol. 1, p. 218). This recommendation was implemented by the Statutory Powers Procedure Act, 1971, section 17 (now Statutory Powers Procedure Act, RSO 1980, c. 484 section 17) which provides: 'A tribunal shall give its final decision and order, if any, in any proceedings in writing and shall give reasons in writing therefor if requested by a party.' It is further provided that the decision and the reasons are to form part of the record of the proceedings (section 20(f)): 'Proper reasons must state the findings of fact and the legal reasoning on which the conclusions are based. Reasons of that sort are necessary to provide an adequate basis for review or appeal . . . reasons must be adequate and intelligible even in a case where these are given voluntarily and are not requested.' (Kavanagh, *A Guide to Judicial Review*, 2nd edn. (1984), 39 citing the *NW Utilities* case—paragraph 3.74 above—and *Miljohns* v. *Scarborough Board of Education* (1980) 29 OR (2d) 251.)

View of the Canadian Law Reform Commission

3.81. The Law Reform Commission of Canada in Working Paper 25, *Independent Administrative Agencies*, published in 1980, proposed that agencies should be required to give reasons on request (Recommendation 6.9, pp. 137–8). The Commission stressed the importance of reasons to enable people to understand the decision, to preserve a record which could be examined, to facilitate appeal and review, and 'to maintain the integrity of the decision-making process'. In its Final Report to Parliament in 1986 (Recommendation 2.4 and paragraphs 174–9) the Commission has reduced the full width of its original proposal and has recommended a compromise. The legal obligation to give reasons would only be imposed where there was a total or partial denial of a requested action or where the agency was obliged to make a choice between competing interests. In other cases reasons would not be mandatory though agencies should be encouraged to give reasons wherever feasible. The Commission adopted this compromise because it feared that a requirement of reasons in all cases would impose an excessive burden and create delay. On the issue of whether reasons should be given with the decision or furnished later the Commission favours the simultaneous issue of reasons. Delay may encourage *post hoc* rationalizations.

Australia

3.82. The generally accepted view in the Australian courts is that no duty is imposed at common law upon an administrator to give reasons for an administrative decision. A decision of the Court of Appeal of New South Wales which took a novel stance on this point was recently overruled by the High Court of Australia. The case is fully discussed in paragraphs 3.100–3.106 below.

Traditional view—no duty to give reasons

3.83. The traditional approach was clearly set out in the judgment of Ellicott J. in *Burns* v. *Australia National University* (1982) 4

ALN No. 93; 40 ALR 707, where he referred to the statutory change made in Federal law in 1977 and said:

It [the statutory provision] confers a basic right which the citizen previously did not have except where legislation expressly required it or the application of rules of natural justice demanded it. Those exercising administrative power under Commonwealth enactments were not under a general duty to give reasons. Up to a point, they were entitled to hide behind a wall of silence. A citizen adversely affected could, of course, attempt to use the prerogative writ procedure to establish that a decision was defective but this procedure was unlikely to be of value if the reasons for the decision could not be proved. Therefore prior to the enactment of [the section], a person whose interests were adversely affected by an administrative decision might be deprived of a remedy even though the decision was actually defective in law. It was largely to remedy this situation that the section was enacted.

3.84. This statement by Ellicott J. is entitled to special weight as he was one of the small group of lawyers who took the lead in overhauling administrative law in Australia and in promoting the legislation which introduced sweeping changes into the system. He was a member of the Kerr Committee, or to give it its formal title, the Commonwealth Administrative Review Committee, which reported to the Australian Parliament in August 1971 (1971—Parliamentary Paper No. 144). One of its recommendations was for the introduction into the law of a general duty to give reasons for administrative decisions (paragraph 266, pp. 78–9 and Recommendation 8, p. 113). As Solicitor-General he was Chairman of the Committee of Review (the 'Ellicott Committee'), which reported to Parliament on Prerogative Writ Procedures in May 1973 (1973—Parliamentary Paper No. 56). This Committee recommended that the Government should proceed to implement those portions of the Kerr Committee's proposals which related to judicial review. The Ellicott Committee dealt with the necessity for reasons to be given (paragraphs 34–8, pp. 8–9). It recognized that conferring a right to receive reasons for a decision '*would clearly alter the existing law*'. It thought, however, that this change was desirable (paragraph 34): 'We think it is in the interest not only of the citizen but also of efficiency in the public service. It may also have the merit that persons who feel that they have been wronged by an administrative decision would abandon their claim when the reasons are known. The recommendation is also in accordance with the principles of open Government.' The Committee recognized that there would have to be exceptions to the general duty to give reasons. It emphasized that the legislation would only be effective if persons affected by decisions were given a real understanding of the basis of the decision. So the applicant should be entitled not only to reasons but to findings of fact and considerations taken into account in reaching the contested decision. It would not be enough for the applicant to be given an uninformative reason, for example that his case was considered not to come within the ambit of a particular statutory provision.

Illustrations of traditional approach

3.85. To illustrate the traditional approach we cite *Taylor* v. *Public Service Board* [1975] 2 NSWLR 278, a decision of the Court of Appeal of New South Wales. The case was affirmed in the High Court of Australia—(1976–7) 137 CLR 208—but on different grounds. Taylor was a public service officer charged with breaches of discipline. He was found guilty by the Public Service Board but it gave no reasons. He had a statutory right to appeal which he did not exercise. Instead he applied for prohibition. One of the grounds on which he relied to support the quashing of the decision was the failure of the Board to give reasons. The Court of Appeal rejected this argument citing the English case of *R.* v. *Gaming Board for Great Britain, ex parte Benaim and Khaida* [1970] 2 QB 417, to which we have referred in paragraph 3.8 above. On the appeal to the High Court this ground of attack was abandoned.

3.86. The Court of Appeal of New South Wales adopted the same approach in 1982 in *Jet 60 Minute Cleaners Pty. Limited* v. *Brownette* (1981) 2 NSWLR 232. The court there decided that a referee, who had power to order the Consumer Claims Tribunal to rehear a case, was not bound to give reasons for refusing to order a rehearing. The argument that it was a breach of natural justice to give no reasons was expressly rejected. Counsel for the appellant felt obliged to concede that there was no general rule that the decision of an inferior tribunal contravened natural justice if reasons for the decision were not given. But it was submitted that a donee of a statutory power of a judicial character must give reasons for his decision where the particular circumstances were such that the failure to do so might excite suspicion that the decision had been based on extraneous circumstances. This limited proposition was also rejected (judgment of Glass JA, pp. 4–5).

Exception where the absence of reasons defeats a right of appeal

3.87. There is, however, some Australian authority for the proposition that reasons ought to be given where an appellant needs to know them for the purposes of prosecuting a right of appeal. *Pettitt* v. *Dunkley* [1971] 1 NSWLR 376 was a case which involved a judge rather than an administrator. In that case the trial judge in an accident case had simply entered judgment for the defendant without giving reasons. The facts given in evidence presented a strong case for the plaintiff. The Court of Appeal of New South Wales held that the judge's failure to give reasons constituted an error of law and it was laid down that the obligation to give reasons was directed to facilitating the exercise of the right to appeal.

The Australian tax cases

3.88. There is also an important line of tax cases in which the High Court has been concerned to ensure that silence on the part of the Revenue as to the reasons for a decision should not deprive the taxpayer of the chance of review by the court. In *Giris Pty. Ltd.* v. *Commonwealth Commissioner of Taxation* (1969) 119 CLR 365 the point at issue was strictly a constitutional question, namely, whether section 99A of the Income Tax Assessment Act, 1936–65, was constitutionally valid. The ground of attack was that the Commissioner of Taxation was, in effect, given a discretion to decide whether a taxpayer should be taxed under one section or under another. The rates of tax differed under the two sections. Tax at the higher rate was due under section 99A unless the Commissioner was 'of the opinion that it would be unreasonable to apply the Section'. It was argued (*inter alia*) that such vaguely drafted legislation created a tax which was unchallengeable. The High Court rejected this argument. Barwick CJ (p. 373), with the concurrence of Windeyer J. (p. 384), said that the Commissioner had a duty in each case to form an opinion; he was bound to inform the taxpayer of it; and on request he 'should inform the taxpayer of the facts he has taken into account in reaching his conclusion'. With the assistance of this material the court would be able, in a suit brought by the taxpayer, to determine whether 'the opinion was formed arbitrarily or fancifully' or upon the basis of relevant considerations (p. 374). McTiernan J. (p. 376) also considered that the opinion of the Commissioner would be open to attack on any of the grounds on which judicial review will lie. Other members of the court, however, appeared to think that there might be difficulties in ascertaining the grounds on which the Commissioner formed his opinion.

3.89. In cases since *Giris* the High Court has adopted the approach of Barwick CJ and, in appeals lodged by taxpayers, has ordered the Commissioner to furnish particulars of the basis upon which he reached his decision. This course has been taken not only where the opinion of the Commissioner or his state of mind forms the basis of the assessment, but also in cases where it is necessary for the taxpayer and the court to know the facts found by the Commissioner and the manner in which he reached his assessment. The authorities were reviewed and the principles were broadly stated in the judgment (effectively that of the whole High Court) of Aickin J. in *Bailey* v. *Commonwealth Commissioner of Taxation* (1977) 136 CLR 214, 222–33.

Legislative intervention

3.90. Following the reports of the Kerr and Ellicott Committees referred to in paragraph 3.84 above and the Interim and Final Reports of the Bland Committee on Administrative Discretions (January and October 1973, ISBN 0 642 00218 5 and 0 642 00466 8) the Australian Parliament enacted a series of measures designed to transform administrative law and to give the citizen much greater opportunities to challenge administrative decisions. The five major steps in this reform may be summarized as follows:

(*a*) the creation of a tribunal empowered to review on their merits administrative decisions of specified classes (the Administrative Appeals Tribunal Act, 1975);

(*b*) the creation of a new court—the Federal Court of Australia— to hear appeals on points of law from the Administrative Appeals Tribunal and to decide applications for judicial review under the procedures introduced by (*e*) below (the Federal Court of Australia Act, 1976);

(*c*) the creation of a body—the Administrative Review Council— charged with the general duty of overseeing law and practice relating to administrative decisions and opportunities for review (section 51 of the 1975 Act);

(*d*) the creation of ombudsman review (the Ombudsman Act, 1976); and

(*e*) the facilitation of judicial review (the Administrative Decisions (Judicial Review) Act, 1977).

The reform committees advocated a statutory duty

3.91. The giving of reasons for administrative decisions was made an integral part of this scheme for reform as all the above committees had recommended. We have given the references to the recommendations about reasons in the Kerr and Ellicott Reports in paragraph 3.84 above. The corresponding passage in the Bland Committee's Final Report is in paragraph 172 (p. 31).

The statutory duty in relation to judicial review cases

3.92. So far as concerns judicial review the applicant is now entitled to apply to the decision-maker to furnish him with 'a statement in writing setting out the findings on material questions of fact, referring to the evidence or other material on which those findings were based and giving the reasons for the decision' (Administrative Decisions (Judicial Review) Act, 1977, section 13(1); the full text is set out in Appendix 8). The application is made before the commencement of proceedings. The intention is that the applicant should be put in a position to know whether it is worth his while to commence proceedings and, if so, on what grounds to put his case. The reasons must be supplied within twenty-eight days. There is no express power to order compliance on default.

The exceptions

3.93. It is significant that the Administrative Decisions (Judicial Review) Act passed in 1977 was not 'proclaimed', that is to say brought into operation, until 1 October 1980. The delay was caused by continuing discussion with government as to the decisions which should be exempted. Two types of exemption were contemplated: exemption which would take the decision right outside the scope of the Act so that no judicial review would be possible; and a more limited exemption which would merely protect the decision from the obligation to give reasons. In the result decisions of the first type were embodied in a new Schedule 1 which was added by way of amendment in 1980, and exclusions of the second type are in the new Schedule 2. The latest versions of these two Schedules are printed in Appendix 8 to this Report.

3.94. Decisions which are removed from the scope of the Act altogether include decisions under certain Arbitration Acts, decisions relating to the assessment of taxes and duties, decisions under the Foreign Takeover Act, 1973, decisions relevant to disciplinary proceedings under naval, military, or air force law, and decisions under enactments dealing with security, intelligence organizations and the interception of telecommunications.

3.95. Schedule 2 of the Act contains a long list of classes of decision which are protected from the statutory duty to supply a statement of findings and reasons (section 13(11)(c)). It is impossible to indicate in a summary the full extent of these exceptions. By way of example, we may mention decisions connected with extradition, consular and diplomatic immunity, decisions relating to the administration of criminal justice, decisions of specified public authorities (such as the Australian Dairy Corporation, Australian Shipping Commission, Australian Wheat Board, and so on) in respect of their commercial activities, decisions of the Reserve Bank in connection with its banking activities, and decisions in connection with personnel management in respect to the Australian Public Services. The Act contains a further power to make regulations declaring that a class or classes of decisions are not decisions to which section 13 of the Act applies (section 13(8)). Regulations may not, however, reduce the list in Schedule 2. Some commentators have deplored the width of these exclusions which have been said to 'undermine' the general operation of the Act (*Administrative Law Service*, ed. D. C. Pearce, Introduction, paragraph 441A). Where a decision is protected by Schedule 2 at the stage before proceedings are brought, the Federal Court will not order reasons to be given once proceedings have commenced (*Murchison* v. *Keating* (No. 1) [1984] 1 FCR 341; 6 ALD 290).

3.96. Further derogations from the duty to give full reasons are created by section 13A, which permits confidential information to be withheld, and by section 14, which authorizes the Attorney-General to certify that disclosure of information would be contrary to the public interest on grounds such as prejudice to the security, defence or international relations in Australia, disclosing Cabinet discussions, and common-law privilege. (The text of these Sections is given in Appendix 8.) The 1980 amendments were controversial and in some significant respects not in accordance with the recommendations of the Administrative Review Council (see its 5th Annual Report 1980–1, pp. 20–3).

The statutory duty to give reasons under the Administrative
Appeals Tribunal Act

3.97. Turning now to the Administrative Appeals Tribunal ('the
AAT'), we find that the same duty to give reasons and to state
findings was imposed by the Administrative Appeals Tribunal Act,
1975. By section 28(1) of that Act the person who is entitled to
apply to the AAT for review may request the decision-maker to
furnish to him a written statement containing reasons, findings, and
references to the evidence. The same language is used as that quoted
in paragraph 3.92 above. Generally the statement must be furnished
within twenty-eight days of the request. The purpose of the statement at that stage is to enable the applicant to understand the
decision and to make up his mind whether to seek review in the AAT
or judicial review in the Federal Court. The applicant may, however,
launch AAT proceedings without asking for reasons. If this happens
it becomes the duty of the decision-maker to send to the tribunal a
statement of reasons, findings, and evidence references. Section
37(1)(a), in imposing this obligation, again uses the same language as
that quoted in paragraph 3.92 above. Section 28(1) and section
37(1)(a) in their original form did not include the words 'referring to
the evidence or other material on which those findings were based'.
These words were added by amendment, thereby rendering the
obligation 'more stringent' (*Re Palmer No. 1* (1978) 1 ALD 183,
192 per Fisher J.). When the decision-maker forwards his written
statement to the AAT he must send with it all relevant documents in
his possession. He can, if necessary, be ordered to give further and
better particulars if his statement is deficient.

The scope and importance of the duty to give reasons

3.98. The obligation imposed by sections 28 and 37 were
described in *Re Palmer No. 1* (above) as 'a crucial feature' of the
current right of the citizen to obtain from an impartial tribunal a
review of an administrative decision. 'Parliament certainly intended
that the citizen should be fully informed' (1 ALD 193). The full
reasons must be given and, if the decision-making process is spread
between more than one person or between two or more departments, the totality of the reasons and relevant findings must be
included. If the decision is founded upon a recommendation or
report from an expert, material findings of fact made by the expert
must be included with references to the supporting evidence. The

reasons which actuated the mind of the expert must also be laid bare. The intent of the sections could be bypassed if it were enough to say that the decision-maker relied upon expert opinion received (ibid., p. 192).

3.99. The Administrative Review Council (to which further reference is made in chapter 4 below) has published an Explanatory Memorandum entitled 'Statements of Reasons' (3rd Annual Report, 1979, Appendix II, pp. 57–63). Basing itself on the English cases cited in paragraph 3.47 and 3.48 above and on the *Palmer* case, the Memorandum states that the purpose of imposing an obligation to furnish statements of reasons includes:

(*a*) overcoming the real grievance persons experience when they are not told why something affecting them has been done; and

(*b*) enabling persons affected by a decision to see what was taken into account and whether an error has been made so that they may determine whether to challenge the decision and what means to adopt for doing so.

More recently, Woodward J. in *Ansett Transport* v. *Wraith* (1983) 48 ALR 500, 507 has said that the decision-maker is required by the statute to explain his decision in a way which will enable a person aggrieved to say, in effect: 'Even though I may not agree with it, I now understand why the decision went against me. I am now in a position to decide whether that decision has involved an unwarranted finding of fact, or an error of law, which is worth challenging.' Accordingly, the decision-maker should set out his understanding of the relevant law, any findings of fact on which his conclusions depend (especially if those facts have been in dispute), and the reasoning processes which led him to those conclusions. He should do so in clear and unambiguous language, not in vague generalities or the formal language of legislation. The appropriate length of the statement will vary with the circumstances.

The *Osmond* case

3.100. In the above paragraphs we have described the changes introduced by Commonwealth legislation in Australia in the years from 1975–80. We return now to look at state law and in particular at a subsequent case decided on the basis of the common law. This is the case of *Public Service Board of New South Wales* v. *Osmond* (1986) 63 ALR 559; 60 ALJ 209 in which the High Court of

Australia emphatically rejected the proposition that there is any general duty at common law to give reasons for an administrative decision. The High Court unanimously overruled the Court of Appeal of New South Wales, which, in a split decision [1984] 3 NSWLR 447, had sought to make a bold advance on the traditional common-law position as described in paragraphs 3.83–3.86 above. In effect what the majority of the Court of Appeal had held was that an administrator is normally obliged to state reasons for his decision if the giving of reasons is necessary to enable a party to make full use of the possibility of appeal or judicial review. The leading judgment was that of Kirby P., who, until his appointment to the Court of Appeal, had served as Chairman of the Law Reform Commission of Australia for ten years.

3.101. The judgment of Kirby P. is erudite and lengthy. It takes account of decisions in most of the common-law jurisdictions considered in this report and also covers India, New Zealand, and Fiji. It is impossible here to summarize adequately the argument developed in his judgment, but it is perhaps possible to select one dictum from an earlier case which forms the springboard for the conclusion reached by Kirby P. This is a dictum of Mahoney JA in a New South Wales Court of Appeal case—*Housing Commission of New South Wales* v. *Tatmar Pastoral Co. Pty. Ltd.* [1983] 3 NSWLR 378, 386. What Mahoney JA said was:

In determining whether, in a particular case, there is a duty to give reasons and the extent of it, regard should, in my opinion, be had to the function to be served by the giving of reasons. Thus, the statement of reasons may be necessary to enable a party to exercise his right of appeal or such other rights as he may have to contest the decision: this is one of the conventional functions of the requirement: see *Pettitt v. Dunkley* ([1971] 1 NSWLR 376) at pp. 387–8. But in my opinion, the requirement that reasons be given should not be limited to cases where there is an appeal. There is as yet no finally authoritative decision on this question. I think that the requirement should been seen as an *incident of the judicial process*.

This passage is cited at p. 459 of Kirby P.'s judgment and the added emphasis is his own.

3.102. At p. 466 of his judgment Kirby P. returns to this seminal idea and says that the suggested limitation of the right to reasons to situations where an appeal is provided and where reasons may be necessary to fulfil that right 'is not conceptually satisfying'. Review by way of appeal is but one means of ensuring compliance with the law. 'To use the expressions of Mahoney J.A. [above], what is really at stake is the 'judicial process', of which appeal is but one instrument. Equally important for the control of power and to ensure compliance with the law is the facility of judicial review'. Kirby P. goes on to say that it is also unsatisfactory to suggest that the right to reasons is limited to the case of judicial officers in courts.

3.103. This line of reasoning leads him naturally forward to the broad proposition which he states as follows:

> The overriding duty of public officials who are donees of statutory powers is to act justly, fairly and in accordance with their statute. Normally, this will require, where they have a power to make discretionary decisions affecting others, an obligation to state the reasons for their decisions. That obligation will exist where, to do otherwise, would render nugatory a facility, however limited, to appeal against the decision. It will also exist where the absence of stated reasons would diminish a facility to have the decision otherwise tested by judicial review to ensure that it complies with the law and to ensure that matters have been taken into account which should have been taken into account or that matters have not been taken into account which ought not to have been taken into account.

3.104. In a separate judgment Priestley JA came to the same conclusion as Kirby P. There is, however, a vigorous dissenting judgment of Glass JA. He had been a party to the *Jet 60 Minute Cleaners* case to which we have referred in paragraph 3.86 above. Glass JA considered (p. 471) that there was binding authority for the proposition that it was no contravention of the principles of natural justice for an administrative tribunal to withhold the reasons for its decision. The power of the courts to renovate the law was not, in the opinion of Glass JA, 'untrammelled' and it was subject to a condition that it be exercised with a due sense of responsibility. He thought the case was one for judicial restraint. The consequences of a judge-made reform of the law in a situation like this were not possible for a court to foresee. All manner of decisions by public and private boards, committees, and officers would become subject to the duty. The social benefits of this 'leap in the dark' (p. 473) could not be quantified. Glass JA then made reference to the fine tuning to be found in the Commonwealth legislation considered in paragraphs 3.90–3.99 above which discriminated between kinds of decision and kinds of supervision. He concluded that judicial innovation was, under the circumstances, unjustified.

3.105. The High Court of Australia reversed the decision of the majority and upheld the viewpoint of Glass JA (1986) 63 ALR 559; 63 ALJR 209. The leading judgment was delivered by Gibbs CJ with whom Brennan and Dawson JJ. concurred. He said (63 ALR 563):

... the conclusion which they [sc. the majority of the Court of Appeal] have reached is opposed to overwhelming authority. There is no general rule of the common law, or principle of natural justice, that requires reasons to be given for administrative decisions, even decisions which have been made in the exercise of a statutory discretion and which may adversely affect the interests, or defeat the legitimate or reasonable expectations, of other persons.

If the law were to be altered this would be a matter for the legislature as it involved departing from a settled rule (p. 567). Gibbs CJ pointed out that the duty to give reasons for a decision once made was quite a different thing from a requirement that a person had to be notified of what case he had to meet before a decision was taken (pp. 563 and 565). While the giving of reasons might generally be thought to be desirable there were arguments to the contrary which had to be considered. He instanced the burden placed on the administrators, the cost and the possibility that a duty to give reasons might in some cases induce a lack of candour on the part of the administrative officers concerned (p. 567). Wilson J. in his separate judgment took up this point and said that in relation to the promotion of senior officers in the public service the legislature must have deliberately refrained from requiring the Public Service Board to give its reasons for preferring one candidate over another. The legislature, he thought:

must have concluded that efficiency and harmony in the higher echelons of the Public Service would be enhanced by having the Board or its delegate keep its reasons to itself and thereby protect the reputations of the protagonists in the sensitive areas of character that a dispute as to relative efficiency might well encompass (p. 571).

3.106. Before leaving *Osmond*'s case it is just worthwhile to consider the actual issue which was there at stake. Mr Osmond had been employed for twenty-eight years in the New South Wales Public Service when in 1982 he applied for an appointment which involved promotion. There was a rival applicant, a Mr Galvin. Under the applicable legislation it was for the Department Head to recommend the most efficient officer for appointment; if all were equally efficient he had to recommend the most senior officer. In the result Galvin was recommended and Osmond was not. Osmond appealed to the Board and his appeal was dismissed in February 1983. No reasons were given. When they were requested they were refused. The statute gave no further right of appeal and declared that the decision of the Board was 'final'. There was also a widely drawn ouster clause in the statute designed to make the appointment or non-appointment of Public Service officers unreviewable by the courts. The effect of the Court of Appeal's judgment in *Osmond* was to require the Public Service Board nearly two years after its original dismissal of Osmond's appeal to furnish reasons which might (but only might) enable Osmond to argue that the preference expressed for Galvin was unlawful. We feel bound to comment that we would not wish to see promotions within the government service in the United Kingdom subjected to these procedural tussles and paralysing delays.

France

3.107. Until the enactment of recent legislation in France there was in French law no general duty on administrators to give reasons for their decisions. Examples can, however, be cited where the Conseil d'Etat has been prepared to ferret out the reasons or to draw adverse inferences from the failure to give any reasons at all where the circumstances called aloud for some explanation. Thus in *Barel* (CE 18 May 1954; Rec. 308; RDP 1954 509 conclusions Letourneur, note Waline; Dalloz 1954, 594) the plaintiffs were five young men who had been refused permission to compete for places in the Ecole Nationale d'Administration. The state authorities had no legal obligation to give any reason for this refusal. The plaintiffs alleged that the only reason for their rejection was the political opinions which they were assumed to hold. The state failed to give any satisfactory reason in rebuttal and in particular failed to produce, at the Conseil's insistence, the full dossier relating to each candidate. In these special circumstances, the Conseil found itself able to conclude that the plaintiffs' case was made out. Accordingly the five decisions were vitiated by error of law and were annulled. Again in *Poncin* (CE 22 June 1963 and 17 June 1964; 1964 RDP 811 conclusions M. Braibant), where the dossier failed to make manifest the reasons which had actuated a jury responsible for the appointment of a public officer, the Conseil ordered an inquiry to establish the true reasons.

3.108. The French Parliament has now enacted a law (Law No. 79–587 of 11 July 1979) which requires administrators to give reasons for their decisions in cases falling within certain categories. The reasons are to be given without delay. The decisions involved are unfavourable individual decisions which:

(*a*) restrain the exercise of public liberties or in a general way constitute a police measure;

(*b*) impose a sanction;

(*c*) attach restrictive conditions to a permission;

(*d*) withdraw or cancel a previous decision which conferred a right;

(*e*) impose a deadline, foreclosure, or forfeiture;

(*f*) refuse a benefit of a sort to which persons are lawfully entitled if they satisfy prescribed conditions.

Critics of the statute argue that it makes little advance over the existing law. They say that the categories are too narrowly drawn and that the law does not automatically render illegal a decision given without reasons.

Israel

3.109. In *Minister of National Revenue* v. *Wright's Canadian Ropes* and in the *dicta* in *Padfield*'s case, discussed in paragraphs 3.26–3.30 above, and also in the Conseil d'Etat's *Barel* case, reliance was placed on the absence of any statement of a valid reason. Silence was held to justify the inference of arbitrariness or the presence of unlawful reasons. The circumstances may not, however, always be such as to make it possible to draw the inference and where this is so the decision once again presents the face of a sphinx. The bold solution to this problem was provided by an Israeli Court, which in *Ahgig* v. *The Controller of Transportation* (H/C 143/56 11 PD, 370) was prepared to hold that all administrators have a positive duty to give reasons for their decisions, unless some special reason (such as the security of the state) justified a departure from the rule. Berinson J. said: 'If a decision is not arbitrary, then it must necessarily be based on certain facts, findings and considerations . . . and if this is so, why cannot these be recorded and brought to the notice of the persons concerned so that they can be reviewed and examined?'

3.110. The Knesset followed up the initiative taken in the *Ahgig* case and passed the Administrative Procedure Amendment (Decisions and Statement of Reasons) Law, 1958, which applies wherever a public servant receives and rejects an application in writing made to him to exercise any power conferred on him under any law. In such circumstances the public servant must inform the applicant 'in writing of the reasons for rejection'. Failure to comply with this requirement does not invalidate the decision but in effect the onus shifts to the public servant to prove that his decision was arrived at lawfully.

3.111. It will be noted that under the Israeli Act the reasons must accompany the decision. The Knesset considered and rejected the solution of making the reasons available on request. According to one commentator 'it was felt that the official should consider and state his reasons at the time of giving his decision and not afterwards' (Judith Pelley-Karp, 'The Israeli Statement of Reasons Act' (1963) 12 AJCL 72). On the other hand, in our Discussion Paper we said that we were impressed by the argument that to require a statement of reasons in every case would in this country be to place a heavy burden on the administration and would be very costly. We thought that a more practicable rule might be one which imposed a duty on the administration to give reasons when demanded. It was possible that this would also lead to the provision of better and more carefully prepared reasons, whereas a requirement that reasons had to be given in every case, whether wanted or not, would be likely to encourage standard form reasons.

3.112. The Israeli Act contains statutory exceptions to the duty to give reasons. These are set out in section 3 which provides:

Notwithstanding the provisions of section 2A, a public servant shall not be bound to notify the reasons for his refusal in any of the following cases—
    (1) if the law which vests the power in him provides that he is authorized to exercise it at his discretion or without giving reasons;
    (2) if the security of the State or its foreign relations requires or require that the reasons for the decision be not disclosed;
    (3) if the application refused by him was for the appointment of the applicant to a particular post or the assignment to him of a particular task;
    (4) if the disclosure of the reasons might, in the opinion of the public

servant, unlawfully prejudice the rights of any person, other than the applicant;

(5) if the disclosure of the reasons will, in the opinion of the public servant, involve the disclosure of a professional secret, or of secret information, within the meaning of any law.

European Community Law

3.113. Under the EEC Treaty, the Council and the Commission are entitled to make and issue 'Regulations', 'Directives', and 'Decisions'. These various instruments differ as to their effects. Regulations have general application, are binding in their entirety, and are directly applicable in all Member States. A Decision is binding upon those to whom it is addressed. A Directive is binding upon each Member State to which it is addressed as to the result to be achieved but it leaves to the national authorities the choice of form and methods (Article 189). All these instruments, of whatever character, must comply with Article 190 which provides: 'Regulations, directives and decisions of the Council and of the Commission shall state the reasons on which they are based and shall refer to any proposals or opinions which were required to be obtained pursuant to this Treaty.'

3.114. It has been held by the European Court that Article 190 is not concerned with mere formality, 'but seeks to give an opportunity to the parties of defending their rights, to the Court of exercising its supervisory functions and to Member States and to all interested nationals of ascertaining the circumstances in which the Commission has applied the Treaty' (Case 24/62 *Germany* v. *Commission*, [1963] ECR 63, 69). The statement of reasons in the challenged Commission Decision in that case (allowing to the extent of only 100,000 hectolitres Germany's applications for permission to import 450,000 hectolitres of cheap foreign wine) was held to be inadequate, vague, and inconsistent. The court annulled the decision. Article 190 would have been satisfied if the decision had set out in a concise but clear and relevant manner the principal issues of law and fact upon which it was based and which were necessary in order that the reasoning which led the Commission to adopt it might be understood.

3.115. The degree of particularity required varies depending upon the nature of the measure in question. If the measure forms part of a series of measures dealing with the same subject matter and where the underlying reasons are generally well known not much is required by way of further reasons. Regulations do not have to be justified by a long recital of all material facts. It is, however, essential that the reasons which are given should make sense. Thus, in one case, a Council Regulation, which purported to prescribe rules for ending abuses resulting from the sale of agricultural products on board ship (the so-called 'butter-buying cruises'), was held to be invalid because it was based upon self-contradictory reasoning. The court said: 'Such a contradiction in the statement of reasons is all the more serious inasmuch as it concerns a provision empowering the Member States to grant exemptions, albeit on a small scale, from import duties, which constitute an essential part of the common agricultural policy.' (Case 156/80 *Rewe* v. *Hauptzollamt Kiel*, [1981] ECR 1805, 1834.)

PART IV

OUR CONCLUSIONS

3.116. In the course of the foregoing analysis of English law and the law of other countries, we have encountered various statements in favour of and some opposed to the imposition of a general duty to give reasons. We will try to summarize these rival arguments and others which are sometimes deployed and we will then state our own position.

The arguments in favour of requiring reasons to be given for decisions

3.117. The arguments in favour of reasons can usefully be marshalled under four headings.

(*a*) *The functioning of the machinery of government*
1. The need to give reasons imposes a healthy discipline on the decision-maker.
2. Consequently, reasoned decisions are likely to be better thought out than those for which reasons are not required.
3. Reasons are a check on arbitrary decision-making and a fundamental of good administration.

(*b*) *The viewpoint of parties affected by the decision*
4. Reasons satisfy a basic need for fair play.
5. Reasons enable a person affected to know whether it is possible to challenge the decision and, if so, upon what basis. The challenge may be by legal process—appeal or judicial review—or by other available routes, such as reference to an ombudsman.
6. Even if the decision is adverse, the person affected may be convinced by the reasons to accept it as a rational and unbiased exercise of discretionary power.

(*c*) *The viewpoint of the reviewing authority*
7. The reviewing authority—whether appellate tribunal, court, or ombudsman—will be better placed to understand the decision and to exercise any relevant appellate, reviewing, or investigatory powers, if the decision is reasoned and if the factual foundation for the decision is laid bare.
8. Proper reasons should expose excess of jurisdiction, error of law, unsubstantiated findings, and extraneous considerations.

(*d*) *The public at large*
9. Public confidence in the decision-making process is enhanced by the knowledge that supportable reasons have to be given by those who exercise administrative power.

The arguments against the giving of reasons

3.118. The arguments against the giving of reasons tend to concentrate on the practical effects on the administration of the imposition of the duty. Thus it is argued:

(*a*) Efficient administration requires free and uninhibited discussion among decision-makers, unimpeded by considerations of what can or cannot be made public subsequently.
(*b*) A general requirement of reasons will impose an intolerable burden on the machinery of government.
(*c*) Delays in the handling of business will inevitably follow and additional expense will be caused. The public at large will suffer. The benefit will not match the cost.
(*d*) The imposition of a general duty will have far-reaching implications for central government, local government, and for many other bodies of a public or semi-public character. Many more decisions will be opened up to the possibility of

legal challenge and a further step down the road of 'judicial-ization' of affairs will be taken.

(e) The imposition of a duty to give reasons will not necessarily mean that the true or complete reasons will be stated. Decision-makers will adapt to the new regime and acquire the art of stating sufficient by way of reasons to preclude success-ful challenge, but candour will not always be displayed.

Our conclusion on the rival arguments

3.119. We believe strongly that the arguments in favour of reasons are compelling and we reiterate the comment made in 1971 in the JUSTICE Committee Report *Administration Under Law* (p. 23): 'No single factor has inhibited the development of English administrative law as seriously as the absence of any general obligation upon public authorities to give reasons for their de-cisions.' It is generally believed that the quality of tribunal decision-making has improved since the imposition of the duty on tribunals in 1958. The same is true in the town and country planning field. We think that the fears of delay and expense are much exaggerated by the opponents of reasons. We record the fact that the respondents to our Discussion Paper were almost unanimous in advocating the introduction of a duty to give reasons.

Legislation or judicial development?

3.120. In the light of the trends in the recent Canadian decisions which we have discussed (paragraphs 3.77–3.79 above) and in particular in the light of the New South Wales *Osmond* case (paragraphs 3.100–3.106), it is necessary at least to pose the question whether the development of a general duty on adminis-trators to state reasons for their decisions can be left in the United Kingdom to the judges. It would certainly be possible for the House of Lords to overthrow the established approach of the common law and to follow the path taken by Kirby P. in *Osmond* in preference to the traditional approach reaffirmed by the High Court of Australia in that case. It would also be possible for the lower courts to undermine the common-law position by repeatedly finding that on the facts of particular cases the absence of reasons caused injustice, or defeated a right of appeal, or in some other way demonstrated an error of law or procedural unfairness. While, however, such develop-ments are possible (and we would not in any way wish to discourage them), given the decision of the High Court in *Osmond* and the long succession of missed opportunities when in England and Scotland judges could have proclaimed (following the Donoughmore Report) that the giving of reasons was the third principle of natural justice, we do not think it at all probable that the judges here will change their basic attitudes. Accordingly, we recommend legislation to introduce a general duty to give reasons. The statement of reasons should be deemed to form part of 'the record' for the purpose of certiorari.

The formulation of the duty

3.121. We have explained why, in our view, a duty which is confined merely to the giving of 'reasons' is insufficient. We favour the American and Australian precedents which go wider than reasons. We are much attracted by the formula used in the Australian statutes which require the decision-maker to state 'the findings on material questions of fact, referring to the evidence or other material on which these findings were based and giving the reasons for the decisions'. If this obligation is duly observed matters will be decided and justice administered according to facts and law and not upon arbitrary or extra-legal considerations.

Reasons—on demand or accompanying the decision?

3.122. The question whether reasons should accompany the decision in every case or should only be given on demand produced less accord among our respondents than the question whether there should be a duty to give reasons. We have referred in paragraph 3.111 above to what we said in our Discussion Paper in favour of the view that reasons need only be given on demand. We know that it can be said that reasons given later may be different from the real reasons that would have been given at the time, but in deciding which view to favour we have kept in mind the fact that we would be recommending the imposition of a new duty which will apply to a vast number of decisions every year. In some cases reasons may be unnecessary and the giving of them simply a waste of time and money. In the end we have concluded that it would be best to follow the Australian model by creating a statutory right to obtain reasons on demand. This does not mean that we would discourage the voluntary provision of reasons accompanying the decision. Wherever this can easily be done and the circumstances are appropriate we consider such a practice highly desirable. Nevertheless, we would confine our statutory requirement to a duty to give reasons following a demand. There is, of course, no reason why the demand for reasons should not be made before the decision is rendered and we certainly would not wish to say anything against this practice. (An analogy may be drawn with the advance requirement to an arbitrator to produce a reasoned award—Arbitration Act, 1979, section 1(6)(a).) Time-limits should be imposed within which the application for reasons would have to be made.

Exceptions

3.123. In our discussion of Israeli law and Federal Australian law we have drawn attention to the problems concerning exceptions to a general duty to give reasons. We accept that it is both right and inevitable that certain classes of decisions will be placed out of the range of the general duty. The precise formulation of these exceptions is likely to be a delicate task. Without attempting to draft or to produce a definitive list it seems to us that exceptions may be found desirable in the following areas:

(a) where the giving of reasons would be prejudicial to the interests of national security, defence, or international relations;

(b) where the reasons would involve disclosing material protected by legal privilege;

(c) where the reasons would disclose information made available to government in confidence (this heading would cover such matters as decisions as to the awarding of commercial contracts, licences, and similar privileges);

(d) where the reasons would reveal professional or trade secrets or otherwise be hurtful to the interests of third parties;

(e) where the decision of which reasons were sought related to the appointment to or promotion in any post or office or to the assignment of any specific task.

The list of exempted categories of decisions ought to be kept as short as possible.

Notification of the right to reasons

3.124. If, as we recommend, legislation is introduced imposing the duty, procedures would have to be adopted whereby persons would be made aware of their right to demand reasons. If a decision were to be issued without a prior demand having been made, the decision should itself inform the recipient of his right to apply for reasons.

Reasons and 'the record'

3.125. The legislation should provide that the statement of findings and reasons should form part of 'the record' for the purposes of certiorari. We dealt in paragraphs 3.15–3.20 above with the current difficulties in relation to what constitutes a record.

CHAPTER 3. RECOMMENDATIONS

1. There should be a general duty on administrators to give reasons for their decisions (paragraphs 3.117–3.119).
2. The duty should be imposed by legislation (paragraph 3.120).
3. The duty should arise upon a demand being made. Such demand could be made before or after the decision. Time-limits for the making of a demand should be imposed (paragraph 3.122).
4. The duty should be expressed in terms making it incumbent to state not only the reasons but also the findings on material questions of fact with references to the evidence or other material on which such findings are based. The statement supplied should be deemed to form part of 'the record' for the purposes of certiorari (paragraphs 3.20 and 3.21).
5. The legislation creating the duty could provide for exempting certain categories of decision from the duty. The list of exemptions should be kept as short as possible (paragraph 3.123).
6. Procedures should be introduced whereby a person affected who believes that a decision-maker has failed to perform the duty altogether or in a particular respect could in the first instance (and within a stated time-limit) apply to the decision-maker to comply with the duty or to supplement in the specified respect the information given and, on continuing default by the decision-maker, could (again within a stated time-limit) apply to the court for an order directing the decision-maker to comply (paragraph 3.59).
7. Persons affected should be informed of their right to require reasons (paragraph 3.124).
8. The Tribunals and Inquiries Act, 1971, section 12(1) should be amended to expand the duty in accordance with the first sentences of Recommendation 4 above. Rules of procedure applicable to tribunals and in the town and country planning field should be similarly amended (paragraph 3.58).

4

Administrative Review Commission

SUMMARY OF ARGUMENT. Administrative decision-making is an enormously important subject. Constant vigilance is required in order to ensure the adequacy of the system of remedies to protect the citizen and to uphold his rights as against the administration. This cannot be done on a casual *ad hoc* basis. What is needed is a standing body, independent of government, which can comment on pending legislation, itself propose reforms, and draw attention to deficiencies in judicial review, in the substantive law, and in the ombudsmen's jurisdiction. Such a body could be created by statute or be set up as a standing Royal Commission. Some link with Parliament would be highly desirable. The Council on Tribunals would remain in being and work alongside the new Commission.

The problem

4.1. There is, at present, no single institution in the United Kingdom the function of which is to keep under constant review all the procedures and institutions whereby the individual may challenge administrative action. The Council on Tribunals only covers part of this ground. The need for an institution that would cover the whole field has often been recognized. The following may be cited:

Machinery should be established (its embryo exists in the Council on Tribunals and the Law Commissions) for handling the on-going problems of the law's development and reform, with special reference to the problems of administrative law. (Lord Scarman, *English Law: The New Dimension*, (Hamlyn Lectures), 1974, p. 82.)

Whatever balance is eventually achieved between the sovereignty of Parliament and the courts as guardians of the liberty of the subject, there would appear to be a significant role for an effective, independent, statutory advisory body in the field of administrative adjudication, with both detailed knowledge and more general insight linked in a systematic manner. (The Council on Tribunals, Special Report 1980, Cmnd. 7805, p. 22.)

The solution

4.2. We believe that there should be an independent body, separate from the executive functions of Government, charged with the duty of reviewing all aspects of administrative law and the process of administrative decision-making throughout the United Kingdom. This body would comment and recommend but would not itself have executive powers. It would not involve itself with the commercial functions of Government or the commercial activities of public bodies.

Australia's Administrative Review Council

4.3. A model is provided by the Administrative Review Council which was established in Australia by section 48 of the Administrative Appeals Tribunal Act, 1975. Its statutory functions and powers were laid down in section 51 (reproduced in Appendix 7 below). The purpose of the Council was set out in its First Annual Report (1977, p. 7) in these terms:

The functions of the Council ... relate both to primary and appellate decision-making; to substance and procedure; to examination of existing law and promotion of reform; to tribunals and individual administrators. The functions relate to the whole of the machinery of Government for making administrative decisions. It is a wide field of enquiry. In this field, the Council is a promoter and not an executor—Council recommends, Government decides, and the public service implements. Accordingly, the Council is a catalyst of action by other parties. Its usefulness will depend upon the quality of its research and of its insights, and upon the practicability of its recommendations. The Council's experience and resources are available to government departments and instrumentalities to assist in their determining appropriate provisions as to the scope, procedure, and review of decision-making powers within their respective areas of responsibility.

This can be summarized by saying that the Council's duty is constantly to examine the whole system of administrative decision-making and to recommend improvements.

4.4. The Council is regularly consulted by Government and tenders its advice by letter or, if time permits a more extended examination of the problem, in the form of a report. Some twenty-three such reports had been issued as at 30 June 1985 of which sixteen were published. Every year the Council submits to the Attorney General an Annual Report giving a full account of its activities. It notes the instances in which Government has implemented its recommendations and highlights the cases in which its advice has not been followed. Occasions have arisen on which the Government has failed to consult it. These have been followed by firm protests from the Council (8th Annual Report, 1983–4, paragraphs 115–16 and 9th Annual Report 1984–5, paragraph 224). Current topics under consideration are Notification of Rights of Review and Damages in Administrative Law.

4.5. The Council has a powerful membership. The three *ex officio* members are the President of the Administrative Appeals Tribunal, the Commonwealth Ombudsman, and the Chairman of the Australian Law Reform Commission. The other nine members are lawyers, civil servants, businessmen, and academics. The present Chairman Mr E. J. L. Tucker has held office since 1981 and succeeded Brennan J. on the latter's appointment to the High Court of Australia.[1] The Council has undoubtedly had an important influence on legislation and on the continuing extension of the jurisdiction of the Administrative Appeals Tribunal.

4.6. Recently the Council has expressed concern about the inadequacy of the resources now being made available to it. Such severe limitations have been placed on the recruitment of research staff that the Council has had to postpone projects which it would have wished to undertake and to abandon a pending investigation, the so-called Impact project, which involved a detailed examination of the impact made both on the administration and on citizens by the new reforms in Australian administrative law (9th Annual Report, 1984–5, paragraphs 33–8 and 284).

New Zealand's Public and Administrative Law Reform Committee

4.7. From 1966 to April 1986 there was in New Zealand a semi-official body known as the Public and Administrative Law Reform Committee. It was once described as 'that well-balanced watch-dog' (by Cooke J. (1975) NZLJ 112). With the creation of a permanent Law Reform Commission the committee was abolished. A new committee called the Legislation Advisory Committee has inherited many of the responsibilities of the old committee. The annual reports of the Public and Administrative Law Committee to the Minister of Justice covered the whole range of administrative law in

[1] Mr Tucker's terms of office as Chairman ended on 8 February 1987. His successor is Dr Cheryl Saunders, a Reader in Law at Melbourne University.

a jurisdiction that has many similarities to that of the United Kingdom. The Committee's 12th Report, for example, considered codification of the grounds for judicial review, delegation of discretionary powers, the liability of administrative authorities, and regulation-making powers and procedures. Its 14th Report dealt with damages. The Committee's earlier recommendations led to the establishment of the Administrative Division of the High Court of New Zealand in 1968, the creation of a new remedy (the application for review) in 1972, and the extension and improvement of that remedy in 1977.

The Administrative Conference of the United States

4.8. In the rather different constitutional context of the USA, the Administrative Conference of the United States was established in 1968, largely under the impetus of pressure by the American Bar Association, to provide:

Suitable arrangements through which Federal Agencies, assisted by outside experts, may co-operatively study mutual problems, exchange information and develop recommendations for action by proper authorities to the end that private rights may be fully protected and regulatory activities and other Federal responsibilities may be carried out expeditiously in the public interest. (Administrative Conference Act, 1964, section 51—now Title 5 US Code Chapter 5, s. 571.)

The Administrative Conference is itself a permanent independent agency of the Federal Government. It has the duty of studying the efficiency, adequacy, and fairness of the administrative procedures used by administrative agencies (section 574). The term 'administrative procedure' is defined as including 'any aspect of agency organisation, procedure, or management which may affect the equitable consideration of public and private interests, the fairness of agency decisions, the speed of agency action, and the relationship of operating methods to later judicial review . . .' (section 572(3)). The Conference has a full-time Chairman, appointed by the President of the United States, a Council of ten (half of whom are governmental, half non-governmental), and a General Assembly of forty-four governmental and about thirty-six non-governmental members (hence Professor Schwartz's description of the Conference as 'a relatively large, not to say unwieldy, group' — *Legal Control of Government* (1972), p. 181). The Conference has nine standing committees and two special committees. Its secretariat is staffed mainly by lawyers. Normally two plenary sessions of the Conference are held every year. At these sessions the Conference debates, with a view to adopting, reports and recommendations which have been worked over in detail by specialist committees. The essential techniques of the Conference are to collect and disseminate information, to rely on 'rational persuasion', and to devote as much time and effort to reform through the accretion of small improvements as through dramatic solutions to major problems. Political influence is considerable in the appointment of the membership of the Conference and this, no doubt, has some bearing on the extent to which its recommendations are adopted by the Federal Government.

The establishment of an appropriate United Kingdom body

4.9. One way of establishing the sort of body which we have in mind would be by legislation. There is, however, an alternative method and that is by the creation of a standing Royal Commission. A precedent for a permanent Commission of this sort is the Royal Commission on Environmental Pollution. The Prices and Incomes Board was initially also set up as a Royal Commission. Such a Commission is entirely different from an *ad hoc* Commission established to produce a report on a specific topic. In the popular mind at least an *ad hoc* Commission is thought of as a recipe for inaction. That emphatically is not what we have in mind in proposing the establishment of a standing Royal Commission.

Membership of the Commission

4.10. In order to be influential it would be necessary for the Commission to be manned by figures of recognized stature. The Chairman should be an eminent lawyer with time and energy to devote to the Commission's work. As our proposed body is to be independent and to stand outside Government it would not be appropriate for the Lord Chancellor to be Chairman. The membership might follow the Australian precedent and include the Parliamentary Ombudsman and the chairmen of the two Law Commissions. Other members would be drawn from senior public servants (both serving and retired), legal practitioners, academics, and businessmen. We attach importance to striking a balance between lawyers and non-lawyers and to securing the representation of experienced administrators. The total membership should not be too large. Personal commitment and regular attendance are all-important. Although we would expect the Government frequently to consult the Commission, it would be free to devise its own programmes and to make recommendations—whether invited to do so or not. In this respect it would be unlike the Law Commission for England and Wales and the Scottish Law Commissions which (as noted in paragraph 1.1 above) were prevented by Government from carrying out the full-scale review of administrative law which they considered necessary.

Research capability

4.11. It is essential that the Commission should have first-class research capability. The experience of the Australian Administrative Review Council shows how important this is. The Commission should in other respects be adequately staffed. In addition to following up projects on its own initiative it would be prepared to receive and evaluate proposals made by others for the improvement of administrative processes. It would propose legislative reform where necessary and, by its reports, provide informed comment over the whole field, thus serving to increase the coherence of the system. It would also have a role in commenting on pending legislation.

Title

4.12. The title which we suggest for our proposed body is 'Administrative Review Commission'. Possibly 'Citizens' Rights Commission' would more easily catch the eye, but such a title could mislead people into thinking that the body was ready to process individual grievances. That would not be its function.

Relationship with the Council on Tribunals

4.13. An important question concerns the relationship between the new body and the existing Council on Tribunals. In paragraph 4.1 above we have quoted from the Special Report made by the Council on its functions. The Council was seeking a wider role for itself. Its proposals for legislation (1980, Cmnd. 7805, pp. 22–3) included:

The Council should be given a clear general power (in addition to the supervision of the tribunals named in Schedule 1 of the Act of 1971) to act as an advisory body over the whole area of administrative adjudication and the general pattern and organisation of tribunal structure. (ii) The Council should be given a clear right to be consulted, and empowered to offer views, in relation to matters arising on draft primary legislation affecting our area of jurisdiction.

The Government turned down the bulk of the Council's proposals. The Lord Chancellor informed the House of Lords (*Hansard*, HL, 27 April 1981, vol. 419, WA c. 1118–19): 'The Government have concluded that, while the Council's present contribution is widely recognised as being of considerable value, the case has not been made out for any substantial widening of their powers or functions on the lines proposed in the report's principal recommendations, particularly as this would create additional demands on resources.' We feel bound to express regret at this negative response.

4.14. We do, however, believe that it would be very difficult to convert a body which has existed for many years and which has had the limited remit of overseeing the work of tribunals and inquiries into the much wider-ranging type of body which we have in mind. We think, nevertheless, that it would be desirable to keep the Council on Tribunals in being. It has a specialist role to perform in relation to the day-to-day operation of the tribunals under its surveillance. The volume of tribunal and inquiry work which it has to oversee is massive. The Council should work in close collaboration with our new proposed Administrative Review Commission. There could be some common membership. The Parliamentary Commissioner for Administration, for example, is already an ex-officio member of the Council on Tribunals.

Influence of the Commission and its accountability

4.15. Finally we must consider the critical question—how much power and influence would our proposed Commission actually wield? We ask the question because we heard complaints from so many quarters about the treatment accorded to the Council on Tribunals. It has been starved of resources and the recommendations which it has made appear often to have been summarily rejected. We have compared this with the influence acquired by the Parliamentary Commissioner for Administration. As we argue elsewhere, much of his strength derives from his links with Parliament, in particular from the Select Committee of the House of Commons. We recommend that our proposed Commission should submit an annual report to Parliament either directly or through a nominated minister. We believe that such Reports would be of great interest to Parliament which might well wish to devise appropriate procedures to handle them. Possibly the appointment of a Select Committee would seem to Parliament the proper machinery or, as there already exists the Select Committee on the Parliamentary Commissioner for Administration, its role might be expanded and its title changed to the Select Committee on Administrative Justice.

Alternative proposals which we have rejected

4.16. The machinery of government seems to be resistant to external criticism and advice. The Report of the Machinery of Government Committee (the Haldane Report—Cd. 9230) published in 1918 is the only full-scale examination of the subject made in this century. The Report devoted a chapter to describing the vast burdens placed upon the Lord Chancellor and his small department. It recommended the creation of a Ministry of Justice. That recommendation has never been adopted by Government. Yet the Lord Chancellor's Office today has much wider responsibilities for the machinery of justice, in particular for the system of civil and criminal courts, than it had in 1918. Theoretically, at least, one way of providing the missing institution for which we are pressing might be by the establishment of a Ministry of Justice which, in addition to its other duties, would be responsible for all aspects of administrative justice. There are, however, objections to this course. We would not be satisfied with a reform agency which was itself part of the government machine. It would be quite unable to perform the role of external critic which is such a notable feature of the Australian system, under which the Administrative Review Council can take the Government to task, for example, for introducing legislation which prejudices the exercise of rights of challenge (9th Annual Report, paragraph 222). In any event, the proposal of a Ministry of Justice goes far wider and touches on far more contentious issues than our more limited suggestion.

CHAPTER 4. RECOMMENDATIONS

1. There should be a permanent body, independent of Government, charged with the duty of overseeing all aspects of administrative justice, drawing attention to defects and proposing reforms (paragraph 4.2).

2. This body could respond to requests made by Government for advice; but it would have an independent role entitling it to act on its own initiative and to set out its own priorities (paragraph 4.10).
3. The body could be set up by Act of Parliament or, more simply, be established as a permanent Royal Commission (paragraph 4.9).
4. We suggest that the new body should be called the Administrative Review Commission (paragraph 4.12).
5. It should have a powerful membership, with possibly an eminent lawyer as Chairman. Other members could include the Parliamentary Commissioner for Administration and the Chairman of the two Law Commissions (paragraph 4.10).
6. The Commission should report annually to Parliament. Other links with Parliament should be established (paragraph 4.15).
7. The Commission should be given adequate resources, in particular a proper research capability, to enable it to carry out its functions effectively (paragraph 4.11).
8. The Council on Tribunals should remain in existence to carry out its heavy work load in relation to the supervision of tribunals and inquiries and should work in close collaboration with the Commission (paragraph 4.14).

5

Ombudsmen

SUMMARY OF ARGUMENT. The introduction of the ombudsman system has improved the position of the citizen *vis-à-vis* the administrator. In investigating allegations of maladministration the ombudsman can probe the inner workings of the administrative agency. He conducts his investigation at no cost to the complainant. The Parliamentary Commissioner for Administration (PCA) is backed by the Select Committee in the House of Commons and, if necessary, by the authority of the House itself. Departments cannot afford to ignore his recommendations.

It is, however, a matter for concern that such a comparatively small number of people seek the help of the PCA. Despite the efforts that have been made to improve access within the existing legislative framework, greater use of the PCA's services is unlikely to be achieved until there is direct access to him (in place of the existing mandatory requirement for a complaint to be referred through an MP). More publicity is needed for what he can do and has done.

Several changes are required in the Local Ombudsman system. There should be no need to refer a complaint through a local councillor. Instead there should be direct access. As regards enforcement, there have been too many cases in which local authorities have failed to comply promptly or at all with recommendations made by Local Ombudsmen. Attention has repeatedly been drawn by the ombudsmen themselves and by others to this unsatisfactory state of affairs. The Select Committee on the PCA has recently involved itself in the debate and has proposed that it should itself assume a supervisory role on compliance. We see difficulties with this proposal. In our view the time has come to follow the statutory precedent already established in Northern Ireland with the Commissioner for Complaints and to make recommendations contained in further reports of Local Ombudsmen enforceable through the courts. We suggest a procedure for giving effect to this proposal with the necessary safeguards to make the system workable.

5.1. Our terms of reference require us to consider the reforms that may be necessary or desirable in law and procedure in order that a person may secure effective redress of grievances suffered as a consequence of acts or omissions of the various agencies of government. Within that general objective it is appropriate that we are specifically required to consider the extent to which 'the redress of grievances against the administration is best dealt with by the existing or an improved ombudsman system', for it is the specific function of the ombudsman to determine whether an aggrieved individual has suffered unjustly from the defective working of the administrative machine and, if so, to ensure that an adequate remedy is provided by the authority concerned. In the first section of this chapter (paragraphs 5.2–5.40) we will consider the Parliamentary Commissioner for Administration and, in one respect only, the National Health Service Commissioner (paragraphs 5.22–5.23), in the second section (paragraphs 5.41–5.105) the Local Government Ombudsmen, and in the final section (5.106–5.110) some matters affecting all ombudsmen.

PART I

THE PARLIAMENTARY COMMISSIONER FOR ADMINISTRATION

5.2. The office of ombudsman was introduced into Great Britain by the Parliamentary Commissioner Act, 1967 ('the 1967 Act'). That Act was itself largely based upon recommendations made after an inquiry by JUSTICE, whose findings were in 1961 published in the Whyatt Report, *The Citizen and the Administration*. Today the Parliamentary Commissioner for Administration ('the PCA') is commonly referred to as the Parliamentary Ombudsman to distinguish his office from other ombudsmen in the United Kingdom. Since 1967 the ombudsman principle has been extended to Northern Ireland (the PCA for Northern Ireland and the Commissioner for Complaints (1969), both posts being held by the same individual), to the National Health Service (that is, the National Health Service Commissioners for England, Wales (1977), and Scotland (1978) respectively—which posts are held concurrently by the PCA for the time being) and to local government (the Local Commissioners for Administration, again for England, Wales (1974), and Scotland (1975)).
5.3. The function of the PCA is to investigate complaints made by members of the public through an MP against the administrative

action of the fifty or so government departments and other authorities listed in Schedule 2 to the 1967 Act. Subject to the statutory exclusion of such matters as government contracts and personnel and civil service issues, substantially the whole of central government is thus subject to his investigatory jurisdiction. In the same way the Northern Ireland PCA can investigate complaints against the principal departments of government there and he can also deal with complaints against the Civil Service Commission, for he (unlike the PCA) has jurisdiction to investigate personnel matters. In its evidence to us the Law Society stressed that while the ombudsman machinery is a valuable part of the system for controlling administration, it is quite distinct from the system of legal control, since the ombudsman's investigations and reports lead not to legal remedies but to recommendations which can be acted upon 'politically'. We readily accept that there are many important differences between the ombudsman approach and judicial control of the administration, but there is in practice a significant overlap in subject-matter between the ombudsman system and judicial control; and the two methods of control should increasingly be seen as complementary to one other. Thus (to take but one example of overlap) the PCA commonly persuades government departments to remedy injustices by paying compensation to aggrieved claimants. In a significant number of these cases it is clear that the claimants had not been paid what was legally due to them. So we do not believe that the ombudsman can appropriately be described as providing just another 'political' remedy against the administration. His unique position is well described by Sir Cecil Clothier KCB, QC, in his Introduction to the PCA's Annual Report for 1983 (HC 322) (p. 1): 'The Office of Parliamentary Commissioner stands curiously poised between the legislature and the executive, while discharging an almost judicial function in the citizen's dispute with his government; and yet it forms no part of the judiciary.'

5.4. For the institution of ombudsman to be fully effective, it needs to command the support of ministers, MPs, and local councillors. An ombudsman's task is not to provide convenient political solutions to administrative disputes, but to encourage public officials, in addition to complying with the requirements of the law, to maintain acceptable standards of good administration in their dealings with private persons. Where these standards have not been observed, and this has caused injustice to an individual, an adequate remedy should be afforded even though the individual's case has little or no political support to back it. What this means in practice is that a recommendation made by an ombudsman should be complied with by the administration and treated with the same deference as a court order.

The PCA's links with Parliament

5.5. The office of PCA is a means of giving protection to the citizen against injustice caused by faulty administration on the part of a department of central government. The White Paper on which the 1967 Act was based (1965, Cmnd. 2767) emphasized that the office was intended to develop and reinforce existing constitutional arrangements for protecting the individual. In particular, the scheme adopted in the 1967 Act emphasized the parliamentary context of the PCA's work. Only members of the House of Commons can refer complaints to the PCA, and it is to individual members and to the House as a whole that the PCA presents his reports. There is also a Select Committee of the House of Commons which examines the reports published by the PCA and by the Health Service Commissioner. In 1979 the Committee's jurisdiction was amended so as to enable it to consider the reports of the Northern Ireland PCA. The Committee has survived two threats to abolish it and can now be regarded as a permanent fixture (Roy Gregory, 'The Select Committee on the PCA, 1967–1980', [1982] Public Law, pp. 49 ff.). As Gregory convincingly demonstrates (pp. 55–70), the work of the Select Committee has often been successful in bringing pressure to bear upon government departments which would otherwise have continued to dispute the PCA's findings and recommendations. The Committee has also been influential in encouraging the PCA to take a broad view of the concept of maladministration. By contrast, it is disappointing that the Select Committee has had so little success in persuading different governments to accept the case for broadening the limits of the PCA's jurisdiction (for example, 4th Report from the Select Committee 1977–8, Review of Access and Jurisdiction, (HC 615/444), 26 July 1978 and the Government's Observations thereon, Cmnd. 7449, January 1979). The case for expanding the PCA's jurisdiction was fully canvassed in a 1977 report prepared by a committee of JUSTICE (under the chairmanship of David Widdicombe QC). Reference should be made to chapter 4 of the committee's report entitled *Our Fettered Ombudsman*. The PCA has himself advocated the widening of the jurisdiction. In 1984 the Select Committee recommended that over fifty non-departmental public bodies should be considered for inclusion within the ombudsman system (4th Report, Session 1983-4, HC 619, November 1984). That recommendation has been substantially implemented by the Parliamentary and Health Commissioners Act, 1987.

Access

5.6. The PCA is currently receiving annually about 750 to 1000 complaints (and the Northern Ireland PCA about 130 to 170 complaints) referred by Members of Parliament. (These figures are based on information given in their respective annual reports for the years 1982-6.) He carries out an investigation in about a quarter of these cases, the remaining three-quarters being outside his jurisdiction or in some other way not appropriate for investigation. The two government departments which give rise to the largest number of investigations are the Department of Health and Social Security and the Inland Revenue. Between them they now account for about half of all cases investigated. As we have said, all these investigations derive from complaints referred by Members of Parliament. We are firmly convinced that the work of the PCA gains much strength from his links with Parliament. We have, however, had to consider whether any change is needed in the statutory rule (section 5(1) of the 1967 Act) that it is only Members of the House of Commons who can refer complaints to the PCA. The JUSTICE committee referred to in paragraph 5.5 above recommended, in chapter 5 of *Our Fettered Ombudsman*, that members of the public should have direct access to the PCA, in the sense that the PCA should be able to investigate complaints without any involvement of a Member of the House of Commons. In practice, many members of the public write or telephone directly to the PCA. Thus in 1983 he had nearly a thousand letters and nearly two thousand phone calls. These figures were much the same in 1984-5; in 1986 there were 838 letters and 1829 phone calls. A high percentage are simply requests for information. A significant number do, however, relate to grievances or complaints. To these the PCA may reply in one of three ways: (i) that the complaint appears to be outside his jurisdiction; (ii) that the problem seems more suitable for reference to the complainant's constituency Member; or (iii) where it appears prima facie that investigation by the PCA would be appropriate, that the PCA can investigate only at the request of a Member and that he will, if the complainant so wishes, write to a Member (not necessarily the constituency Member) to ask if an investigation is desired. The number of cases in category (iii) is admittedly small (rarely more than ten a year). The machinery described under (iii) was introduced in 1978. It does not bypass the statutory need for an MP to agree that the complaint should be investigated by the PCA, but it does provide the complainant with a positive response to his initial approach to the PCA. Both the House of Commons and the Government rejected the proposal in the 1977 JUSTICE report that the need for the intervention of a Member of Parliament should be dispensed with.

5.7. There are now a hundred or so national ombudsmen in the world and it appears that there are only two who cannot receive complaints direct from the public. The two exceptions are the French *Médiateur* and the PCA (Annual Report 1983—Introduction, paragraphs 7 and 8). The 1977 JUSTICE Report quoted figures which strongly supported the argument that direct access was causally linked with a high work load. The Report also drew attention to the fact that the original Whyatt Report had recommended that direct access should be granted after an experimental period of about five years. If direct access were allowed it seems to us that the PCA would be able to project himself to the public in a far more positive way. He could advertise the availability of his services more vigorously and could supply direct to complainants (and, with their consent, to the Press) copies of his case reports.

5.8. Sir Cecil Clothier once argued that the need for missionary work is perhaps less in this country than in others where there is direct access (Annual Report 1982, paragraph 13). Later, however, he began to have doubts about the wisdom of the present arrangements. An MP who raises a matter direct with a minister has neither the time nor the resources to probe the answer which he receives. Sir Cecil was inclined to favour a compromise whereby the citizen first asks his MP to take up his grievance with the department concerned; if the citizen is dissatisfied with the progress that is achieved he should have the right to refer the case direct to the PCA (Annual Report 1983, paragraph 7). We take a somewhat different view. We believe that there is an urgent need for missionary work by the PCA. It will only be when the value of his services is well publicized nationally to all sections of society and when the public are invited to submit grievances direct that the present low volume of complaints will increase significantly. We recognize that some Members of Parliament will be reluctant to allow direct access as they may fear that this move will reduce the importance of the services which they offer to constituents through 'surgeries' and in other ways. But we believe that the public interest makes the change necessary. We recognize a further danger, namely, that the jurisdiction of the PCA might become too popular, leading to an overwhelming work load and the risk of inferior investigations. This consequence could be avoided by making available to the PCA additional resources. The links with Parliament would have to be maintained by the PCA keeping the Select Committee of the House of Commons fully informed of all his investigations. Many complaints would, as now, be passed on by MPs to the PCA for investigation.

5.9. Accordingly we recommend that the 1967 Act should be amended by providing for direct access to the PCA by all complainants. Members of Parliament would still be able to refer cases themselves, but this would cease to be the only route.

Investigating on his own initiative

5.10. We have considered whether, as the ombudsman may do in some other countries, the PCA should have the right on his own initiative to carry out investigations into administrative matters— where, for example, reports are published in the press of alleged incompetence by a government department on a matter of current concern. A related question is whether the PCA should be able to conduct a general investigation into how a government department has dealt with certain matters, or to inspect the running of a particular institution or branch of a department. At present one or more complaints about a particular establishment may make it necessary for the PCA to examine how other individuals similarly placed have been treated.

5.11. In 1978 the Select Committee recommended that if, on the basis of individual complaints, the PCA had reason to believe that a particular branch of a department was not dealing efficiently with its business, the PCA should, subject to the Select Committee's approval, be able to carry out a systematic investigation of the work of that branch. The aim would be to identify the causes of the problem and to make recommendations for improving the position (see the 4th Report from the Select Committee referred to in paragraph 5.5 above). This recommendation by the Select Committee was rejected by the Government on the ground that these additional powers of inspection were not necessary and would distract the PCA and his staff from their task of investigating individual complaints (January 1979, Cmnd. 7449).

5.12. We have been struck by the fact that the PCA in the course of investigating one or more complaints may have to examine how a whole class of cases has been handled by a department. For example, in 1981 industrial action in the civil service led, among other things, to delay in the issue of passports and the PCA received a number of complaints (Annual Report 1981, paragraph 25). In the end he decided to investigate seven of them. His general attitude was that departments were bound to make every effort to alleviate the effects on the citizen of strikes by civil servants. 'I decided therefore', he wrote (1982 Report, paragraph 47), 'that I should widen the scope of my investigation into these complaints so as to look in detail at the steps which the Passport Office had taken to reduce inconvenience to the travelling public arising from their staff's industrial action.' He was impressed by the measures which had been taken.

5.13. More recently the PCA submitted to Parliament his 4th Report for the Session 1983–4, entitled *Investigation of a Complaint about Delay in Reviewing a Conviction for Murder* (HC 191). In September 1977, a forensic scientist, Dr Clift, was suspended from duty by the Home Office and a pending prosecution was abandoned because his evidence was regarded as untrustworthy. The complainant, Mr Preece, had been convicted of murder in Scotland in 1973. The forensic scientific evidence against him had been given by Dr Clift. Although the suspension from duty took place in 1977 it was not until 1981 that Mr Preece's conviction was referred to the High Court of Justiciary in Scotland and the conviction quashed. In investigating the particular complaint the PCA had perforce to look at the way in which the Home Office had reacted once it knew (as it did in September 1977) that Dr Clift gave evidence which was unsafe to support convictions. The PCA concluded that the Home Office's reaction to the discovery of 'an unprecedented pollution of justice at its source' (Report, paragraph 58) was inadequate and he made a number of serious criticisms in his report.

5.14. It seems to us that in cases such as those which we have cited (and many more examples could be given) the PCA's investigations carry him into a review of the way one or more departments deal with a class of case or category of work. We do not think that what the Select Committee recommended involves any major extension of this role. Hence, while we accept that the PCA should not assume the general remit of inspecting the administrative efficiency of government departments, a task that would be beyond his resources, we consider that the limited recommendation made by the Select Committee in 1978 would be beneficial and would not lead to a wasteful diversion of resources away from the PCA's primary task. We recommend accordingly.

Exposing a defect in statute law

5.15. When an individual complains that he has suffered injustice through maladministration, investigation may show that the sense of injustice has arisen out of the application to the individual of a rule which is contained in a statute or statutory instrument. In such a case, the administrative decision may have been a correct application of the statutory rule in question, but the PCA's investigation may have shown that the rule produces consequences which were not intended and which give rise to hardship or unfairness. From an early stage the Select Committee has encouraged the PCA to take up with the department concerned the issue of whether a statutory rule has been the subject of a departmental review; and the PCA's report on an investigation may include an account of the review and sometimes a statement of the outcome. We have considered whether the PCA should be expressly authorized by statute to draw Parliament's attention to unforeseen injustices resulting from primary legislation. In fact he does already point out instances of unfairness which he considers to result from legislation. He may also bring to the notice of the Law Commission any instance where his investigations suggest that the law is defective or unjust. Since this is already his practice, we do not consider that the 1967 Act needs to be amended in this respect.

The language of the Parliamentary Commissioner Act 1967—'injustice in consequence of maladministration'

5.16. The central phrase of the 1967 Act on which the PCA's jurisdiction is based empowers him to investigate written complaints by members of the public who claim 'to have sustained *injustice in consequence of maladministration*' in connection with action taken in the exercise of the administrative functions of a government department or other authority to which the Act applies (sections 5(1)(a) and 10(3)). Neither 'injustice' nor 'maladministration' is defined in the 1967 Act but each term has been applied broadly in the case-work of successive holders of the office of PCA. The 1977 JUSTICE report recommended that the PCA should instead be empowered to investigate *unreasonable, unjust, or oppressive action* by government departments. This matter was examined in 1978 by the Select Committee of the House of Commons. The Select Committee reported that the proposed change in the definition of the PCA's competence would not enable him to investigate or criticize anything that did not already fall within his remit (4th Report from the Select Committee referred to in paragraph 5.5 above). Although it was more than once suggested to us in the written evidence which we received that a change in the statutory test of 'injustice in consequence of maladministration' was desirable, Sir Cecil Clothier told us that in his opinion the present statutory test was a wholly adequate basis for his investigations. He also stated that while some potential complainantts might not understand what the statutory test meant, very many more complaints were received from persons who understood it well, in the sense of mismanagement of their affairs by persons in authority. Moreover, the PCA need not express his conclusions at the end of an investigation in terms of the statutory formula. Thus, he may state in his conclusion that a particular complainant has good cause for dissatisfaction at the way in which the department has handled his affairs, or that a serious but isolated error was made. As to the word 'injustice', the PCA very reasonably takes the view that this should be construed as personal injustice suffered by the person aggrieved rather than injustice (or a feeling of injustice) suffered by the community at large or by a substantial section of it. On this ground he refused to investigate complaints relating to the Revenue's agreement concerning the Fleet Street casual workers who had evaded their tax obligations and which subsequently gave rise to the case of *R* v. *Inland Revenue Commissioners*, ex parte *National Federation of Self-Employed* [1982] AC 617 (Address by Sir Cecil Clothier to JUSTICE 11 July 1984 at pp. 4–5). For these reasons, we do not recommend that any change should be made in the phrase 'injustice in consequence of maladministration' as the basis of the PCA's jurisdiction.

Relations between the PCA and the courts

5.17. Many differences exist between the work of the ombudsman and the role of the courts in controlling administrative acts. While it is dangerous to resort to generalizations it may be said that the courts are primarily concerned with the legality of administrative decisions, whereas the ombudsman is primarily concerned with whether standards of good administration have been observed. The adversary procedures of civil litigation bear little resemblance to the inquisitorial process followed by the PCA, the costs of whose investigations are met from public funds. The highly co-operative attitude of nearly all departments and bodies subject to his jurisdiction, reinforced where necessary by a hint as to his statutory powers, ensure to the PCA ready access to the relevant official files. A litigant, on the other hand, has to rely upon the procedure of discovery. The outcome of these two processes also differs sharply. Judicial control culminates in an authoritative judgment by the court which may quash the offending decision, award damages, or provide other relief. The PCA's finding on whether the complaint is justified is authoritative in quite a different sense, for he has no power to force the department to provide any particular remedy.

5.18. None the less there are points of comparison between the role of the courts and that of the ombudsman. Some of the grounds upon which the ombudsman might base a finding of maladministration (such as the unreasonable exercise of a statutory power or the failure to consider all the relevant circumstances) could also be grounds for judicial review. In other instances the PCA may find maladministration where a court would deny relief (as where an official has given an assurance as to future executive action which is later found to conflict with a statutory duty). Although the PCA cannot in any of these cases award damages to a complainant, he may recommend payment of compensation or other financial benefits or the remission of a claim, and the recommended payment or waiver (as the case may be) will then be duly provided by the department which was the subject of criticism. What matters to an individual who has suffered loss is that he should recover appropriate compensation, and it is immaterial to him whether this takes the form of damages awarded by a court or *ex gratia* compensation paid by the department (though he will naturally prefer the route that costs him nothing).

Investigations by the PCA where the complainant has (or had) other avenues of redress open to him

5.19. Under the 1967 Act, the PCA may not investigate any administrative action in respect of which the person aggrieved has or had a right to go before a tribunal or has or had a remedy in any court of law (section 5(2) of the 1967 Act). By the proviso to that subsection the PCA is allowed to investigate action where he is satisfied that 'in the particular circumstances' the individual cannot reasonably be expected to resort (or to have resorted) to his right or remedy. The PCA not infrequently refuses jurisdiction where a complaint should properly be the subject of an appeal to a tribunal, but it is rare for him to refuse to investigate a complaint on the ground that the person aggrieved has 'a remedy by way of proceedings in any court of law' unless the facts alleged fall into a category of case which is well within the normal jurisdiction of the courts (such as a case of personal injury occurring on departmental premises) or unless a writ has actually been issued. The statutory language gives the PCA some measure of discretion, for it may not be possible to tell until after the investigation has been completed whether the complainant 'has or had' a remedy at law.

5.20. There have in fact been cases where the PCA has investigated a matter which subsequently came before the courts. A well-known example is provided by the incident when the Home Office threatened to revoke the television licences of persons who had (quite lawfully as it transpired) taken prompt action to renew their licences at the old cheap rate instead of waiting for the expiry date and then being obliged to pay an enhanced rate. The PCA in a special report (HC 680, 1974–5) criticized the Home Office for inefficiency and lack of candour with the public. In a subsequent law suit (*Congreve* v. *Home Office* [1976] QB 629) the Court of Appeal held that the threat to revoke the licences was unlawful. The Home Office subsequently refunded the additional monies obtained from the licensees under the threat of revocation.

5.21. Another instance of overlap is afforded by the case of *Barty-King* v. *Ministry of Defence* [1979] 2 All ER 80. The judge (May J. as he then was) there held that the Ministry was bound to issue a certificate under section 71 of the Finance Act, 1952, stating that the fourth duke of Westminster had died from a war wound. The effect of the certificate was to exempt the duke's estate from death duty. Four applications for such a certificate had earlier been refused. It emerged at the hearing that the PCA had investigated the first two refusals of the certificate and had criticized the procedures adopted. The case had been referred to anonymously by the PCA in his Annual Report for 1971 (at p. 26) and its significance was commented on by Gregory and Hutchesson in *The Parliamentary Ombudsman* (1975) at pp. 312–13 and 351–2. After the High Court judgment the Government undertook to review other cases in which a certificate had been refused (*Hansard*: House of Commons, 26 November 1979, cols. 501–2).

Undertakings not to sue

5.22. The Health Service Commissioner has a difficult path to tread in some cases. Not only does his empowering statute have the same provision as section 5(2) of the 1967 Act, to which reference has been made in paragraph 5.19 above (National Health Service Reorganization Act, 1973, section 34(4)), but also he is specifically excluded from investigating (*inter alia*) 'action taken in connection with the diagnosis of illness or the care or treatment of a patient, being action which, in the opinion of the Commissioner in question, was taken solely in consequence of the exercise of clinical judgment, whether formed by the person taking the action or by any other person' (1973 Act, section 34(5) and Schedule 3, paragraph 1).

5.23. In exceptional cases, for instance where a complaint of maladministration in a hospital relates to the treatment of a patient who has died, the Health Service Commissioner may, before exercising his discretion to investigate the case, require an undertaking from the complainant not to sue the hospital authorities. While it might be argued that such undertakings are in principle undesirable (and perhaps legally unenforceable) we can well understand why the relatives of a child or old person who has died in hospital may be willing to give the undertaking so that an impartial investigation may be made into the circumstances. Such persons may have no intention of bringing an action against those responsible. We can also understand that the giving of such undertakings enables the Commissioner to investigate complaints which he might otherwise have to decline. No doubt it smoothes the way for the Commissioner to be able to assure those whose actions he is investigating that such an undertaking has been given. But when we reflect upon the fact that the undertaking may be required to be given by persons still in a state of

grief or shock and that at the time when they give the undertaking
they may have no just appreciation of the strength of any possible
civil action, we have been led to the conclusion that undertakings not
to sue should be sought by the Health Service Commissioner only in
very special circumstances and we recommend accordingly. We
further express the hope that neither the PCA nor the Local
Ombudsman will ever require such undertakings to be given by
complainants.

The question whether the relationship between the PCA and the
courts should be changed

5.24. We have considered whether the present overlapping of
functions between the courts and the PCA is satisfactory or whether
section 5(2) of the 1967 Act should be revised. Three broad options
might seem to be open: (*a*) to integrate the administrative jurisdiction of the civil courts and the PCA into a single system, with a
common procedure for investigating and reviewing acts of the
administration; on this basis all claims against the administration
would be made in the same manner but the actual procedure to be
followed would depend upon the nature of the claim; (*b*) to mark out
the functions of the courts and the PCA more precisely, specifying
which types of complaint must go to the courts and which must be
referred to the PCA; (*c*) to maintain the status quo, leaving the
complainant to choose his preferred avenue of redress and, if he
complains to the PCA, entrusting the PCA with a discretion to
refuse to investigate a complaint which he considers should come
before the courts.

5.25. The first of these courses would involve a radically new
approach to controlling the administration which we do not consider to be practicable. The traditional role of the courts in this
country is to decide issues which are brought before them after
preparation by the parties. The courts' role is essentially a passive
one. It would be a fundamental departure for the courts to undertake
an active role and to initiate inquiries and investigations in relation to
pending law suits. (We may comment in passing that if the courts
were to be obliged to undertake such a role there would seem to be
no particular logic in confining its application to cases involving
challenge to administrative action.) Many problems would arise. It
would be difficult to decide in what cases and at what stage the court
ought to start to investigate of its own motion. It is a well-known fact

that a very high percentage of actions commenced in the courts are either settled or abandoned. Who would pay the costs of the abortive investigations? Presumably this wasted expenditure would have to be borne by the state. A further problem is whether the investigation by the court should be in substitution for or in addition to the ordinary processes such as discovery of documents and interrogatories. Many lawyers would want to preserve these traditional weapons for establishing the facts and would be sceptical of the court's ability to carry out equally rigorous research. It is scarcely necessary to add that there would have to be a large increase in the staff of the courts if they were to undertake such an investigatory role. But perhaps the conclusive objection to any attempt to integrate the PCA with the court system is the fact that the PCA gets the support and co-operation of departments in answering questions and revealing records precisely because he operates outside the regime of the courts of law. If the PCA came to be regarded as the investigatory arm of the court we believe that the whole atmosphere would change and that departments would act strictly in accordance with their legal obligations and disclose only such documents as were discoverable at law. So we see no net gain to be derived from adopting the first option.

5.26. The second course referred to in paragraph 5.24 above (a more precise demarcation of the roles of the courts and of the PCA respectively), would be likely to restrict the future development both of judicial control and the work of the PCA. It would also cut out the right of the individual to choose his preferred avenue of redress. This consideration was given prominence in a report to the Attorney-General of Australia submitted by the Administrative Review Council (*The Relationship between the Ombudsman and the Administrative Appeals Tribunal*—Report No. 22 (1985), paragraph 47):

It is the Council's view that a major benefit of having overlapping jurisdictions is to offer aggrieved individuals a range of distinct review venues in which they can pursue administrative justice according to the particular circumstances of their cases. Administrative justice cannot be achieved by both review bodies in all cases because of their distinct jurisdictions, roles and procedures and the remedies available from each body.

In evidence to us the Commission for Local Administration in England argued that the individual should continue to have freedom of choice as between the ombudsman and the courts. In the Commission's experience the potential overlap between the courts and their own jurisdiction creates no problems.

5.27. Our conclusion, therefore, is to favour the third course of action outlined in paragraph 5.24 above, namely, maintaining the status quo and thereby allowing for future developments in the work both of the ombudsman and of the courts. We say this being well aware of the substantial degree of overlap which exists between the two systems. We have also taken note of the case histories summarized in the PCA's recent annual reports which demonstrate that, in addition to the many small cases where benefits are paid belatedly or unreasonable tax demands are abated, there are also certain cases in which the PCA's intervention leads to the payment of substantial sums of money (£57,000 in one case in 1982, a similar sum in 1983, in another 1983 case pension arrears of £2,600 with the department undertaking the review of 600 to 700 potentially similar cases, and in 1984 £131,000 paid to 140 war pensioners). In a case concerning wrong advice about the duty liability of a mixture of beer and cider (known as 'Snakebite'), when, on reference to headquarters some time after production had started, the correct duty, which rendered the mixture commercially unprofitable, was discovered, HM Customs and Excise agreed to make a payment of £30,000 in settlement of the brewer's claim for development costs (Annual Report, 1986, HC 248, p. 11).

5.28. As regards the choice between the ombudsman and the judicial control of administration, we are convinced that the ombudsman in many situations is a more effective way of securing redress against the administration than recourse to the courts. As Sir Cecil Clothier said in evidence to us,

The clear intention behind the institution of the ombudsman was to afford a mode of redress for those administrative ineptitudes and inequities which could not reasonably be the subject of litigation. Even those countries with highly developed systems of administrative law and law courts have found that there remains ample scope for the functions of an ombudsman.

There will, however, always be some disputes between the government and the governed that are better resolved by an authoritative application of the law to facts established by the adversary procedure. Difficult points of law are also best resolved by the courts after full argument between the parties in dispute.

5.29. We are, therefore, broadly in favour of maintaining the present role of both courts and ombudsman. But we have to ask whether there are any specific changes which are needed in the relationship between the two institutions.

Preserving the status quo while the PCA investigates

5.30. The 1967 Act gives the PCA no power to intervene directly in the administrative work of departments. In particular, the department may continue dealing with a matter even where it is the subject of a pending complaint to the PCA (1967 Act, section 7(4)). This power enables a department to correct its mistakes and to issue a fresh decision in favour of the citizen as soon as the mistakes are discovered. But in some circumstances (such as those involving the demolition of a building, the construction of a motorway, or the destruction of natural environment) the department could take or authorize action that would pre-empt the outcome of an investigation by making it impossible to restore the status quo ante. We have considered whether, so as to provide a safeguard against abuse of a department's powers, the 1967 Act should be amended to permit the complainant or the PCA himself to apply to the civil court for an order declaring that certain action should not be taken by the department pending the outcome of his investigation. We have, however, concluded that there is no case for this extension of the court's powers. The normal rule is that no injunction can be granted against the Crown (Crown Proceedings Act, 1947, section 21); though see the opinion of Hodgson J. in *R.* v. *Governor of Pentonville Prison*, ex parte *Herbage* [1987] 6 CL 87, discussed at paragraph 6.4 below. If one assumes a situation, as may commonly be the case, where the complainant has no legal remedy against the department, it would be anomalous for the court to be able to intervene so as to enjoin the department from doing what it was legally entitled to do. If, on the other hand, the complainant's legal rights are being infringed, he is free to pursue his remedy in the courts subject to the general disability in relation to injunctions against the Crown.

Whether the PCA should be entitled to ask the court for an advisory opinion on a question of law

5.31. We have considered a proposal that the PCA should be expressly empowered to ask the court for an advisory opinion on a matter of law. It seems that a distinction needs to be drawn between a question of law relating to the jurisdiction of the PCA and a question of law which arises in the course of an investigation. The PCA cannot be compelled to carry out an investigation in a case that is, or may be, within his jurisdiction. The words of section 5(1) of the 1967 Act ('*may* investigate') confer on him a discretion not to investigate (*Re Fletcher's Application* [1970] 2 All ER 527, CA and HL).

5.32. But a case could theoretically arise in which the PCA asserted a right to investigate and a department argued that on the true construction of one of the paragraphs in Schedule 3 to the 1967 Act ('Matters not subject to investigation') he had no jurisdiction to do so. The PCA takes the view that in the event of such a challenge it would be open to him to get a declaratory judgment from the court as to the scope of his jurisdiction (Address by Sir Cecil Clothier to JUSTICE 11 July 1984, pp. 15–16). We see no reason to doubt the correctness of his view. There have been many suits elsewhere in the Commonwealth against ombudsmen brought to establish whether a particular investigation was or was not within jurisdiction. (For a recent example involving the Ombudsman of British Columbia, which reached the Supreme Court of Canada—*British Columbia Development Corporation* v. *Karl Friedman* (1984) 14 DLR (4th) 129 and cases there cited.) A Local Ombudsman has been taken to court in England in a case of the same type—*R.* v. *Local Commissioner*, ex parte *Bradford Council* [1979] QB 287. If suits can be brought against ombudsmen, it must in principle be possible for the PCA to take the initiative and bring an action himself. In practice, no such confrontation requiring recourse to the courts has yet arisen. The PCA takes independent legal advice (not, as was formerly the case, from the Treasury Solicitor) and acts accordingly. For example, there has been a long-standing difference of view between the PCA and the Lord Chancellor's Department as to whether the court staff fall within or without the PCA's jurisdiction. The matter is referred to in the PCA's Annual Report for 1986 (HC 248), p. 16. If necessary, this issue could be decided by the court.

5.33. As regards questions of law which arise in the course of a reference, it can happen that the PCA is able to point out to a department an obvious mistake of law, as in one case where the Home Office accepted that it had erroneously construed a provision in the Prison Act, 1952, relevant to the calculation of parole (David W. Williams, *Maladministration: Remedies for Injustice* (1976), p. 50). If, on the other hand, a difficult question of law lies at the heart of the allegation of maladministration, the PCA can do no more than satisfy himself that the department has taken skilled legal advice and acted on it. This is what the PCA had to do when the complaint raised the question whether the Water Authorities (Collection of Charges) Order, 1974 (SI 1974 No. 448) was *ultra vires* the Water Act 1973 (Case C 380/J—First Report 1974–5, p. 63). The issue was subsequently taken to court and a divided House of Lords held by three to two that the Order was invalid (*Daymond* v. *Plymouth City Council and South West Water Authority* [1976] AC 609).

5.34. In Australia the Commonwealth Ombudsman has power to cause questions relating to the taking of action in pursuance of a power conferred by an enactment or relating to the exercise of such power to be referred to the Administrative Appeals Tribunal by the principal officer of the authority concerned (Ombudsman Act, 1976, section 11 as amended by the Ombudsman Amendment Act, 1983, section 14). The questions that can be put go wider than questions of law but certainly include them. In fact only two such references have been made since the passing of the Act and as one of these was settled there has been only one advisory opinion (the Administrative Review Council's 6th Annual Report, 1981–2, p. 75). In the opinion in that case Brennan J. stressed the delicate nature of the jurisdiction and said that the AAT should only give an answer if the question was real (not hypothetical) and the answer was likely to be definitive (*Re Reference under Section 11 of Ombudsman Act 1976 for an Advisory Opinion*; ex parte *Director-General of Social Services* (1979) 2 Administrative Law Decisions 86, 90–1). It seems that no appeal lies from the AAT's advisory opinion (per Brennan J. at p. 91). The judge thought that if the question referred to the AAT was solely or principally a question of law and if that question was also raised or about to be raised in separate court proceedings, then 'considerations of prudence' might deter the AAT from answering the question. It is noteworthy that the department involved in that case at first objected to being forced by the ombudsman to refer the question and sought legal advice as to whether it was obliged to do so. Subsequently there were further problems in relation to compliance with the opinion: Commonwealth Ombudsman 3rd Annual Report, 1979–80, pp. 48–9 and 4th Annual Report, 1980– 1, p. 12. The Administrative Review Council has recommended to the Attorney-General (Report No. 22, paragraphs 73–4) that the 'fiction' involved in requiring another person to refer to a question should be done away with and that the ombudsman should be given power to refer questions himself direct to the AAT. We have asked ourselves whether it would be desirable to confer on the PCA a similar statutory right to seek or to require others to seek an advisory opinion from the court on a question of law which arises in the course of his investigation. The practical objections are considerable. The reference to the court would delay the investigation, particularly if appeals were permitted. It might be necessary to confer a right on the complainant and on the department to appear and argue before the court. Considerable expense would be involved.

5.35. Having considered the difficulties involved and the Australian experience we conclude that it is neither necessary nor desirable to confer on the PCA any power to cause questions of law to be referred to the courts. It seems to us preferable to let him continue with his existing practice of seeking such independent legal advice as he needs for his own purposes when confronted by any difficult matter of law. Where a serious question of law arises (as in *Daymond*), it is for a litigant to ask the court to resolve it.

Whether the recommendations of the PCA should be enforceable through the courts

5.36. We have considered whether there should be legislation to permit findings of the PCA to be enforceable in the courts (for example, where the PCA recommends that compensation should be paid to the complainant). The theoretical argument in favour of this is that an injustice would remain unremedied and harm would be done to the standing and reputation of the PCA if, after he had found a complaint of maladministration to be justified and had recommended that a certain remedy be provided by the department to cure the injustice, the individual were not to receive that remedy because of the department's refusal to comply. We consider, however, that this argument is outweighed by a number of opposing considerations.

5.37. In practice we are satisfied that there is no problem that has to be tackled. Although there have been instances of non-compliance in the past (Wade, *Administrative Law*, 5th edn., p. 89), the fact is that departments do now comply and do carry out his recommendations. In the background there is always the Select Committee and, if necessary, the authority of Parliament. The fact that the departments remain fully responsible for providing a remedy is an important strength of the present arrangements, since the PCA relies upon the co-operation of departments both in carrying out his investigations and at the stage of remedy. If ultimate recourse to the courts were possible it would be necessary to specify whether the PCA's conclusions would be binding on the courts or whether the court could in some way provide a forum of appeal against the PCA's findings.

5.38. We think that to make the PCA's recommendations enforceable through the courts would be to alter an essential aspect of his office; and we consider that the advantages thereby obtained would be offset by the disadvantages. As we have commented in paragraph 5.25 above, the key to the PCA's success is that the departments co-operate with him and give him full access to their files just because he represents a system which stands apart from the courts and contentious litigation.

5.39. For those reasons, although, as we explain in detail in paragraphs 5.77–5.82 below, in Northern Ireland a recommendation of compensation made by the Commissioner for Complaints may be enforced by the complainant through the courts, we do not consider that a similar provision should be applied to the PCA.

The 'case law' of the ombudsman

5.40. The PCA has produced a large number of reports on individual cases since the office was first established. The more important of these cases have been included in the 'Select Cases' reports which the PCA regularly makes to Parliament. We believe that the volume of material is now such that it constitutes a valuable reference source to be used in the preparation of the general principles of good administration which we advocate in chapter 2 above. Quite apart from the formulation of these principles, there is much to be said for the preparation by or under the authority of the PCA of a digest instancing the main areas in which he has investigated and found maladministration. At present the material is scattered through numerous Annual Reports, 'Selected Cases' reports, and unpublished reports. A single volume epitomizing his case work would be extremely useful in improving the general level of knowledge about his services. (On this aspect see further paragraph 5.111 below.) As the publication would be merely illustrative of the standards which the PCA has in the past required to be observed there is no reason why his future discretion should be in any way fettered.

PART II

THE LOCAL GOVERNMENT OMBUDSMEN

5.41. The foregoing discussion has concentrated on the office of the PCA whose work is carried out against the background of the constitutional principle that the departments investigated are headed by ministers who are responsible to Parliament for their departments. The constitutional position is very different for the Local Government Ombudsmen (or to give them their full title, the Local Commissioners for Administration in England, Wales, and Scotland). The Local Ombudsmen do not report upon their investigations to Parliament but simply to the complainant and to the local council and member concerned. Copies of their reports are available to the public on request and in practice are supplied regularly to the press.

5.42. In England and Wales the system has now been in operation for twelve years. The Local Government Act, 1974, established 'the Commission for Local Administration in England' and 'the Commission for Local Administration in Wales'. There has only been one Local Commissioner for Wales though there have always been three Local Commissioners for England, each responsible for a defined geographical area. (We will refer to them as Local Commissioners or Local Ombudsmen.) The PCA is an ex-officio member of each Commission but he takes no part in the investigations carried out by the Local Commissioners. The 1974 Act also provided for the establishment of bodies to be called 'the representative body for England' and 'the representative body for Wales', to consist of bodies appearing to the Secretary of State to represent local authorities in the two countries (section (24(1) and (2)). Currently the Representative Body for England consists of ten persons—three members each from the Association of County Councils, the Association of District Councils, and the Association of Metropolitan Authorities and one representative from the Water Authorities Association. In Wales it consists of four County Council, four District Council, and two Welsh Water Authority representatives. The function of the Representative Bodies is to receive and (if appropriate) to comment on the annual reports made by the Local Commissions and the individual reports made by each Local Commissioner. A Representative Body may also comment on any recommendations made or conclusions reached by a Commission in carrying out its statutory duty of reporting annually on the operation of the Act. An additional function of each Representative Body is to review the budget which each Commission prepares of its estimated expenditure in the year ahead and to make its comments thereon to the Commission and ultimately to the Secretary of State if the Commission insists on proceeding with a budget estimate which the Representative Body regards as excessive. The costs of the Commissions are borne by the county councils.

5.43. The Local Government (Scotland) Act, 1975, section 21, created the office of Commissioner for Local Administration in Scotland (no separate Commission was created) and provided for the appointment of the 'designated body for Scotland' to receive the Commissioner's annual reports. This body (the Convention of Scottish Local Authorities) is responsible for defraying the reasonable expenses of the Commissioner and his officers.

5.44. In 1980 the record of the Local Ombudsmen was examined in detail by a Committee of JUSTICE (under the joint chairmanship of Victor Moore and Harry Sales) in a report entitled *The Local Ombudsmen, A Review of the First Five Years*. The report contains much useful statistical information and records the results of extensive research work carried out in interviews with complainants, local councillors, and others. The nineteen recommendations made in that report cover many facets of the work of the Local Ombudsmen as well as such matters as the limitations then (and now) placed on their jurisdiction. For our part we propose to concentrate on what we regard as the salient deficiencies in the system as they now manifest themselves after some eleven years' experience. We will not repeat the arguments for (and against) the extension of the Local Ombudsmen's jurisdiction in the respects discussed in chapter 2 of the JUSTICE Report. We note, however, that the Commissions for England and Wales made a further submission to the Secretary of State in August 1984 pressing for a widened jurisdiction and the Government has made a response (Report for the year ended 31 March 1986, Appendix 4). The Government turned down (not for the first time) proposed extensions covering complaints concerning *all* commercial and contractual matters, concerning personnel matters, and about conduct and discipline in schools and colleges. The renewed proposal that the Local Ombudsmen should be able to investigate on their own initiative a matter coming to their attention where injustice may have been caused by faulty administration was also rejected.

5.45. We will first give some indication of the complaints work-load of the Local Commissioners. The figures in Table 5.1 are taken from five recent annual reports and are confined to complaints properly referred to a Local Commissioner in accordance with the statute (a concept which we discuss further below).

TABLE 5.1 Complaints to Local Commissioners

Year ended 31 March	England	Wales	Scotland	Total
1982	2706	147	357	3210
1983	2753	295	468	3516
1984	3034	213	478	3725
1985	3389	249	441	4079
1986	3802	216	578	4296

It is interesting to contrast the totals column with the figures published by the PCA for complaints properly referred to him. His figures for the same five calendar years (1982–6) are respectively 838, 751, 837, 759 and 719. It follows that the Local Commissioners handle roughly four to five times more complaints annually than the PCA. In England and Wales the complaints submitted to the Local Commissioners have tended to break down fairly consistently into a pattern—one-third housing, one-third planning, and one-third miscellaneous, though in the last year to 31 March 1986 housing complaints (in England) moved ahead of planning complaints (41 per cent against 29 per cent). In Scotland housing complaints predominate (54 per cent in the year to 31 March 1986) with planning and building control complaints in second place (15 per cent). Many of the complaints which reach the Local Commissioners are found to be outside their jurisdiction for one reason or another; other complaints are not entertained because the Commissioners in the exercise of their discretion consider that they do not merit investigation. An appreciable percentage is disposed of by amicable settlement during the course of the investigation.

Access

5.46. The 1974 Act provides that a complaint shall not be entertained unless it is made in writing to a member of the authority concerned specifying the action alleged to constitute maladministration and is referred to the Local Commissioner, with the consent of the person aggrieved, by that member, or by any other member, with a request to investigate the complaint (section 26(2)). By way of exception to this basic rule, it is provided in section 26(3) that a Local Commissioner may nevertheless entertain a complaint if he is satisfied that a member of the authority concerned has been asked to refer the complaint and has not done so. (The corresponding provisions for Scotland are section 24(2) and (3) of the 1975 Act.)

5.47. In practice these provisions have operated as a serious curtailment of the jurisdiction of the Local Commissioners. The reason is that large numbers of people wish to complain direct to their Local Commissioner. Even when the correct statutory procedure is pointed out, many of them abandon their complaints rather than refer them through a member of the local authority.

5.48. The JUSTICE Report referred to in paragraph 5.44 above highlighted this problem and recommended that, as an alternative to a complaint being referred through a member of the authority concerned, it should be permissible for a person to make a direct complaint to the Local Commissioner (Report, paragraph 104). The recommendation envisaged that, on receipt of a direct complaint, the Local Commissioner would first have to refer it to the local authority to give it an opportunity to investigate and reply. The English Commissioners agreed with the approach in the JUSTICE Report and on 18 August 1980 recommended to Government that the 1974 Act should be amended so as to permit direct access (Report for year ended 31 March 1981, Appendix VI, paragraph 24 and Appendix VII, paragraph 6). The Representative Body for England opposed the amendment, being of the opinion that the channelling of complaints through members should remain a fundamental feature of the local ombudsman system (see Report for year ended 31 March 1984 at p. 48). The Commission for Local Administration in Wales agreed with the English Commissioners and made the same recommendation to Government. At first the Representative Body for Wales endorsed this view but it subsequently changed its mind and opposed direct access (Report for year ended 31 March 1982, p. 49).

5.49. Since 1980 the volume of direct complaints, which did not subsequently develop into properly referred complaints, has continued to give concern to the Local Commissioners. Thus, in her Chairman's Foreword to the English Commissioners' Report for the year ended 31 March 1982, Baroness Serota wrote:

Whilst fully accepting that in some cases a Member can help to get a complaint reconsidered, and perhaps resolved, there are undoubtedly many cases where a local settlement is just not possible. The requirement to refer a complaint through a Member is thus no more than another barrier between the citizen and the Local Ombudsman and the people most in need of help are often those ill-equipped to overcome such barriers. Experience over eight years clearly supports the Commission's proposal that people should be able to complain *either* direct *or* through a Member.

5.50. The figures for direct complaints in England as recorded in the five annual reports up to March 1986 were as in Table 5.2. About half of these complaints were subsequently referred through a member. Inevitably cost and delay were involved in rerouting the complaints. Nevertheless, the fact remains that approximately half of them were simply 'lost'.

TABLE 5.2 Direct Complaints in England

Year ended 31 March	Complaints
1982	1953
1983	2045
1984	2145
1985	2050
1986	2007

5.51. The reports of the Commission for Local Administration in Wales give the figures for direct complaints for the years ended 31 March 1982 to 1984 as in Table 5.3 (In view of the change in procedure described in paragraph 5.56 below the figures are not given for subsequent years.). Again about half this number became 'lost' in the process of trying to have them referred by the statutory route. The Welsh Local Ombudsman, Mr D. E. A. Jones, commented in the first of his reports referred to above (p. 39): 'It is disturbing to reflect that some of [those who complained direct] may have preferred to forego seeking a remedy for that injustice rather than identify themselves as complainants to elected members.' In his report for the year ended 31 March 1984 (p. 6) he said that some of those who complained direct were not aware of the referral system 'but others thought that direct referral would ensure that the consideration of their complaints would be entirely independent'.

TABLE 5.3 Direct Complaints in Wales

Year ended 31 March	Complaints
1982	215
1983	203
1984	209

5.52. In his report for the year ended 31 March 1984 the Local Ombudsman for Scotland (the late Mr Eric Gillett) also deplored the absence of direct access. He wrote (p. 4):

There are also serious restrictions on the methods of access to me. It remains the case, in spite of the representation which my predecessors and I have made, that I cannot deal with complaints unless the complainant has first asked a councillor to refer the matter to me, even though the councillor may well have been a party to the decision complained against. This year over 80 complaints were lost as complainants did not reply after being asked to seek referral by a councillor.

Pursuing this theme in his report for the year ended 31 March 1985 he observed (p. 3):

I remain convinced that the fact that complainants have to submit their complaint to a councillor in the first instance deters many people from making a complaint at all ... This seems to me fundamentally wrong, and a considerable deterrent to people exercising their statutory right to submit complaints. It is based on a false analogy with complaints against government departments, which must be submitted through MPs. ... It is high time that these defects in the framework of the local ombudsman system were remedied.

The Convention of Scottish Local Authorities has publicly supported Mr Gillett on this issue.

5.53. In the light of these sustained pleas by all the Local Ombudsmen it was disappointing indeed to learn that, after the Department of the Environment had cogitated for three and a half years on the English Commissioners' submission originally made on 18 August 1980 (see paragraph 5.48 above), the Secretary of State on 8 March 1984 finally rejected the proposal for direct access (Report of the Commission for Local Administration in England for the year ended 31 March 1984, p. 33, paragraph 92 and Appendix IV at p. 48). The basis for this rejection was stated to be that, 'It is important that locally elected councillors, as part of their responsibility towards their electors, should continue to be involved in considering complaints against the local authority on which they serve, and thereby have the opportunity to deal with complaints themselves if this is practicable.' In our view, although this goal is important (and is often attained when complainants are willing to route their complaints through local councillors), it is no less important to ensure that electors can in all cases freely invoke the aid of their Local Ombudsmen to remedy injustices (real or supposed) which they attribute to the maladministration of the local councils and councillors. The evidence is compelling to the effect that in many cases complainants who have been at loggerheads with their local councils, possibly for many months, will simply refuse to use the services of a councillor in order to get their cases reviewed by the Local Ombudsman. The figures for 'lost' complaints which we have quoted cannot be ignored. The Local Commissioners in reports published since the Secretary of State's announcement expressed their disappointment at his decision (Reports for the year ended 31 March 1984—England (p. 33) and Wales (p. 27)).

5.54. Although the Secretary of State set his face against an alteration in the law he told the English Commissioners that he was 'concerned' that a number of complaints, which might well justify investigation, did not reach the Commission under existing procedures. He therefore intended to discuss with the Commission and the Representative Body whether improved procedures could be devised within the existsing legislative framework (p. 48 of the English Commissioner's Report for the year ended 31 March 1984).

5.55. In England, a modified referral procedure was introduced on 1 June 1984. The procedure is used by the Local Commissioners with the backing of the Representative Body and with the support of the Secretary of State. When a complaint is received direct by the Commission it is sent by the Commission to the civic head of the local authority concerned with a request that he should seek to settle the complaint locally and that, if settlement proves impossible, he should refer the complaint to the Local Commissioner. By a further refinement to this procedure the Commissioners now advise the chief executive when they have sent a direct complaint to the civil head. In Wales direct complaints are sent to the chief executive, clerk, or chief officer with a request that he draw the matter to the attention of the chairman or mayor and the relevant local members.

5.56. An account of the above procedure is given in the Report of the English Commissioners for the year ended 31 March 1985 at paragraphs 95 to 97. They comment as follows: 'The result so far has been a marked increase in the number of direct complaints becoming properly referred through a Member. But further experience is needed to judge whether the procedure is a truly effective substitute for giving the citizen freedom of choice in how to pursue a complaint.' The Report of the Local Commissioner for Wales for the same year is more sanguine about the new procedure (p. 21): 'Happily, the new procedures for complaint referral which are described in the Commission's general report, and which were readily approved by the Representative Body and by the Local Authority Associations, are likely to provide a complete solution to the long-standing problem of "lost complaints".' As no figures are given it is difficult to judge from the outside how effective the innovation has been, but it seems that there must still be a significant number of direct complaints annually that are neither settled nor properly referred. This is because the new procedure puts the complainant at the mercy of the civic head of the authority so far as the further progress of his complaint is concerned. Although most authorities act fairly in relation to complaints and in all their dealings with the Local Commissioners, there is unfortunately a large body of evidence (provided by the Commissioners in their annual reports and in other public pronouncements) to show both that authorities are capable of displaying animosity to particular complainants and that they may not always be zealous in supporting the work of the ombudsman. No doubt these comments apply only to a minority of authorities.

5.57. The new procedure has not been adopted in Scotland. The Convention of Scottish Local Authorities had reservations about it

and the Local Commissioner considers that it somewhat undermines the case for direct access without providing an adequate
substitute for it. However, direct access has been provided in
Scotland, with effect from 1 January 1986, in the case of two
extensions of the Scottish Local Commissioner's jurisdiction—to the
housing functions of the New Towns and to the Scottish Special
Housing Association—by the Law Reform (Miscellaneous Provisions) (Scotland) Act of 1985.

5.58. We ourselves are not satisfied that the palliative which has
been introduced goes to the heart of the problem. The essential flaw
in the existing legislative framework described in paragraph 5.46
above is that a member of the council which is being attacked by the
complainant has to be involved in the referral process, either
willingly (section 26(2)(b)) or unwillingly (section 26(3)). There is a
class of complainants who do not want any councillor to be so
involved and the present system does not cater for them.

5.59. We recommend that the proper solution is to amend the
legislation so as to allow for direct access as an alternative to referral
through a member. The safeguard recommended in the JUSTICE
Report whereby the ombudsman would forthwith refer the complaint to the local authority for investigation and reply (see paragraph 5.48 above) could be written in if thought desirable, but we
would not press the point. The existing statutory provisions do
already ensure that the local authority has ample opportunity to
remedy the grievance before a Local Commissioner investigates.
Section 26(4) of the 1974 Act requires that a complaint, to be
eligible, must have been made to a member within a year of its
arising. The local authority must have had an opportunity to investigate and reply (section 26(5)) and the Local Ombudsman is not to
proceed with his investigation until the local authority has had an
opportunity to comment (section 28(1)). Similar safeguards are
contained in the Scottish Act.

Failure or refusal to implement recommendations made by Local
Ombudsmen

5.60. A Local Ombudsman, having first satisfied himself that a
complaint is within jurisdiction and merits investigation, will carry
out his investigation and report. He is bound by statute to report (*a*)
to the member of the authority who referred the original complaint
to him, (*b*) to the complainant, and (*c*) to the authority concerned

(section 30(1) of the 1974 Act and, for Scotland, section 28(1) of the 1975 Act). If in the report the Local Ombudsman finds that injustice has been caused to the complainant in consequence of maladministration, the Acts provide that the report 'shall be laid before the authority concerned'. It is thereupon the duty of the authority to consider the report and to notify the Local Ombudsman of the action which it has taken or proposes to take. If a reasonable time elapses and he receives no such notification or if the local authority does not take action to his satisfaction, the Acts state that 'he shall make a further report setting out these facts'. (See section 31(2) and section 29(2) of the respective Acts.) The further report has to be sent to the same recipients as the first report. Curiously, in the 1974 and 1975 Acts there is no requirement that this further report must be 'laid before' the authority concerned. This defect in the statutes was brought to the attention of Government in 1978 by the Local Commissioners for England. In 1979 the Government accepted that a statutory amendment was desirable. The requisite amendment was achieved for Scotland by the Local Government (Miscellaneous Provisions) (Scotland) Act, 1981, section 24 and Schedule 1, which added a new subsection to section 29 of the 1974 Act as follows: '(2A) It shall be the duty of the authority concerned to consider a report made under subsection (2) above, and to notify the Commissioner of the action which the authority have taken, or propose to take.' An attempt was made in 1979 to introduce a similar provision for England and Wales in the Local Government, Planning and Land Bill, but the Bill in its original form was withdrawn, and no attempt has since been made to remedy this obvious lacuna in the 1974 Act (Report of the English Commissioners for the year ended 31 March 1985, pp. 46 and 51). We recommend that the required amendment should be made in the 1974 Act.

5.61. The successive annual reports of the Local Ombudsmen establish clearly that the great majority of local authorities loyally accept the rulings which the Local Ombudsmen give in their first reports and do not make the issue of a further report necessary. Authorities vary in the alacrity with which they comply and in the amplitude of the remedy provided, but, in the language of cricket (which is commonly used in this context in the Local Ombudsmen's reports), they accept the umpire's decision even though they may think it mistaken. Unfortunately, the reports establish with equal clarity that, from the commencement of the Local Ombudsmen system, there has been a minority of local authorities prepared to defy both an original report and a further report on the same matter.

5.62. At one time it was possible for local authorities to refuse to comply with a report, using as the excuse that they had no legal authority for making the payment that ought to be made to redress a grievance upheld by a Local Ombudsman. This excuse was removed by section 1 of the Local Government Act, 1978, which amended section 31 of the 1974 Act (and, for Scotland, section 29 of the 1975 Act) by adding a subsection empowering authorities to make any payment that appears to them to be appropriate in the light of the contents of the report. This amendment does not deal with the situation which arises where the authority wishes to settle the case and to make a payment for acknowledged maladministration before the Local Commissioner has investigated. The Secretary of State has indicated that in such circumstances local authorities may apply to him for sanction to make the payment pursuant to section 19(1) of the Local Government Finance Act, 1982, and that, while each case will turn on its own facts, he will give sympathetic consideration to such applications (Report of the Commission for Local Administration in England for the year ended 31 March 1984, Appendix 4, paragraph 15).

5.63. In England the position is, that in the first twelve years of operation of the scheme (that is up to 31 March 1986), the Local Commissioners had to issue a further report on no less than 140 occasions. In only 38 of these cases did a satisfactory remedy follow. It follows that there has been a failure with about three out of every four further reports. To put this in perspective it is necessary to look at the figure of 102 as a percentage of all cases (including, of course, those where it was only necessary to issue one report) in which a finding of maladministration causing injustice has been made and where the outcome was known at 31 March 1986. The total of such cases was 1534. Accordingly the failure figure of 102 represents about $6\frac{1}{2}$ per cent of the total. Perhaps a more disturbing statistic is the fact that as at May 1984 there were 68 of all local authorities in England (19 per cent) which had at one time or another failed to provide a remedy as required by a Local Commissioner, 17 of them had failed on two or more occasions, and one had failed no less than six times (Minutes of Evidence before the Select Committee on the PCA, Session 1983– 4, HC 622, Evidence of

15 May 1984 at p. 13, per Dr David Yardley, Chairman of the English Commissioners).

5.64. The reports of all the Commissioners have regularly contained details of the cases in which further reports have had to be issued. An analysis of the English cases up to 1979 and of the excuses (if any) proffered by local authorities for non-compliance will be found in the JUSTICE Report referred to at 5.44 above (at paragraphs 114, 119–21, and Appendix C). The need to issue a further report naturally creates further delay for the complainant. For the twenty further reports issued by the English Commissioners in 1982–3 the average time between the first report and the further report was thirty-seven weeks.

5.65. In the Report for the year ended 31 March 1982 one of the English Commissioners (Mr H. B. McKenzie Johnston, CB) drew attention to the seven further reports which he and his predecessor had had to issue in his area that year (p. 42). He deplored the excuse given by one local authority for non-compliance, namely, that if they gave a remedy to the complainant they would incur considerable expense in providing a similar remedy to others in like case. Another Commissioner, Mr F. P. Cook, wrote (p. 46): 'a small hard core who appear unprepared to accept the umpire's decision do give growing concern for the efficacy of a system which rests at present upon acceptance and consent, rather than legislative enforcement. A particular worry is that four authorities . . . have failed twice to take satisfactory action following Second Reports on different complaints.'

5.66. In the Report for the year ended 31 March 1983 the Commission recorded their concern and contrasted their success rate with that of the PCA (p. 7, paragraph 21). 'The Commission', they wrote, 'have not so far advocated any change in the present arrangement (for example, adoption of Northern Ireland's provision). They would much prefer authorities to abide by findings of Local Ombudsmen, to act on them if required, and to act quickly and with good grace.' The Chairman of the English Commissioners, Dr David Yardley, was still taking the same position in an article which he published in 1983 ([1983] Public Law p. 522, at p. 531). He wrote that persuasion was the method favoured by the Local Ombudsmen, but 'we recognise that if the number of "failures" increases, or if the recalcitrant authorities become more determined in their rejection of adverse criticism from Local Ombudsmen,

Parliament may well find the movement for the introduction of more teeth into the powers of the Commission becomes irresistible.'

5.67. The continuing anxiety of the English Commissioners was again manifested in their report for the year ended 31 March 1984. By this time the Select Committee on the PCA had begun to take an interest in the problem of non-compliance by local authorities and the English Commissioners were showing a greater readiness to contemplate the possibility of coercive powers. In this report (p. 34, paragraph 98) they wrote:

Over the years the Commission have expressed their concern about those authorities who do not provide a remedy for injustice found by a Local Ombudsman. They have so far stopped short of recommending legislative action to remove this added injustice for some of those whose complaints are upheld after independent investigation. The matter will be carefully considered in course of the 1984 review mentioned earlier, and will be a matter discussed, at their request, with the Select Committee on the Parliamentary Ombudsman who have indicated their concern that the failure of some authorities to remedy injustice 'risks bringing the ombudsman system into disrepute'.

5.68. Mr D. E. A. Jones, the then Local Commissioner for Wales, had by 31 March 1985 issued nine further reports out of a total of 192 containing a finding of maladministration leading to injustice. None of the nine further reports resulted in the provision of a remedy for the injustice caused by maladministration which he had found. In each of his last four annual reports he commented on the further reports which he was obliged to issue. In the year ended 31 March 1982 he issued 22 reports finding maladministration and resulting injustice and he issued one further report (Report, pp. 4 and 40). The following year the figures were 32 and 2 respectively (Report, pp. 4 and 24–5), for the year ended 31 March 1984 they were 21 and 1 (Report, p. 4), and for the year ended 31 March 1985 13 and nil. In his 1984 report he bemoaned the 'obduracy' of a council which had refused to adopt the remedy which he suggested and which had rejected the result of his investigation 'by arguments which, when properly examined, can be seen to have no substance' (p. 18).

5.69. The Scottish Commissioner had by 31 March 1985 issued a total of eleven further reports, seven of which were in the last three years. Only one further report produced a satisfactory response. In

total 200 reports have been issued in Scotland in which maladministration causing injustice has been found. In his annual report for the
year ended 31 March 1984 Mr Eric Gillett, the then Scottish
Commissioner, commented that while he had made twenty findings
of maladministration with injustice, he had also had to issue four
further reports that year. This figure was 'the highest ever' (paragraph 13) and, measured against the twenty other findings, represented 'an unacceptably high number of failures'.

5.70. Mr Gillett stated that the Scottish local authorities are 'to an
increasing extent' (the trend began in 1982–3) refusing to take
action on the recommendations which he made after full and
impartial enquiry, 'and the public are increasingly aware that this is
so' (paragraph 6). He felt that he could no longer offer complainants
the reasonable certainty that they would be given a remedy if investigation showed that injustice due to maladministration had occurred.
He was conscious of 'widespread scepticism about the effectiveness
of the Local Ombudsman service'. Many people, he believed, must
be deterred from submitting complaints for this very reason. He
contrasted his own success rate with that of the PCA (see paragraph
5.61 above). 'Athough I shall continue', he wrote, 'to try to persuade
local authorities to accept a finding of maladministration, I fear the
situation may well get worse, as more and more officials and local
authorities are prepared to ignore the basis on which the Ombudsman system works in Great Britain, namely, that there would be
voluntary compliance with the recommendations made in a full and
impartial report, or certainly after a further report'.

5.71. The conclusion to which the Ombudsman for Scotland
found himself driven was that there was a need for enforcement
machinery through the courts on the lines of the provisions which
apply in Northern Ireland in respect of findings made by the Commissioner of Complaints there. (We comment further below on the
relevant statutory provisions in force in Northern Ireland.) Mr
Gillett summarized his position as follows (paragraph 6): 'My predecessors and I have been very reluctant to come to this conclusion,
feeling that it was much better to retain the voluntary system as long
as failures to comply were a rarity, but the time has now come to say
that the voluntary system is not working adequately.' In his report for
the year ending 31 March 1985 Mr Gillett observed (paragraph 3):
'What we must seek, either through better adherence by local
authorities to the recommendations of myself and my successors, or

if not, through legislation, is something approaching virtual certainty that a justified complaint will be properly remedied.'

5.72. Further reports have continued to be issued since that date and, notwithstanding the warnings given by the Commissioners, such further reports have been largely ignored. Thus in the four cases reported on by Dr Yardley in the English Commissioners' Report for the year ended 31 March 1985 the authorities generally accepted the findings of maladministration but nevertheless refused to remedy them (Report, paragraphs 32–35) and there were two cases of intransigence the following year (Report for year ended 31 March 1986, paragraphs 24–6). In the ten cases reported on by Mr F. G. Laws in his same Report for the year ended 31 March 1985 only three ended with an attempt by the authority to remedy the injustice (ibid., paragraphs 48–58). Six out of ten acted in response to further reports the following year (Report, paragraph 35). It is only fair to add that Mr Cook in his last year (ended 31 March 1985) issued no further reports and secured satisfactory results by persuasion. In the same Report he commented (paragraph 73): 'The invariable voluntary acceptance of critical findings will be far preferable to some form of statutory enforcement. . . . Even so, local government cannot afford to lose sight of the fact that a single injustice unremedied is one too many.' His successor, Mrs P. A. Thomas, issued no further reports in her first year, ended 31 March 1986 (Report, paragraph 77).

Other instances of lack of co-operation by local authorities

5.73. The following matters have come to our attention.

1. In November 1982 the English Commissioners discussed the question of remedies with the Representative Body and invited their help in improving the situation in the small minority of cases where authorities failed to provide a satisfactory remedy following an adverse verdict. Help was needed in order to prevent increased pressure for compulsion. By way of response to this appeal the Representative Body were recorded as having felt that 'outside pressure on the matter was unnecessary and ill-founded', but they nevertheless agreed to recommend to the individual associations of local authorities that they should write to all their members urging them always to respond positively and speedily to the Local Ombudsman's findings. We were surprised to read that this simple recommendation came to nothing as the three associations declined

to act on it (Report for the year ended 31 March 1983 at p. 7, paragraph 25 and p. 12, paragraph 44 and Report for the year ended 31 March 1984 at p. 35, paragraph 101). A letter advising prompt compliance was ultimately written to all Chief Executives by the three associations some time after 16 November 1984 but this was clearly written as a defensive response to the interest being taken by the Select Committee for the PCA (Report for year ended 31 March 1985, p. 34, paragraph 112 and Appendix 6).

2. It appears from what the Local Ombudsmen write that it is not uncommon for local authorities to challenge their findings and to enter into contentious correspondence on their reports. The ombudsmen may finally convince such authorities that they should comply, but much time and effort has to be expended on the exercise of persuasion. (See, for example, the comments by Mr McKenzie Johnston in the English Commissioners' Report for the year ended 31 March 1984, p. 10, paragraph 29 and Dr David Yardley in *Judicial Teeth for the Local Ombudsmen?*, Report of a conference held at Edinburgh in December 1984, p. 28 ('Edinburgh Conference').)

3. The last cited report also makes a generalized protest about the time taken by many authorities in providing a satisfactory remedy for injustice. 'In ten years of operation, in some 25% of cases more than six months elapsed between the issue of a first critical report, and the date when the local ombudsman was satisfied with the authority's response' (p. 26, paragraph 75).

4. Local authorities often dispose of pending complaints by entering into arrangements for settling the matter in advance of a report by the Local Ombudsman. At the time such settlements appear satisfactory to the complainants. This is a very commendable practice and much to be encouraged. Unfortunately, doubts sometimes arise subsequently as to whether the authority kept its word and carried into effect the agreed solution. The Commissioner for Local Administration in Scotland has had some investigations made among complainants. The inquiry showed that in almost one-third of the cases the complainants asserted that the remedy which the council had proposed was not in fact implemented in full or indeed was subsequently altered (Report for year ending 31 March 1984, p. 9, paragraph 21).

5. A Local Ombudsman (Mr F. P. Cook) was twice taken to court to debar him from investigating as he saw fit. In the first case, the Council succeeded in preventing him from seeing statutory reports

which he wanted to examine when investigating the boarding out of a child with foster parents; *In re A Complaint against Liverpool City Council* [1977] 1 WLR 995. (The case turned on the construction of a provision in the Local Government Act, 1974. The law was later altered—in favour of the ombudsmen—by the Local Government, Planning and Land Act, 1980, section 184.) In *R. v. Local Commissioner for Administration for the North and East Area of England*, ex parte *Bradford Metropolitan City Council* [1979] QB 287, the Council failed in arguments that the Local Ombudsman had exercised his discretion improperly and that in any event he could not investigate because the complainant had not specified anything that could amount to maladministration. These cases demonstrate that some local authorities are reluctant to co-operate with the local ombudsmen unless required to do so by law.

6. It seems that on occasions some local authorities go out of their way to treat Local Ombudsmen contemptuously. Instances were cited at the Edinburgh Conference. Dr David Yardley said that he was now constantly trying to avoid issuing further reports because this was 'a very weak thing to do'. He had to be prepared to overlook 'stinging remarks' made by local authorities about his first report so long as he was able to ensure that the recommended remedy was granted to the complainant. The Local Ombudsman for Wales cited a case where the local authority had not only refused to pay the compensation which he recommended but had gone on to pass a resolution complimenting for his excellent work in the affair one of its officers whose conduct had been criticized in the first report and in the further report (Edinburgh Conference, pp. 20 and 23–4).

Intervention by the Select Committee

5.74. In 1984 the Select Committee on the PCA began to interest itself in the problem of non-compliance by local authorities. The members of the Committee had begun to form the view that the failure by local authorities to carry out recommendations by Local Ombudsmen had reached significant proportions. This failure was not only bringing the Local Ombudsman system into disrepute but was also having an effect on the credibility of the PCA himself. The Select Committee took evidence from ministers, the Local Ombudsmen, the PCA, the Representative Bodies for England and for Wales, the Northern Ireland Commissioner for Complaints, the National Consumer Council, and civil servants. The evidence was taken on various dates between May 1984 and November 1985. The Committee reported on 10 June 1986 (3rd Report of the Select Committee on the PCA, Session 1985–6, *Local Government Cases: Enforcement of Remedies*; HC 448). The minutes of evidence are attached to the report.

5.75. The Committee's main recommendation (ibid., paragraph 3) is as follows:

Despite the lack of precedent which was touched on by ministers we consider that the best method of providing support for local ombudsmen's reports would be for our remit to be extended to allow the possibility of our calling recalcitrant local authorities to account. If experience showed that our involvement did not, however, have an improving effect on the treatment of the reports of local ombudsmen we would recommend serious consideration of the involvement of the courts along the lines recommended by JUSTICE, supported by the local ombudsmen and successfully operated in Northern Ireland.

Before commenting on this proposal we will refer in more detail to the JUSTICE recommendation and to the Northern Ireland system.

5.76. Various solutions to the enforcement problem have from time to time been canvassed. We have considered them all and rejected them. The first two were discussed in the JUSTICE Report mentioned in paragraph 5.44 above (at pp. 43–4 of that Report).

1. *Making the Local Ombudsmen's proposed remedy binding on the local authority*. The effect would be to give direct executive authority to the Local Ombudsman over a local authority. The JUSTICE Committee rejected this solution as undesirable in principle. We agree.

2. *Giving the Secretary of State power to direct a local authority to comply with a Local Ombudsman's recommendations*. This would involve an extension of central government control over local government and it seems to us, as it did to the JUSTICE Committee, an objectionable solution. There would, moreover, be practical difficulties. The Secretary of State would have to carry out a separate investigation in order to satisfy himself that the case was a proper one in which to give a direction to comply. If he declined to give such a direction the standing of the Local Ombudsman concerned would be put at risk. The minister would be answerable in Parliament for his decision (whichever way it went) and there would be a strong

probability that a series of cases would be debated in the politcial arena and the essential independence of the Local Ombudsman would be seriously compromised.

3. *Giving the ombudsmen sufficient resources to enable them to make direct financial awards themselves*. This solution, which was one of those advocated by Mr Jeremy Mitchell, the Director of the National Consumer Council, in his evidence to the Select Committee (3rd Report—attached Minutes of Evidence for 17 July 1984, pp. 42–3, paragraphs 13 and 14; HC 448) would only go part of the way to meeting the problem. It would not help where what was recommended by the ombudsman was executive action by the local authority, such as the provision of housing or the grant of a licence or permission. In any event the solution involves an abandonment of a basic principle of the ombudsman system, namely, that it is for the local authority itself to put right the injustice which it has caused by its maladministration.

The Northern Ireland Commissioner for Complaints—
enforcement through the courts of findings of maladministration
causing injustice

5.77. In Northern Ireland the same individual holds the two posts of Parliamentary Commissioner for Administration and Commissioner for Complaints. In his first capacity complaints must be made to him through Members of Parliament; in his second capacity complaints may be made to him direct. As Commissioner for Complaints he may investigate complaints against local bodies (harbour authorities and local authorities) and against public bodies. The full list of these public bodies is set out in Annex C to his Report for 1983 (HC 445) and includes the ten additional bodies which were added by the Commissioner for Complaints (Extension of Jurisdiction) Order (Northern Ireland), 1983 (SI 1983 No. 235). Many of the functions which would in England be discharged by an elected local authority are in Northern Ireland carried out by a non-elected public body. The most important of these in the present context is the Northern Ireland Housing Executive. This can be demonstrated by the statistics in Table 5.4. About one-third of the housing complaints relate to repairs. Other principal areas of complaint are housing allocations and housing transfers. The jurisdiction of the Commissioner for Complaints also extends to personnel matters and to commercial and contractual matters. (These

areas are excluded from the jurisdiction of the Local Ombudsmen in
England, Wales, and Scotland: see paragraph 5.44 above.)

TABLE 5.4 Complaints against the Northern Ireland Housing Executive

	1981	1982	1983	1984	1985	1986
Total number of complaints received in the year	477	504	569	551	398	370
Number of complaints against the Northern Ireland Housing Executive	289	349	320	332	214	213

5.78. The statutory provision of particular relevance to the
present discussion about the failure or refusal of local authorities to
implement ombudsman recommendations is section 7 of the Commissioner for Complaints Act (Northern Ireland), 1969. We repro-
duce the text of this section in Appendix 11 to this Report. Section
7(1) spells out clearly the purposes of the Commissioner's investigation. These are (*a*) to ascertain whether the complaint is a proper
one and true in fact and whether maladministration is disclosed and
(where it appears to be desirable) (*b*) to effect a settlement, or if that
is not possible, to state what action should be taken to effect a fair
settlement or to remove the cause of complaint. It may be noted that
the Local Commissioners in England, Wales, and Scotland are not
given the task of effecting a settlement.

5.79. Two enforcement powers are provided. Section 7(2) states
that if the Commissioner in his report finds maladministration and
injustice caused thereby to the person aggrieved that person may
apply to the county court and the court may award 'such damages as
the court may think just in all the circumstances to compensate' the
applicant for loss or injury suffered on account of (*a*) expenses
reasonably incurred and (*b*) lost opportunity of acquiring benefit.
Notice of the application has to be given to the body complained
against. If it appears to the court that justice can only be done by
ordering that body to take or refrain from taking some action then
the court may, if satisfied that in all the circumstances it is reasonable
so to do, grant a mandatory or other injunction (section 7(3)). As is
clear from the language quoted, under both subsections (2) and (3))
the court has full discretion as to the appropriate relief to grant and is

in no sense a 'rubber stamp' to enforce the remedy pointed out by the Commissioner. A right of appeal is given (subsection (4)) and the normal limitations on the jurisdiction of the county court are displaced (subsection (9)).

5.80. It is further provided that if maladministration coupled with injustice has been found and if it appears to the Commissioner that the body concerned has previously engaged in conduct of the same kind and is likely to continue to engage in future in conduct of the type which he has condemned, the Commissioner may request the Attorney-General to apply to the High Court for appropriate relief, such as a mandatory or other injunction or a declaration. The defendants to the application can be the body concerned or any officer or member of it (section 7(5)). Mr Hugh Kernohan, the Northern Ireland Commissioner for Complaints, is on record as saying that the Attorney-General has never to date been asked to make an application under this subsection.

5.81. A highly important practical question concerns the status of the Commissioner's report in any legal proceedings under section 7. This problem is faced in subsection (8) in the following terms: 'For the purposes of any proceedings authorised by this section, a recommendation of the Commissioner and any report of the Commissioner relating to the complaint in connection with which the recommendation is made shall, unless the contrary is proved, be accepted as evidence of the facts stated therein . . .'

5.82. According to the Northern Ireland Commissioner for Complaints he issues annually about 300 reports and makes findings of maladministration in about twenty of them. Over the last ten years on average three applications have been made to the county court each year by successful complainants. No difficulties have so far arisen in connection with the operation of subsection (8) quoted above. In practice where a court case arises both parties normally accept his report as a true statement of fact and the case is argued in court on the basis of the report.

5.83. The Northern Ireland Commissioner for Complaints believes that it is a significant advantage to him to know from the outset that at the end of the road there exists the possibility of court enforcement proceedings to back his recommendation. He has absolute freedom to express his views and findings and his suggestions for a remedy.

Such freedom is, however, lacking in a situation where a commissioner has to tone down his language, his criticism and even his report and its findings for the purpose of ensuring that the report will in the end be acceptable to and acted upon by a particular body. Plea bargaining should not be part of any commissioner's functions ... The rights of an aggrieved citizen who has suffered an injustice as a result of maladministration should never be prejudiced, compromised or whittled away, as a consequence of a so-called 'toothless' commissioner having to seek by compromise some sort of redress from an unco-operative and unhelpful body. (Edinburgh Conference, p. 29.)

Appraisal of the Select Committee's recommendation

5.84. The proposal of the Select Committee on the PCA (quoted in paragraph 5.75 above) that it should supervise the compliance by local authorities with the recommendations of the Local Ombudsmen deserves serious consideration. In its favour it may be said that supervision by the Select Committee would afford the opportunity for regular oversight rather than the episodic review which might result from a system of *ad hoc* court enforcement. Moreover, there is logic in the proposal in the sense that maladministration is common to both central and local government. Such supervision would fill a gap. The Representative Bodies cannot in any way be compared with the Select Committee. The chief advantage of the proposed extension of jurisdiction is said by the Select Committee to be that it would not create a direct method of enforcement imposed on authorities; but instead the force of persuasion would be enhanced by the prospect of recalcitrant authorities being summoned to explain themselves before a Parliamentary Committee (3rd Report, paragraph 2.9; HC 448).

5.85. There are, however, counter-arguments. In the first place there is the inevitable encroachment on the independence of local government. The spectre of political contests being fought between local councillors and a Parliamentary Committee over local issues is an unattractive one. The ultimate consequence of continued defiance by a local authority would presumably be that it would be in contempt of Parliament and subject to punishment accordingly. Unlike ministers, who are in contention with the Select Committee, councillors cannot take part in debate and defend themselves on the floor of the House of Commons.

5.86. Our own conclusion on this matter is that the implementation of the Select Committee's proposal is likely to be so hazardous that it should only be adopted if there is no better answer to hand. Accordingly, we turn to consider the strength of the arguments against the court enforcement route.

The arguments against court enforcement

5.87. The Representative Body for England has argued that if the Northern Ireland enforcement model were to be imported here every investigation by a Local Ombudsman would start off as one likely to end up in the courts. The investigation would virtually be on a judicial basis, the system would be lengthened, more costly, and to the detriment of the complainant because of the longer time taken in arriving at a decision. (For the views of the Representative Body see Appendix 5 to the Report of the English Commissioners for the year ended 31 March 1985 and for a similar expression of opinion by the three local authority associations see the letter written by them to the chief executives of all member authorities at Appendix 6 of that Report.)

5.88. At the Edinburgh Conference the arguments against judicial enforcement were forcefully put by Mr Ian Wilson, Chief Executive of the Inverclyde District Council, and by Mr Percival Buchanan, the Director of Administration and Legal Services, Central Regional Council. In addition to the arguments summarized in paragraph 5.87 above they were critical of the way in which the ombudsman system sometimes works. The troublesome cases tended to be those in which the ombudsman's findings of maladministration were felt by the authorities concerned to be wrong. Sometimes the ombudsmen were thought to be entering into the forbidden area of policy and into the merits of the particular decision under investigation rather than confining themselves (as they should) to the steps by which the decision was reached. Mr Wilson also criticized the inquisitorial methods followed by the Commissioners if these were to form the procedural prelude to a recommendation which could be judicially enforced. Thus, he said that the local authority did not usually see the full terms of the complaint and was put in the position of having to answer specific questions while ignorant of the case made against it. There was no provision for a meeting or confrontation between the two sides, no evidence on oath, and no opportunity for testing by cross-examination. Finally, it was contended that there would be no objection to making maladministration which caused injustice justiciable by the courts. What was objectionable was to bring within the ambit of the court's powers only those cases where an opinion on the issue of maladministration had already been formed by an ombudsman on facts found by him. (See generally Edinburgh Conference, pp. 40–52.)

Our proposal on enforcement in relation to further reports made by the Local Ombudsmen

5.89. While recognizing the force of the above objections, we have concluded that enforcement through the courts does offer the best solution to what has become a major problem. We have recounted the continuing history detailed above of failures by a minority of local authorities to comply with the recommendations contained in further reports made by Local Ombudsmen. The combined total of further reports issued in England, Wales, and Scotland was at 31 March 1986 160, of which 120 ended in failure. We have taken into account the other evidence which we have recounted (paragraph 5.73) of lack of co-operation and the lukewarm support of the local authorities associations. As we have shown, the Local Commisioners are treated contemptously by some local authorities and the public are repeatedly being made aware of their inability to achieve results. Thus, the impotence of the Local Ombudsmen formed the theme of three articles published in *The Times* on successive days (25, 26, and 27 November 1985) under the titles 'Investigators without enforcement power', 'Case still drags on after three years', and 'Injustices that go unresolved'. The second article detailed a current case where the complainant, having failed to receive the remedy recommended in two reports by the ombudsman, lodged a new complaint alleging maladministration by the council in not implementing the first two reports.

5.90. We think that the time has now come to add teeth to the ombudsman scheme by making it possible for successful complainants to apply to the county court or, in Scotland, the sheriff court for appropriate relief. The time has passed for saying 'One day it may be necessary to consider enforcement powers'. The hour has come. As regards the objections which we have set out in paragraphs 5.87 and 5.88 above, we think that the fears on the grounds of delay and formalism are exaggerated. The system has worked well in Northern Ireland and we think that it should now be tried in England, Wales, and Scotland. If, as is asserted (though without any citation of specific instances), ombudsmen stray outside their statutory jurisdiction, the powers of the court can be invoked to restrain them.

5.91. As the system of first reports and further reports is already well established we would not propose any change in that. The 'mischief' at which we are striking is failure or refusal to comply with further reports. The conditions precedent to the application to the court would be:

(a) a first report containing a finding in favour of the person aggrieved that he had suffered injustice in consequence of maladministration;

(b) a further report (following on the authority's failure or refusal to implement the first report) containing a recommendation as to the action which it would be appropriate for the authority to take to remedy or compensate for the injustice;

(c) a certificate from the Local Ombudsman issued to the complainant to the effect that the local authority had had a reasonable time within which to comply with his further report and that no action to his satisfaction had been taken by the local authority, and further certifying that the case was, in his opinion, an appropriate one for application to the court for relief.

5.92. We propose a certificate as in (c) above because, in the first place, the authority must have some time within which to comply with the further report and we feel that it would be wrong to allow legal proceedings to be launched prematurely. What is a reasonable time will vary with the circumstances. In some cases it may be very short. In other cases, for instances, where drainage works have to be undertaken or the surface of a road made up, it may be longer. We think that the Local Ombudsman is the best judge of what is a reasonable time. Secondly, we think that it is important that the Local Ombudsman should officially record his view that there has been no compliance or that the purported compliance does not satisfy him. As we have seen, some local authorities go through the motions of redressing a grievance but fail to provide the remedy that the Local Ombudsman regards as adequate. Finally, we have a special reason for requiring the Local Ombudsman to certify that in his opinion the case is an appropriate one for an application to the court. A study of the annual reports of the Local Commissioners shows that in some cases where a further report has been ignored the only recommendation made was that the authority should make a written apology. Other cases have involved a recommendation for the payment of a trifling sum of money or for a local authority to take action in relation to some highly personal matter (such as altering the precise language of an entry in a Book of Remembrance at a council crematorium). The system might be brought into ridicule if the coercive power of the court were to be invoked in such cases or others of a sensitive nature where a Local Commissioner would judge that more harm than good would be done by permitting the complainant to go to court. In the ordinary case, however, where there was a recommendation for a substantial payment or for the taking of action that could appropriately be enforced by injunction there would be no difficulty in obtaining the certificate. Nevertheless we think that it is too facile simply to suggest that all recommendations which have not been complied with should be enforceable in the courts.

5.93. We propose that the court itself should have the same discretion as regards the relief to be granted as is conferred upon the county court in Northern Ireland when dealing with cases where the Commissioner for Complaints has found maladministration causing injustice. We have explained this in paragraph 5.79 above. The effect would be that the court has both a discretion as to the type of relief which should be granted and a discretion to withhold relief altogether.

5.94. We also consider that while section 7 of the Northern Ireland Act provides a valuable precedent to which reference may be made, it would be inadvisable to follow its provisions literally. We are particularly concerned about section 7(8) which makes the Commissioner's report available as evidence in the legal proceedings. The report is not made conclusive evidence; the subsection goes no further than to state that the report 'shall, unless the contrary is proved, be accepted as evidence of the facts stated therein'. This raises the possibility that the defendant authority in any legal proceedings might try to reopen the whole matter investigated by the Local Commissioner and seek to establish that the facts found in his report were wrong and that his conclusions on maladministration and resulting injustice were also ill-founded. As we have shown, recalcitrant authorities not infrequently adopt the line that the ombudsman's report is mistaken, that there has been no maladministration, and that the complainant is in any event not entitled to a remedy. Such local authorities, which are already undermining the voluntary system, based (as it is supposed to be) on the willing acceptance of the umpire's verdict, would not hesitate to use the law courts as the forum for seeking to demolish or gravely impugn ombudsmen's reports.

5.95. We are also concerned about the disadvantageous position of the complainant (plaintiff) in the litigation. He would be trying to uphold the Commissioner's report but he would be at a financial disadvantage in taking on the local authority in what might become protracted litigation. Furthermore, he might well be unable to give strict proof of all the material facts in the report. Sources of information which were available to the Local Ombudsman in preparing his report might not be available to him as a private litigant. This could come about because the Local Ombudsman in making his inquiries is backed by formidable statutory powers for obtaining evidence and documents (see section 29 of the 1974 Act). To give only one example, under section 29(4) the Local Ombudsman is entitled to have access to documents which would in ordinary litigation be protected by public interest immunity (or, as it used to be called, Crown privilege). Quite apart from the existence of these powers, the Local Ombudsman, by virtue of his status and authority, can at the investigation stage sometimes procure voluntary co-operation from bodies and persons who might not lend their aid to an ordinary litigant.

5.96. These considerations make it necessary, in our view, to entrench and protect the findings of fact made by the Local Ombudsman in his report and further report and his conclusions that there has been maladministration causing injustice to the person aggrieved (the plaintiff). We agree with the view of the Local Commissioners for England who in their submission made to the Secretary of State on 17 August 1984 said: '7. The court should not repeat work already done by the Local Ombudsman, and in enforcement proceedings his investigation report should be conclusive, save only for the nature and extent of the remedy required for the injustice.' (Report for the year ended 31 March 1984, p. 53.) Similar protection should be given to the certificate referred to in paragraph 5.91 (c) above.

5.97. The statutory protection for the reports and findings of Local Ombudsmen which we advocate would not, of course, preclude a local authority from showing that in a particular instance the ombudsman had stepped outside his jurisdiction. On ordinary principles the protection would not avail the ombudsman in such circumstances.

5.98. We further recommend that a special rule should be introduced as regards the legal costs of the successful complainant who was obliged to take the local authority to court for its failure to implement a further report. The presumption should be that the local authority was in the wrong and was putting the complainant to unnecessary expense. Accordingly it should be laid down that in any such proceedings the plaintiff should be entitled to recover his costs on a common fund basis from the defendant authority unless in the opinion of the court there were exceptional circumstances which made some other form of costs order appropriate.

5.99. One further point which we should mention is the matter of settlements made by the local authority with the complainant during the course of the Local Ombudsman's investigations or indeed at any time after the lodging of the complaint with the ombudsman. These settlement arrangements are often made with his approval. We have referred to the problem which on occasion arises when the local authority defaults on the arrangement (paragraph 5.73(4) above). We think that the power to apply to the court should also apply in a case where an authority fails to provide the remedy which the complainant has agreed to accept and which the Local Ombudsman has approved and on the basis of which he has abandoned his investigation. It may be that a remedy would lie in contract at common law but the entitlement of the aggrieved person in such circumstances should be put beyond doubt by statute. A similar costs provision to that recommended in paragraph 5.98 above should apply.

Relations between the Local Ombudsmen and the courts

5.100. What we have said about relations between the PCA and the courts at paragraphs 5.17–5.19 above applies also to those between the Local Ombudsmen and the courts. A restriction corresponding to section 5(2) of the 1967 Act for the PCA (see paragraph 5.19 above) is imposed on the Local Ombudsmen by section 26(6) of the Local Government Act, 1974 (in Scotland, section 24(6) of the Local Government (Scotland) Act, 1975) with a corresponding proviso. However, the Local Ombudsmen consider it unreasonable to expect the average person aggrieved to resort to High Court proceedings for review, having regard to their cost and to the limited availability of legal aid. The consequence is that sometimes, though not always, the Local Ombudsman may secure a better result for the complainant than he would be likely to obtain from the court—notably in the matter of compensation, because the court's capacity to award damages in proceedings for judicial review is somewhat circumscribed. Examples where the aggrieved citizen probably secured a better result from the Local Ombudsman than he or she would have done from the courts are considered in an article by M. Macpherson, 'Local Ombudsman or the Courts?' [1987] JPL 92. On the other hand, the court, because it has the power to quash a decision, may offer the aggrieved person a better result than he could have obtained from the local Ombudsman. Thus, in *R.* v. *Castle Point District Council*, ex parte *Brooks* [1985] JPL 473, the court quashed the planning authority's approval of reserved matters where outline planning permission for a house had been granted. In another case, where the facts were similar, the Local Ombudsman found maladministration, but the complainant had to be content with an apology: *Test Valley Borough Council* (No. 622/J/83).

'Injustice in consequence of maladministration'

5.101. The phrase 'injustice in consequence of maladministration', which we discussed in paragraph 5.16 above in the context of the PCA's statute, is also found in the Local Ombudsman legislation (Local Government Act, 1974, section 31(1)). For the reasons given in paragraph 5.16 above, we do not recommend any alteration in the statutory formula, though it is only right that we should record the fact that in evidence to us the Commission for Local Administration in England stated that the word 'maladministration' is disliked by councillors and officials and means little to many complainants. That hostility to the term 'maladministration' also exists in Scotland was made clear by Mr Wilson at the Edinburgh Conference (p. 44).

5.102. The effect of the present legislation (Local Government Act 1974, section 31(1) and, in Scotland, section 29(1) of the 1975 Act) is that a council is required to consider a Local Commissioner's report only when it records the opinion of the Commissioner that injustice has been caused to the complainant in consequence of maladministration. Such a conclusion can be misunderstood as being a general indictment of the manner in which a council's affairs have been conducted, whereas the complaint may have concerned an isolated error or failure of service. It should be open to a Local

Ombudsman, having investigated an allegation of maladministration, to report in terms critical of the local authority but falling short of a finding of maladministration and it should then be obligatory for the local authority to consider such a report with a view to taking any necessary remedial action. The Commission for Local Administration in England have pointed out that the PCA is not bound to use the word 'maladministration' in his reports and they have sought to be put in the same position. We cannot however agree with the recommendation which they made to the Secretary of State that they should in effect be able to make a finding of maladministration but without using 'a word which has sinister overtones for some' (Report for the year ended 31 March 1981, Appendix vii, paragraphs 19 to 21, p. 51). In our view a spade should be called a spade and we think that the Secretary of State was right to reject that proposal (Report for the year ended 31 March 1984, Appendix 4, paragraph 12, p. 51).

5.103. We do not think that our proposal would run foul of section 34(3) of the 1974 Act (in Scotland section 32(2) of the 1975 Act) which states: 'It is hereby declared that nothing in this Part of this Act authorises or requires a Local Commissioner to question the merits of a decision taken without maladministration by an authority in the exercise of a discretion vested in that authority.' A provision in similar terms applies to the PCA (section 12(3) of the 1967 Act). This has not inhibited the PCA in his work. By what he calls 'a sensible understanding' between successive ombudsmen and departments, a discretionary decision is treated as being one made by a Minister of the Crown, informed by his political judgment, to exercise which he was elected and appointed. The purely administrative decisions of non-political officials must plainly be open to investigation and the PCA does in fact investigate very many of them (Sir Cecil Clothier's Address to JUSTICE, 11 July 1984, p. 14). In the context of the Local Ombudsmen the statutory restriction is aimed merely at precluding them from challenging what may be called the political decisions of local authorities.

Internal arrangements within local authorities for consideration of critical reports made by Local Ombudsmen

5.104. The English Commissioners have more than once drawn attention to the undesirability of having a critical report considered in the first instance by those members of the council who were the subject of the criticism. This matter was again discussed in their Report for the year ended 31 March 1985 (at paragraph 47 and 70(1)). Mr F. P. Cook suggested that such reports should go first to a detached group of senior and experienced members. (By way of example he suggested the Policy and Resources Committee). A report could then, if necessary, be passed on to another committee if its expertise were to be involved. In our view, the receipt of the critical report should thereafter be reported to the full council with an indication of the steps being taken to comply with the recommendations made. It should not be permissible to delegate to a committee, subcommittee, or officer the final consideration of a report or further report. Local authorities should consider their own procedures with a view to bringing them into line with these recommendations.

Investigating the work of a department

5.105. A Local Commissioner may often want to investigate the methods of working of a section or department of a local authority in order to decide whether in a particular case some injustice has occurred to the complainant or to a group of complainants. The Local Commissioner has, nevertheless, no specific power to conduct a systematic investigation of the work of a department or part of a department even where, on the basis of individual complaints, the Commissioner has reason to believe that the department (or part thereof) is not dealing with its business properly. For the reasons developed in paragraphs 5.10–5.14 above in relation to the PCA, and notwithstanding the Secretary of State's contrary opinion (noted at paragraph 5.44 above), we consider that the Local Commissioners should have power to make such a general investigation provided that either (*a*) the local authority consents, or (*b*) the Secretary of State gives his approval.

5.106. In arriving at the above conclusion we have not overlooked the fact that wide powers are now conferred on the Audit Commission under sections 26 and 27 of the Local Government Finance Act, 1982. These include the power to undertake studies of various kinds designed to enable the Audit Commission (*a*) to make recommendations for improving the economy, efficiency, and effectiveness of services provided by, and the management of, local authorities and other public bodies within the jurisdiction of the Commission; and (*b*) to prepare reports on the impact of statutory provisions or of directions or guidance from ministers on the effectiveness of such services. These powers are aimed at a different target and we do not anticipate that any difficulties will arise if the Local Commissioners are given the additional investigatory powers which we recommend. The Local Commissioners are primarily dealing with the effects of administration upon individuals rather than protecting the public as ratepayers.

Government support

5.107. There have been strong expressions of concern by the Local Commissioners for England, Wales, and Scotland at the tardy response of the Government to their various recommendations for improving the system and for implementing the reforms for which the need has been accepted by the Government (Reports for the year ending 31 March 1985, English: paragraphs 75, 90, and 101; Welsh: p. 7; and Scottish: paragraph 4). We share the view of Mr Cook that the most immediate need is for central government to support more positively in these two respects a service created for the citizen by Parliament.

PART III

MATTERS AFFECTING ALL THE OMBUDSMEN

The case for an integrated ombudsman service

5.108. The existence of ombudsmen at national level, at local government level, and for the National Health Service had led to suggestions for a unified ombudsman service under which all ombudsmen would operate under the same legislation. The matter has been examined by the Select Committee in its report *The System of Ombudsmen in the United Kingdom* (2nd Report, 1979–80; HC 254), but the Select Committee did not make any definite proposals for reorganizing the present arrangements. We do not ourselves recommend the creation of a single integrated service but we do urge that the closest possible co-operation between ombudsmen should continue to be maintained.

5.109. It is clear that every effort is now made within the offices of the PCA and the Local Commissioners to ensure that complaints reach their appropriate destination (PCA's Annual Reports 1983,

p. 38, paragraph 82 and 1984, p. 35, paragraph 69). Furthermore, satisfactory arrangements appear to have been made for the carrying out of composite investigations, that is to say, investigations which involve two or more of the PCA, the Health Service Commissioner, and a Local Ombudsman. Section 33 of the 1974 Act (in Scotland, section 31 of the 1975 Act) authorizes the required co-operation. The Chairman of the English Commission has given particulars of a case where an allegation of unchecked flooding to a house beside a trunk road involved a complaint against one government department and three local authorities (Report for year ended 31 March 1984, p. 4, paragraph 9). Four other composite investigations were carried out with his participation in that year and two more in the year ended 31 March 1985 (Report p. 4, paragraph 10). He described the procedure in these cases in 'Local Ombudsmen in England: Recent Trends and Developments' [1983] *Public Law* 522, 524. (For the PCA's account see his Annual Report 1982, p. 10, paragraph 15.) In the absence of any evidence that these arrangements are not working smoothly we have no proposal to make.

Publicity

5.110. Finally, while considerable efforts have been made both by the PCA and by the Local Commissioners to secure publicity for the services they offer, our impression is that there is still much ignorance both about what has been done by the ombudsmen and about what more could be done. We hope that these efforts to improve public knowledge of the ombudsmen will continue and will bear fruit. We believe that our proposals for direct access to the PCA and to the Local Commissioners would, if implemented, greatly facilitate the necessary additional publicity.

5.111. We also consider that members of the legal profession have a special responsibility to be well informed about the assistance which an ombudsman may be able to give to their clients. In giving advice about available remedies in the courts lawyers should also refer in appropriate cases to the possibility of the alternative route via the ombudsman. We have already indicated (in paragraph 5.40 above) the need for a digest of the PCA's case law. Such a publication would, of course, have to make full reference to the work of the Local Ombudsmen. Those responsible for legal education should ensure that administrative law courses include instruction on the ombudsmen.

CHAPTER 5. RECOMMENDATIONS

(*i*)   *Parliamentary Commissioner for Administration* (*'PCA'*)

1. The Parliamentary Commissioner Act, 1967, should be amended so as to allow the public direct access to the PCA without the need for any intervention by an MP (paragraphs 5.8–5.9).
2. The links between the PCA and Parliament should be preserved (*a*) by MPs continuing their present practice of referring complainants to the PCA and (*b*) by the PCA informing the Select Committee for the PCA about his investigations (ibid.).
3. If, on the basis of individual complaints received, the PCA has reason to believe that a particular branch of a department of government is not dealing with its business properly, the PCA should, subject to the Select Committee's approval, be able to carry out a systematic investigation of the work of that branch. But the PCA should not have a general remit to conduct investigations on his own initiative (paragraphs 5.10–5.14).
4. It is not necessary to confer a further express power on the PCA to notify Parliament of unforeseen injustices of which he has become aware resulting from primary legislation (paragraph 5.15).
5. It is not necessary to amend or to find a substitute formula for the statutory phrase 'injustice in consequence of maladministration'. These words have proved very flexible and wide-ranging in operation and are now sufficiently well understood (paragraph 5.16).
6. Requiring a complainant to give an undertaking not to sue as a condition precedent to the commencement of an ombudsman investigation is undesirable in principle. The Health Service Commissioner should only require such an undertaking in very special circumstances (paragraph 5.23).
7. The existing relationship between the PCA and the courts should be preserved. No attempt should be made to integrate the administrative jurisdiction of the civil courts and the activities of the PCA into a single system with a common procedure for investigating and reviewing acts of the administration (paragraphs 5.24–5.29).
8. The PCA should not be given power to apply to the court to restrain administrative action while he investigates (paragraph 5.30).
9. It seems that the PCA already has the capacity to apply to the court to determine a question relating to his jurisdiction to carry out an investigation. No further express statutory power need be conferred on the PCA to seek the court's opinion on a point of law which arises in connection with his investigation (paragraphs 5.31–5.35).
10. Although recommendations made by the PCA are not legally binding on departments they are in fact always complied with. No statutory

mechanism to provide for the enforcement of his recommendations is therefore required (paragraphs 5.36–5.39).

11. It would be helpful if a one-volume digest could be prepared under the authority of the PCA giving illustrative examples of the cases of maladministration which he has investigated. Reference should be made to the work of the Local Ombudsmen (paragraphs 5.40 and 5.111).

(ii) The Local Commissioners for Administration in England, Wales and Scotland ('Local Ombudsmen')

12. Direct access to Local Ombudsmen should be provided for complainants. They should have the option of either taking their complaints direct to their Local Ombudsman or referring them through a councillor (paragraphs 5.46–5.59).

13. A statutory amendment should be introduced (bringing the law in England and Wales into line with the law in Scotland) imposing an obligation on a local authority to consider a further report and to notify the Local Ombudsman of the action which the authority has taken or proposes to take (paragraph 5.60).

14. When a local authority fails to provide a remedy for injustice caused by maladministration and defies the recommendation of a Local Ombudsman made in a first report and repeated in a further report, it should be open to the complainant to apply to the county court for appropriate relief (or, in Scotland the sheriff court). Legislation to give effect to this proposal is urgently required in view of the number of cases in which local authorities have failed to comply on a voluntary basis (paragraphs 5.89–5.90).

15. Legislation should provide that following a further report which had been ignored a potential plaintiff would have to obtain from the Local Ombudsman a certificate to the effect that the local authority had failed within a reasonable time to provide a remedy to his satisfaction and that the case was an appropriate one for an application to the court (paragraphs 5.91 and 5.92).

16. The court should have a discretion as to the relief to be granted and as to whether any relief at all should be granted (paragraph 5.93).

17. In the court proceedings the findings of fact made by the Local Ombudsman in his report and further report and his judgments on such matters as maladministration and injustice should be made conclusive. This would not extend to matters affecting remedy as to which the court would have a discretion in accordance with 15 above; nor would there be any protection in respect of matters outside the jurisdiction of the ombudsman (paragraphs 5.94–5.97).

18. In the court proceedings the plaintiff would be entitled to his costs

against the defendant authority on a common fund basis unless in the opinion of the court there were exceptional circumstances which made some other form of costs order appropriate (paragraph 5.98).

19. A complainant should be entitled to obtain a court order in appropriate terms against a local authority in circumstances where the authority had reached a settlement with him after the lodging of his complaint with the ombudsman but which subsequently failed to provide in full the agreed remedy as approved by the ombudsman. A similar costs provision to that in recommendation 17 above should apply (paragraph 5.99).

20. It is not necessary to amend or to find a substitute formula for the statutory phrase applicable to investigations by Local Ombudsmen 'injustice in consequence of maladministration' (paragraph 5.101).

21. It should be obligatory for a local authority to consider any critical report made by a Local Ombudsman even if the criticisms do not involve a finding of maladministration causing injustice (paragraph 5.102).

22. Local authorities should have internal procedures whereby critical reports by Local Ombudsmen are not considered in the first instance by members of the council who have been criticized. The final consideration of a first report or a further report should always be undertaken by the council as a whole and should not be delegated to a committee, subcommittee, or officers (paragraph 5.104).

23. Greater priority should be given by Government to the needs of the Local Ombudsman system. Agreed amendments to the relevant legislation should be introduced promptly and not (as in the past) indefinitely postponed. Government should respond expeditiously to the statutory submissions made by the Local Ombudsmen reviewing the operation of the 1974 Act (England and Wales) and the 1975 Act (Scotland) (paragraphs 5.53, 5.60, and 5.106).

24. The jurisdiction of the Local Commissioners should be expanded to allow them to investigate the work of a department of a local authority if individual complaints give grounds for believing that the department is not dealing with its business properly. Such investigation should not, however, be undertaken without either (a) the consent of the local authority or (b) the approval of the Secretary of State (paragraph 5.105).

(iii) *Matters affecting all the Ombudsmen*

25. No case had been made out for an integrated ombudsman service. The existing arrangements for carrying out composite investigations are working satisfactorily (paragraphs 5.108 and 5.109).

26. There is still a need for greater publicity to be given to the availability of the services of all the ombudsmen (paragraph 5.110).
27. The legal profession should be well informed about the work of the ombudsmen. Those responsible for legal education should be mindful of this requirement (paragraph 5.111).

6

The Application for Judicial Review

SUMMARY OF ARGUMENT. English law developed special procedures which could be used to challenge decisions of public authorities and orders made by inferior tribunals. These were certiorari (to quash the decision), prohibition (to stop proceedings), and mandamus (to enforce the carrying out of a public duty). Alongside these historic remedies there grew up over the last 100 years the practice of using the action for a declaration, with or without joined claims for injunctions and damages, as a means of enforcing the law and controlling illegal conduct by public bodies. In Scotland, on the other hand, the Court of Session made available its ordinary remedies—reduction (to quash), declarator (to declare rights), and interdict (to restrain). In clear cases there was a summary statutory procedure for enforcing the performance of statutory duties.

The English procedures were each subject to special rules and were confusing for litigants. The choice of the wrong remedy involved starting again from scratch. In Scotland (the statutory procedure apart) the proceedings were too slow and cumbersome.

The position for England and Wales was transformed by the introduction in 1977 of the special procedure known as the application for judicial review. In 1985 Scotland, modelling itself on this precedent, introduced a specially adapted swift procedure for handling administrative law cases.

Experience has brought to light certain defects in the English procedure. In particular, litigants are being compelled to use the new procedure and being debarred from the remedy by action. They are made to get the leave of the court before they can start and too short a time-limit is imposed upon them.

In addition to procedural changes, which would ameliorate the current position, there is a need for a single statutory statement of the grounds on which an application for judicial review may be based.

6.1. In this chapter we comment on the new procedural arrangements which have been made in England and Wales and, more recently, in Scotland, for dealing with administrative law cases in the courts. We deal separately in chapter 8 with all issues relating to standing to sue (*locus standi*) in administrative law cases.

PART I

ENGLAND AND WALES

Procedural innovation—Order 53 of the Rules of the Supreme Court

6.2. An important reform was made in 1977 with the introduction of the new form of procedure known as 'the application for judicial review'. The change had been proposed in 1976 by the Law Commission of England and Wales in *Remedies in Administrative Law* (Law Com. No. 73 Cmnd. 6407). Earlier Commonwealth precedents were Ontario's Judicial Review Procedure Act, 1971 (now Revised Statutes of Ontario 1980 c. 224), and New Zealand's Judicature Amendment Act, 1972 as subsequently amended. The Australian Parliament in 1977 enacted the Administrative Decisions (Judicial Review) Act, though for the reasons which we have explained elsewhere, the Act was not proclaimed until 1 October 1980.

6.3. Before the reform was introduced the law was in an untidy state. The aggrieved citizen who wanted to have set aside an unfavourable decision rendered against him by a public authority could apply for a prerogative order of certiorari. If he wanted the authority to perform a duty he could apply for the prerogative order of mandamus; and if he wanted to prevent it from exceeding its jurisdiction the remedy of prohibition (another prerogative order) was available. The applicant, however, could not get sight of the relevant files of the authority nor could he cross-examine its witnesses. The general rule was that discovery of documents and interrogatories were not available and that evidence was confined to affidavit material. Different time-limits applied in relation to each remedy. If the applicant applied for the wrong remedy the whole proceedings would fail and he would have to start again (if still in time). The court had no power to award the right remedy. The cases were heard by the Divisional Court of the Queen's Bench Division, consisting of three judges.

6.4. The prerogative orders were not, however, the only means by which wrongful conduct by public authorities could be brought before the courts. If that conduct amounted to an actionable wrong (a tort in English law, a delict in Scotland), damages could be recovered and an injunction sought (though if the Crown were the defendant, no injunction could be—or can now be—granted and, in relation to damages, special procedures had to be followed until the passing of the Crown Proceedings Act, 1947; as regards the injunction, Hodgson J. has pointed out that the statute has a restricted application (*R. v. Governor of Pentonville Prison*, ex parte *Herbage* [1987] 6 CL 87)). In addition, litigants could avail themselves of the declaration (in Scotland, the declarator) by the use of which remedy the court was enabled to make a binding declaration that the defendant's actions or proposed actions were illegal. The first statutory power to grant declarations, section 50 of the Chancery Procedure Act, 1852, was restrictively construed and a more expansive form was provided by Order 25 rule 5 of the Rules of the Supreme Court made in 1883 under the Judicature Act. This made it possible for the court to grant a binding declaration of right without granting consequential relief and it was enabled to do this 'whether any consequential relief is or could be claimed or not'.

6.5. Litigants were quick to take advantage of the new remedy. Resort was had to it in cases which had a 'public-law' flavour. Thus, in *London Association of Shipowners and Brokers* v. *London and India Docks Joint Committee* [1892] 3 Ch. 242 a declaration was granted to the effect that regulations issued by the defendants had no binding force as they had not been validly made and confirmed as by-laws. So far as proceedings against the Crown are concerned, the landmark case is *Dyson* v. *Attorney General* which went twice to the Court of Appeal ([1911] 1 KB 410 and [1912] 1 Ch. 158). It was held that Mr Dyson was entitled to have it declared that a tax form, which he (and some 8 million other citizens) had been sent to fill in, was invalid.

6.6. Since that time very many plaintiffs have sought relief from the court in the form of a declaration. The cases are classified by de Smith in *Judicial Review of Administrative Action*, 4th edn. (1980), chapter 10. He distinguishes between classes of cases in which declarations may be granted and those in which they may not. In the former category he includes declarations to impugn legislative instruments, administrative acts and decisions, and orders of a judicial character; declarations as to status, rights of public employees, and rights in relation to the carrying on of a trade or occupation; and declarations as to the existence and scope of public rights, powers and duties.

6.7. Many of the well-known authorities in administrative law were actions for a declaration. We may give as examples *Vine* v. *National Dock Labour Board* [1957] AC 488, *Pyx Granite Co.* v. *Ministry of Housing and Local Government* [1960] AC 260, *Ridge* v. *Baldwin* [1964] AC 40 and *Anisminic Ltd.* v. *Foreign Compensation Commission* [1969] 2 AC 147. Such cases were treated like any other High Court action. There was full discovery of documents. The case was tried by a single judge. Witnesses could be called and cross-examined.

6.8. The plaintiff suing for a declaration did not have to get the leave of the court before proceeding. If, on the other hand, he decided to apply for one of the prerogative orders he was obliged to get leave and he usually had to move fast. Certiorari, for example, was subject to a six months' time-limit. Actions for declarations were not subject to such short limitation periods.

6.9. In general, the differences in the procedures applicable to the various remedies presented a confusing picture to the potential litigant. So it was appropriate that when the Law Commission was not entrusted with the task of carrying out the full-scale re-examination of administrative law which it wished to undertake, it should turn its attention instead (at the direction of the Lord Chancellor) to the procedural problems which we have described. Its first proposals (set out in Working Paper No. 40 of 1971) involved too much rigidity. According to the plan provisionally put forward, judicial review was to be 'an exclusive remedy not only where an administrative act or order is challenged directly, but also where it is challenged collaterally in an action for tort or contract and in other cases which essentially involve the exercise of public powers' (paragraph 154(2) of Working Paper No. 40). It is not difficult to imagine the inconvenience which this proposal would have caused had it been implemented. However, in 1976 the Law Commission, in the light of comments received on its Working Paper, produced a revised set of proposals in its report Law Com. No. 73 (Cmnd. 6407) and recommended the introduction of a new procedure to be called the application for judicial review. It no longer proposed that it should be an exclusive avenue for seeking redress. The new Order 53 of the Rules of the Supreme Court followed a year later. In 1981, as doubts had arisen as to whether the Order was *intra vires*, Parliament included in the Supreme Court Act, 1981, a section providing for the application for judicial review (section 31). The texts of the latest version of

Order 53 and of the relevant sections of the 1981 Act are given at Appendix 12 below.

6.10. The fundamental change introduced by the new Order is that the applicant, by commencing proceedings by way of an application for judicial review, can now seek in the same proceedings any one or more of the separate remedies referred to above, namely, certiorari, mandamus, prohibition, declaration, injunction, and damages. The applicant needs the leave of the court in order to start proceedings. If the court considers that the applicant ought not to be using the judicial review route, it can order that the application should continue as if it were an action begun by writ. (There is no provision, as there should be, for the reverse to occur, that is for enabling the court to order that proceedings wrongly commenced by writ should continue as if they were an application for judicial review.) Facilities have also been provided for discovery of documents, interrogatories, and cross-examination of witnesses (though in practice they are subject to certain restrictions on which we comment below).

6.11. A further important change was made in 1980 when Order 53 was amended so as to make it possible for applications for judicial review in the administrative field to be heard by a single judge. The procedure which formerly applied where an applicant sought one of the prerogative orders (certiorari, mandamus, prohibition) was, as has already been pointed out, that the case had to be dealt with by a Divisional Court of the Queen's Bench Division. This court consisted of three judges (normally the Lord Chief Justice and two other judges). The Divisional Court had not only to deal with the prerogative order cases but also with an extensive range of criminal cases. A serious backlog of cases developed during the 1960s and 1970s. The position had been reached where even an urgent application for an order of certiorari might have to wait months before it was heard. This situation was transformed by making it possible for a single judge to hear any case. Although there is nothing in the Rules laying down criteria for the judges who are to be selected to hear applications for judicial review, in practice the judges who are now selected are generally those who have a familiarity with this class of work. This system is working well according to the evidence which we have received from practitioners.

6.12. As we pointed out at the beginning of this Report, the introduction of the application for judicial review appears to have had a dramatic effect on the flow of administrative law cases. Although the substantive law was not itself modified, the flexibility of the new procedure has made it very much easier to use and hence more attractive to litigants. It is utilized not only by private individuals and corporations to challenge public bodies, but also by public authorities themselves to resolve their disputes with one another. The volume of work is now such that some fourteen judges are required to handle the Crown Office list. The judges have continued to build on the developments in the common law which we outlined in section G of our Discussion Paper. It would be a task well beyond the confines of the present Report to give an account of the many significant decisions that have been given on applications for judicial review and we will not attempt this task. It may, however, be worth noting that there are already some signs that the pendulum is starting to swing in the other direction. In various categories of cases we find appellate courts holding back and declining to interfere with the decisions of the authority entrusted with the function of making the primary decision. Examples can be cited from recent cases dealing with homeless persons (*Puhlhofer* v. *Hillingdon LBC* [1986] 1 All ER 467) prisoners (*R.* v. *Deputy Governor of Camphill Prison*, ex parte *King* [1985] QB 735, and immigrants (*R.* v. *Secretary of State for the Home Department*, ex parte *Swati* [1986] 1 AER 717).

6.13. So long as courts are confined to judicial *review* there will always be a line beyond which the judges cannot trespass without overtly usurping the role which the law has entrusted to some other body or person. Where the line is to be drawn in any particular case is a matter for judicial judgment. If the judges hold back they are accused of being 'timorous'; if they intervene they may run the risk of being accused of 'dabbling in politics', especially where they are called upon to review a decision made by a minister or a local authority. The ridgeway of perfection which separates these two chasms is not easy to walk. A full review on the merits is not possible under the system. Tribunals can, and regularly do, review the merits of decisions made by officials (as in the social security field). In Australia a general tribunal, the Administrative Appeals Tribunal (AAT) has been created and given the tasks in relation to prescribed categories of decision, of reviewing decisions on their merits (Administrative Appeals Tribunal Act, 1975). The AAT may substitute its decision for that of the original decider; its task is to reach the correct or preferable decision; it is even free to criticize and differ from policy statements by ministers. The AAT, however, constitutionally forms part of the administration. This is so, even though judges hold office as the President and Deputy Presidents of the AAT. We do not press for the adoption of such a system in the United Kingdom. There already exists an elaborate structure of tribunals to adjudicate on many types of disputed claims and rights. We discuss the AAT more fully in chapter 9 (paragraphs 9.74–9.76).

Defects in the current system of judicial review

6.14. We turn now to consider certain criticisms which we have to make of the current law and practice in relation to the application for judicial review. These are:

  (*a*) the mandatory use of Order 53;
  (*b*) the imprecision of the term 'public law';
  (*c*) the need to obtain the leave of the court;
  (*d*) the shortness of the time-limit;
  (*e*) discovery and evidence;
  (*f*) the absence of a statutory statement of the grounds for judicial review.

(*a*) *The mandatory use of Order 53*

6.15. As we noted in paragraph 6.9 above, the Law Commission in putting forward its revised proposals in 1976 (which led to the introduction of the new procedure) abandoned its earlier view that the application for judicial review should be the exclusive route for challenging the legality of actions by public authorities. The Law Commission formulated its revised recommendations in the light of evidence which it had received. The Rules Committee followed the Law Commission's approach and did not attempt to provide for exclusivity. Similarly, when Parliament enacted section 31 of the Supreme Court Act, 1981, it did not provide that the application for judicial review was to be the exclusive route. The House of Lords, however, decided in *O'Reilly* v. *Mackman* [1983] 2 AC 237 that it is prima facie an abuse of the process of the court to use any procedure other than the application for judicial review in a case which falls within the scope of Order 53.

6.16. In *O'Reilly*'s case four prisoners sought to establish that the Board of Visitors of Hull Prison had improperly made an award against each of them decreeing that they should forfeit remission of sentence. The main ground of attack was an allegation that the Board of Visitors had refused to allow the prisoners to call alibi witnesses. In one case bias on the part of the Chairman of the Board was alleged. Three of the prisoners brought actions by writ and one started proceedings with an originating summons in the Chancery Division. The actions were launched three and a half years after the Board's decisions; the originating summons was issued sixteen months after the relevant decision. The House of Lords struck out all the proceedings on the ground that they were an abuse of the process of the court. It was said ([1983] 2 AC at 285) that they were 'blatant attempts to avoid the protections for the defendants for which Order 53 provides'.

6.17. The 'general rule' laid down in *O'Reilly* (p. 285) is that it is 'contrary to public policy, and as such an abuse of the process of the court, to permit a person seeking to establish that a decision of a public authority infringed rights to which he was entitled to protection under public law to proceed by way of an ordinary action and by this means to evade the provisions of Order 53 for the protection of such authorities'. The foregoing is the general rule. Two exceptions are mentioned. The first is where the invalidity of the decision arises as a collateral issue. The second is where none of the parties objects. It is left for subsequent case law to establish what other exceptions there may be. Presumably relator actions will have to be treated as an exception.

6.18. In our view *O'Reilly* v. *Mackman* is an unfortunate decision. As we argue below, the tests for deciding what is a 'public-law' case are uncertain, so the effect of the decision is quite imprecise. The judgment proceeded on an erroneous basis in so far as it suggested that 'all' the disadvantages previously associated with the prerogative orders (certiorari, prohibition, and mandamus) have been removed. Some of the surviving objectionable features are considered later in this chapter under heads (*c*), (*d*), and (*e*). Nor is it correct to say, as Lord Diplock's judgment in *O'Reilly* reasons, that prior to 1977 courts had allowed actions for declarations to be brought because they recognized that the prerogative orders (formerly the prerogative writs) had features that were unsatisfactory for litigants. No case has been cited where a judge in giving a plaintiff his remedy in an action for a declaration made any statement to this effect. There are, on the contrary, several statements to the effect that certiorari and an action for a declaration were alternative remedies available to the plaintiff at his option (de Smith, *Judicial Review of Administrative Action*, p. 519 n. 48).

6.19. The main objection to *O'Reilly* v. *Mackman* is, however, that it has all the appearances of judicial legislation without the benefit of the consultative and debating process normally associated with legislation. Counsel for the plaintiffs in that case was not even permitted to cite the Law Commission's report in which it explained why it was *not* recommending that the application for judicial review should be an exclusive remedy. No thought appears to have been given by their Lordships, in formulating their doctrine about 'an abuse of the process of the court', as to what the position of a defendant would be if he wished to raise in his defence a challenge to the validity of a 'public law' decision on which the plaintiff's claim in an action depended. It took a subsequent House of Lords case to make clear (what would formerly have been obvious) that such a defence could legitimately be raised (*Wandsworth LBC* v. *Winder* [1985] AC 461). It seems apposite to quote the words of Lord Simon of Glaisdale in *Miliangos* v. *Frank (Textiles) Ltd.* [1976] AC 443, 480:

I do not think that this is a 'law reform' which should or can properly be imposed by judges; it is, on the contrary, essentially a decision which demands a far wider range of review than is available to courts following our traditional and valuable adversary system—the sort of review compassed by an interdepartmental committee.

(b)   The imprecision of the term 'public law'

6.20. *O'Reilly* v. *Mackman* draws a sharp distinction between rights protected by public law and private law rights. We do not believe that any such clear-cut distinction can consistently be drawn. The term 'public law' has been useful to remind courts and practitioners that in many administrative law cases there are values and interests to be upheld which transcend the private rights normally the subject of litigation between individuals, but it is, in our view, dangerous to suppose that there is a category of right which can be clearly identified as a public law right. The perilous nature of the attempt to apply labels to rights was demonstrated in the second House of Lords case decided on the same day as the *O'Reilly* case, namely, *Cocks* v. *Thanet District Council* [1983] 2 AC 286. The

House was there examining the duties of housing authorities under the Housing (Homeless Persons) Act, 1977. Lord Bridge's speech contains the judgment of the House. He said that it was for the housing authority to decide whether the facts gave rise to a duty of inquiry or to a duty to provide temporary housing. It was for the housing authority then to decide whether the facts gave rise to a 'limited' duty to house the applicant and his family or to the 'full' duty to house them. 'These', he said (p. 292), 'are essentially public law functions'. He went on to point out that a housing authority is charged with executive functions: 'Once a decision has been reached by the housing authority which gives rise to the temporary, the limited or the full housing duty, rights and obligations are immediately created in the field of private law.' The decision-making functions and the executive functions fell into 'two wholly distinct categories'. Lord Bridge had to confess that his failure to appreciate this 'dichotomy' had vitiated his own earlier judgment in the Court of Appeal in *De Falco* v. *Crawley Borough Council* [1980] 1 QB 460. It seems to follow that in this context the process of decision-making is a matter of public law, while the decision itself (if favourable to the applicant) creates a private law right. The applicant presumably has a public (but not private) law right to the effect that the housing authority should consider his case in accordance with proper principles and he will acquire a private (but not public) law right that a favourable decision should be implemented. The end result of all this unconvincing logic-chopping is that if the applicant wants to challenge what happens at the decision-making stage he must apply by way of judicial review. If he wants to challenge the failure to implement a decision in his favour he may (and perhaps must) do so by action. The artificiality of the distinction is also evident on the facts of *O'Reilly* v. *Mackman* where it was held that remission of sentence was a matter of indulgence and involved no private law right. The prisoners had merely a 'legitimate expectation' that good conduct would be rewarded by full remission.

6.21. Lord Wilberforce expressed his reservations about the use of the term 'public law' in *Davy* v. *Spelthorne Borough Council* [1984] AC 262, 276. He said:

The expressions 'private law' and 'public law' have recently been imported into the law of England from countries which, unlike our own, have separate systems concerning public law and private law. No doubt they are convenient expressions for descriptive purposes. In this country they must be used with caution, for typically, English law fastens, not upon principles but upon remedies. The principle remains intact that public authorities and public servants are, unless clearly exempted, answerable in the ordinary courts for wrongs done to individuals. But by an extension of remedies and a flexible procedure it can be said that something resembling a system of public law is being developed. Before the expression 'public law' can be used to deny a subject a right of action in the court of his choice it must be related to a positive prescription of law, by statute or by statutory rules. We have not yet reached the point at which mere characterisation of a claim as a claim in public law is sufficient to exclude it from consideration by the ordinary courts: to permit this would be to create a dual system of law with the rigidity and procedural hardship for plaintiffs which it was the purpose of the recent reforms to remove.

6.22. We agree with Lord Wilberforce's views. *Davy* v. *Spelthorne BC* itself is an illustration of the procedural hardship to which Lord Wilberforce refers. The case revolved round a planning enforcement notice served on the plaintiff and also involved the circumstances (alleged to include negligent advice from council officers) which led the plaintiff not to appeal against the notice. The plaintiff had three causes of action, all arising out of the same set of facts. The result of the procedural battle, which ended in the House of Lords, was that two causes of action had been identified as 'public law' matters which should have been raised in an application for judicial review and not in an action. The third cause of action, raising allegations of negligence by council officials, was held to be an ordinary claim in tort which could properly be the subject of an action. It was, therefore, necessary for there to be two sorts of proceedings. The hardship, not to say absurdity, of handling a composite case in this manner, is further emphasized by the suggestion made by Fox LJ when *Davy*'s case was in the Court of Appeal, that it might ultimately prove convenient to consolidate the two sets of proceedings and hear them together (81 LGR 580, 597).

(c) The need to obtain the leave of the court

6.23. The requirement for leave to proceed with an application for judicial review in an administrative law case should in our view be abolished. Although the statistics show that leave is refused in a significant number of cases, they do not distinguish between administrative law cases and those from magistrates and the Crown Court.

The Law Commission recommended, albeit with some hesitation, the retention of the requirement of leave, but (as noted above) only in the context that judicial review should not be an exclusive remedy. Leave is not required in Scotland under the new procedure introduced in 1985 (see paragraph 6.46 below) nor is it required in those Commonwealth countries which have judicial review procedures. Parliament has not thought it necessary to impose a leave requirement in the numerous cases in which the prerogative orders have been replaced by a statutory procedure (such as compulsory purchase orders and town planning decisions). Indeed, we are not aware of any other jurisdiction, including the continental systems, in which the citizen requires leave of the court to challenge the legality of administrative acts. We look upon it very much as a matter of principle. The citizen does not require leave to sue a fellow citizen and we do not think that he should have to obtain leave in order to proceed against the state and administrative bodies. In particular, we cannot agree with the philosophy advanced by the House of Lords in *O'Reilly* v. *Mackman* that leave, time-limits, and other restrictions are necessary for the protection of the administration.

6.24. It is sometimes argued that the leave requirement is beneficial to the litigant. With very little expenditure of time and money he hears from the court itself that his case has no prospect of success. It would be impossible to assess the validity of this argument (in terms of benefit perceived by the litigant) without making a study of the reactions of those litigants who have had their cases summarily dismissed in this manner, but we venture to doubt whether the paternalistic attitude implicit in the argument is one that the courts ought to adopt. In any event it is surely preferable for the case to be dismissed on its merits, as now happens in Scotland under the new procedure to which we have already made reference.

6.25. In *R.* v. *Inland Revenue Commissioners*, ex parte *National Federation of Self-Employed and Small Businesses Ltd.* [1982] AC 617 it was said that the justification for leave is to prevent litigation by 'busybodies, cranks and other mischief makers' (per Lord Scarman). In *O'Reilly* v. *Mackman*, the phrase used in relation to Order 53 generally was 'protection against groundless, unmeritorious or tardy harassment' ([1983] 2 AC 237, 284). The number of cases in this category is not known to us, but we think the administrative bodies concerned can safely be left to their remedy of striking out, which, together with the penalty of costs for an unsuccessful application for judicial review, affords, in our view, quite sufficient protection for the administration from the activities of busybodies and such like. Pleadings may be struck out under the rules of court (Order 18, rule 19) if they disclose no reasonable cause of action, if they are scandalous, frivolous, or vexatious, or if they otherwise constitute an abuse of the process of the court, and the action may be dismissed (Order 18, rule 19(1)). If, as we recommend, the leave requirement is abolished the rule that we have cited should be extended to applications for judicial review. In our view this amendment would give the administration perfectly adequate protection against bogus claims. There may be critics of our proposals who will seek to justify the status quo on the ground that the leave requirement acts as a useful filter and that its removal will open the floodgates and lead to a massive increase in the list of pending cases with attendant delays in obtaining a hearing date. We do not seek to minimize the problem of delay. It already takes far too long in many cases of judicial review to get the decision of the court. But this is part of a more general problem. Even the Commercial Court, which twenty years ago could boast of its expedition, is now seriously overloaded and incapable of offering to suitors generally the service it once provided. What we regard as wrong in the current situation is that one category of litigants, namely those seeking judicial review, should be subjected to an impediment which is not put in the way of litigants generally. It would not matter if leave were always granted on a benevolent basis, with every allowance made in favour of the would-be applicant (though this approach would rather weaken the force of the 'useful filter' argument). But we know from recent experience that judges sometimes refuse leave where the Court of Appeal subsequently grants it and the case is finally decided in the applicant's favour *R. v. Commissioner for the Special Purposes of the IT Acts*, ex parte *Stipplechase Ltd.*, *The Times*, 23 January 1985). There must, therefore, be a real risk at present that applicants, having been wrongly refused leave by a judge, give up their cases and never have them heard on the merits.

6.26. A further reason why the requirement for leave should be abolished is that the House of Lords in the *National Federation of Self-Employed* case (followed in *R. v. Boundary Commission*, ex parte *Foot* [1983] QB 600) has altered the character of the leave required where standing is in issue. It used to be thought that standing was a threshold requirement. The court would consider the matter at the outset and decide whether to grant leave. If leave were granted it would not thereafter be withdrawn. The House of Lords case has now demonstrated that in many cases the issue of standing is intimately connected with the substance of the case. But the rule links standing to leave. The practical result is that, as regards a case where standing is in issue, the court may not be able to decide finally whether there should be leave until the case has been argued out on the merits. This undermines the argument commonly advanced in favour of leave, namely, that it is a useful filter for weeding out unmeritorious cases before the defendant is put to the expense of making his defence[1].

6.27. Finally, it may be noted that if the Court of Appeal refuses to grant leave to apply for judicial review the House of Lords has no jurisdiction to entertain an appeal, there being no order or judgment to appeal against, within the meaning of section 3 of the Appellate Jurisdiction Act 1876 (*In re Poh* [1983] 1 All ER 287, HL). We think that the ordinary rule should apply and that the House of Lords should be able to give leave to appeal in an appropriate case. A clause which would have had the effect of taking away even the right to appeal to the Court of Appeal from a refusal of leave by a judge appeared in the Administration of Justice Bill, 1985. Fortunately, when the Bill was before the House of Lords the clause was withdrawn. What may be described as a compromise was subsequently rejected on a division in the House of Lords and was not revived in the Commons. This would have provided for an appeal to a three-judge Divisional Court, one of the members being a Lord Justice of Appeal.

(d) The shortness of the time-limit

6.28. Before the new Order 53 was introduced the only time-limit in respect of the prerogative orders was the six months' limit for certiorari. That time-limit could be extended if the delay was satisfactorily explained to the court. The Law Commission recommended the repeal of the six months for certiorari, and the application of a general rule for judicial review that 'relief should not be refused by the Court solely on the ground that there has been

---

[1] Sir William Wade proposes a different solution to the present unsatisfactory state of the law—to fit the prerogative remedies into the mechanism of an ordinary action and to build in a procedure for expedition: (1985) 101 LQR 180. 189.

delay in making the application, unless the Court considers that the granting of the relief would cause substantial prejudice or hardship to any person or would be detrimental to good administration' (paragraph 50). This was implemented by the new Order 53, rule 4(1), introduced in 1977, except that it added a three months' time-limit for certiorari. In 1980, the three months' time-limit was extended to *all* applications for judicial review 'unless the Court considers that there is good reason for extending the period within which the application shall be made'. The Supreme Court Act, 1981, section 31(6) lays down the general rule envisaged by the Law Commission in the passage quoted above, but there is a saving for 'any rule of court which has the effect of limiting the time within which an application for judicial review may be made' (section 31(7)). (The full text of the section is in Appendix 12.)

6.29. The three months' time-limit, which is contrary to the liberalizing recommendation of the Law Commission, has been much criticized and is a defect of the judicial review procedure. It should, we think, be removed. Three months is too short. Some administrative defaults do not come to light immediately and in some cases an applicant may want time in which to try to negotiate a solution before deciding whether to start proceedings for judicial review. We think the Law Commission's recommendation, now contained (albeit in a slightly modified form) in section 31(6) of the Act of 1981, gives the court ample powers for dealing with unjustified delay. We do not read the decision of the House of Lords in *O'Reilly* v. *Mackman* as endorsing the three-month period, only the general concept of a time-limit.

6.30. We therefore recommend the revocation of the present Order 53, rule 4, thus removing the three months' time-limit and leaving the question of delay to be dealt with by reference to the statutory test in section 31(6) of the 1981 Act. We are, of course, aware that there are situations in which third party interests are involved; in such cases the court would understandably consider with great care whether to grant a tardy application. If our recommendation of a right to reasons for an administrative decision becomes law, we think it should be made clear that any time limitation for the start of proceedings only begins to run from the date when the reasons are received by the applicant, subject to the proviso that the request for reasons is made promptly after knowledge of the decision.

6.31. We would add that there are some administrative law matters which clearly ought not to be subject to any time-limit. The validity of delegated legislation, for example, on which criminal liability sometimes depends, should be open to question without a time-limit. Another example is where the right to use land is affected by the validity of a planning permission or planning condition granted in the past (for example, *Kingsway Investments (Kent) Ltd. v. Kent CC* [1971] AC 72; *Newbury DC* v. *Secretary of State for the Environment* [1981] AC 578).

(e) Discovery and evidence

6.32. Although the court has power on judicial review to make interlocutory orders, the summary nature of the proceedings and the fact that under the prerogative orders discovery, interrogatories, and cross-examination were only allowed in very exceptional cases, have resulted in a climate unfavourable to procedural steps of this kind. In many cases of judicial review an interlocutory stage is not necessary, but we think it should be freely available in cases where it is needed. Judicial review would be a more attractive procedure for litigants if it became known that the judges were sympathetic to applications for discovery and cross-examination, and that the traditional 'prerogative order' attitude was dead. We had hoped that what Lord Diplock said in *O'Reilly* v. *Mackman*, to the effect that leave for discovery and cross-examination in judicial review cases is governed by the same principles as in actions begun by originating summons ('it should be allowed whenever the justice of the particular case so requires' [1983] 2 AC at 283A), would have been liberally implemented. Recent evidence from practitioners tends to confirm, however, that there has been little change in old attitudes. The objection to the criterion of 'justice' in the particular case is, in any event, that the applicant may not know what documents the defendant authority has in its possession. Moreover, 'justice' is not the criterion for disclosing documents in an ordinary action. The normal test there is relevance.

(f) The absence of a statutory statement of the grounds for judicial review

6.33. The lawyer who is expert in administrative law is well aware of the various grounds on which it is possible to challenge the validity of administrative action. But many, perhaps most, lawyers do not deal with administrative law cases in the course of their day-to-day practice and there are many litigants or potential litigants who would be assisted by a clear statement of the grounds of challenge. We believe that it is very important to make the law as clear as possible and to make it accessible and intelligible to ordinary people. Reference is made in chapter 2 of this Report (paragraph 2.20) to two statutes which have endeavoured to state in simple terms the grounds of review. They are the Australian Administrative Decisions (Judicial Review) Act, 1977 (as amended) section 5, and the Barbados Administrative Justice Act, 1980, section 4. (The sections are quoted below in Appendices 8 and 9 respectively.) The objection that such a codification measure would freeze the law in a mould and prevent further growth is answered by paragraph (j) of section 5(1) of the Australian Act which states as a last ground of review 'that the decision was otherwise contrary to law'. Moreover, the other grounds are no more than convenient shorthand labels for established grounds of challenge and the law can continue to develop under each heading. For example, paragraph (a) in the subsection, referring to 'a breach of the rules of natural justice', leaves the court free to develop these rules in accordance with the common law doctrine of precedent. We would, however, deem it prudent in any English version of this statute to add after the quoted words the phrase 'or of the duty to act fairly'. This would eliminate barren discussion as to whether the duty to act fairly is part and parcel of natural justice or a distinct concept.[1] The only paragraph of the subsection which is explained in any detail is (e) ('an improper exercise of the power conferred'). Subsection (2) of section 5 helpfully elaborates on this by listing nine types of cases which are to be taken as referred to. The somewhat restricted language of paragraph (h), 'that there was no evidence or other material to justify the making of the decision', may need redrafting in the light of the authorities which we discuss in paragraphs 7.6 to 7.11 below.

6.34. In our view an enactment along the lines of the Australian legislation (suitably modified to take account of the points which we have mentioned and any other desirable drafting changes) would be beneficial and we recommend its adoption.

[1] Reference may be made to the article 'Fairness and Natural Justice – Distinct Concepts or Mere Semantics?' by Dr G. D. S. Taylor in (1977) 3 Monash University Law Review 191 with its reflections upon the judgment of Wootten J. in *Dunlop* v. *Woolahra Municipal Council* [1975] 2 NSWLR 446.

PART II

SCOTLAND

Remedies

6.35. Apart from those statutory remedies which are essentially the same in England and in Scotland (for example, the six-week right of application to the courts to challenge a compulsory purchase order or a planning decision), the judicial remedies available in Scotland for administrative law purposes are in origin quite different from those in England. In particular, the prerogative orders of certiorari, prohibition, and mandamus, along with the writ of habeas corpus, never formed part of the law of Scotland. Historically it has always been by the ordinary procedures of the Court of Session in Edinburgh that an individual sought redress against public authorities. Thus by an action for *reduction* an individual may seek to quash (reduce) an official decision on grounds of *ultra vires*, excess of jurisdiction, or breach of natural justice. By an action for *declarator*, the court may be asked to declare the rights and duties of the parties. A public authority may be restrained by *interdict* (the equivalent of the English injunction and prohibition) from infringing the rights of the individual or from otherwise exceeding its powers. Such remedies can be combined with a claim for damages where loss has been caused unlawfully. By the summary procedure of petition under section 91 of the Court of Session Act, 1868, an order may be obtained for the performance of a statutory duty where the law and the facts are clear. A full account of the law of judicial review of administrative action in Scotland is now available in the *Stair Memorial Encyclopaedia, The Laws of Scotland* (1987), vol. 1, 'Administrative Law', pp. 147–66).

6.36. One consequence of the fact that the prerogative orders are not known in Scotland is that the remedies available in administrative law are mainly general purpose remedies available for all matters of civil right. Scotland has not developed a specialized 'public law' jurisdiction similar to that which in England is now associated with applications for judicial review under Order 53. The administrative law work of the Court of Session is handled as part of the general work of the court and no specialization of judicial tasks has occurred comparable to the work of the Divisional Court in

London. While Scotland avoided the problems associated with choosing the right form of action (a serious weakness of English law before 1977), the major weakness of the Scottish position was for many years perceived by critics to be that the effectiveness of judicial scrutiny of the decisions of administrative agencies and tribunals was seriously impeded because litigation tended to be too elaborate, too expensive, and too long-drawn-out. Section 91 of the 1868 Act referred to above provided an exception to this generalization in relation to the enforcement of statutory duties. Now, as a result of the recent reform referred to below, a streamlined procedure of general application has been introduced designed to meet these criticisms.

6.37. In 1969 the Law Commission for England and Wales and the Scottish Law Commission were each asked by Government 'to review the existing remedies for the judicial control of administrative acts and omissions with a view to evolving a simpler and more effective procedure'. In England, this led to the report of the Law Commission in 1976 recommending the introduction of the application for judicial review. How that report was implemented has already been described. The Scottish Law Commission published a memorandum on *Remedies in Administrative Law* in 1971 and invited observations on certain questions set out in the memorandum from the legal profession and others concerned. Those observations were received but no further action was taken on the subject by the Scottish Law Commission, presumably because other subjects for law reform were regarded as having greater priority.

6.38. While Scotland has not experienced the recent rapid increase in administrative law litigation which has occurred in England, there has been sufficient use of the Scottish courts to draw attention to certain problems. One question raised in 1971 by the Scottish Law Commission's memorandum was whether the Court of Session had the same jurisdiction as the English High Court has by certiorari to review errors of law within jurisdiction made by tribunals and other bodies. In *Watt* v. *Lord Advocate* 1979 SC 120, the Inner House of the Court of Session decided, in an unemployment benefit case, that the court may not review an error of law made by an inferior tribunal unless that error caused the tribunal to exceed its jurisdiction. That decision produced an evident inequality in the remedies available to social security claimants north and south of the border and the Social Security Act, 1980, section 14 established an appeal on points of law from the Social Security Commissioners to an appropriate appellate court (the Court of Appeal for England and Wales, the Court of Session for Scotland, and the Court of Appeal for Northern Ireland).

Jurisdiction of the sheriff court

6.39. Another question raised in the memorandum of 1971 was the jurisdiction of the sheriff court in administrative cases. In matters of private law the sheriff court has a more extensive jurisdiction than the county court in England. In the field of public administration, very many Acts of Parliament have provided for a right of appeal from local authorities to the sheriff, on such matters as housing, public health, allocation of pupils to schools, and licensing. But the broader question was whether the sheriff court had a general jurisdiction that could be exercised without specific statutory authority to review the acts and decisions of public bodies.

6.40. This question arose for decision in *Brown* v. *Hamilton District Council* 1983 SC (HL) 1, under the Housing (Homeless Persons) Act, 1977. That Act imposed new duties upon local housing authorities in respect of homeless persons but provided no right of appeal against a housing authority's decision turning down a request for assistance made under the Act. In Scotland there was no doubt that the housing authority's decision could be challenged by the individual concerned raising an action in the Court of Session to seek review of the housing authority's decision. For reasons mentioned in paragraph 6.36 above, however, this was not suitable for resolving urgent issues. In *Brown* v. *Hamilton DC*, it had to be decided whether decisions under the Housing (Homeless Persons) Act, 1977, could be reviewed in the sheriff court. In the Inner House of the Court of Session, the court by a majority (Lord Dunpark dissenting) decided that the sheriff court did have power to supervise the administrative decisions of local authorities under such Acts as the 1977 Act. Lord Justice Clerk Wheatley emphasized that the sheriff court was a very suitable forum for reviewing controversies arising under the Act, saying, 'To require the Court of Session to find time to determine the kind of issue likely to be involved is somewhat akin to taking a sledgehammer to crack a nut . . .'. The decision of the majority was overturned by a unanimous House of Lords. It was held that in the absence of express legislative provision conferring jurisdiction under the 1977 Act upon the sheriff court, that court had no authority at common law to review decisions taken by housing authorities and had no power to provide an appropriate remedy quashing such decisions.

Comparisons made between English and Scottish procedures

6.41. In the course of his judgment in the *Brown* case, Lord Fraser asked whether there might not be advantages in developing special procedures in Scotland for dealing with questions in the public-law area, comparable to the English prerogative orders. Having mentioned the beneficial effects of recent reforms in English procedure, he stated that the prerogative orders now had advantages over ordinary procedures such as declaration, 'particularly by making available remedies which are speedy and cheap and which protect public authorities from unreasonable actions'—a reference to Lord Diplock's speech in *O'Reilly* v. *Mackman*, discussed above.

6.42. In a subsequent House of Lords decision, *Stevenson* v. *Midlothian District Council* 1983 SC (HL) 50, Lord Fraser referred again to his suggestion that there might be advantages in developing special procedures in Scotland comparable to the Order 53 procedure in England for obtaining judicial review of the decisions made by public bodies. In *Stevenson*'s case, it appeared that the individual's action was wholly without merits and under a procedure modelled on English lines the court could either have refused leave at the outset or could have reached a decision on the merits of the application upon affidavit evidence much more quickly than was possible under existing Scottish procedure.

6.43. In the light of Lord Fraser's remarks in *Brown* and *Stevenson*, the Lord President of the Court of Session, after consultation with the Lord Advocate, decided in May 1983 to establish a small working party under the chairmanship of Lord Dunpark to devise and recommend for consideration a simple form of procedure for bringing before the Court of Session (*a*) complaints against acts or decisions of inferior courts, tribunals, public bodies, authorities, or officers, where no right of appeal is available, based on grounds of *ultra vires* or failure to comply with statutory procedures, and (*b*) complaints of failure of any body or person to perform a statutory duty coming within the scope of section 91 of the Court of Session Act, 1868.

6.44. Our own Working Group in Scotland made submissions to

Lord Dunpark's Working Party. So far as the decision in *Brown* v. *Hamilton District Council* was concerned, they submitted that it would not be desirable for Parliament to vest in the sheriff court a general power to review all administrative decisions by local authorities and other public bodies. As Lord Fraser's speech in *Brown* had made clear, supervisory jurisdiction over inferior courts and other public authorities had always been exclusive to the Court of Session. In this respect a close parallel existed with the role of the High Court in England. However, the Housing (Homeless Persons) Act, 1977 (as modified by section 76 of the Housing Act, 1985), should be amended so as to confer on sheriff courts power to review decisions taken by housing authorities in exercise of their duties under the Act. A remedy of this kind would be consistent with many other existing rights of recourse to the sheriff court in local government matters. The Licensing (Scotland) Act, 1976, section 39(4) provided a recent example of specialized jurisdiction being conferred on the sheriff court and this appears to be working satisfactorily.

6.45. As regards remedies in general, our Working Group submitted that a new summary two-stage procedure for judicial review of decisions by public authorities should be introduced into Court of Session practice. The aim should be to produce a remedy which would be cheaper, speedier, and less cumbersome than present judicial remedies. It should resemble the present procedure under section 91 of the Court of Session Act, 1868 except that it would be heard by a single judge and not by a division of the Inner House. The new procedure would take the form of a petition submitted to the court by the complainant and naming the public authority whose decision was being challenged. It could be called a petition for judicial review. The petition should set out or otherwise identify the decision being challenged, should state the names of the other parties, should specify in brief the grounds of challenge and should indicate the relief sought. This would usually be of a negative character, to have the offending decision set aside, the public authority restrained from giving effect to it, and the way thus opened for a fresh decision to be made. But the petition might also seek a declarator of the petitioner's right, and it should be competent on a petition to seek an order for the performance by a public authority of its public duties (thus superseding in this field the remedy by petition under section 91 of the Court of Session Act, 1868). It would not be appropriate for a petition of this kind to include a claim for damages or compensation, whether as ancillary to the main relief sought or as a remedy in its own right. The procedure on the petition should be simple and expeditious and should be at the discretion of the court. All petitions should be heard by a single judge in the Outer House, and the Lord President should nominate one or two judges specifically to deal with these petitions, since the judge or judges concerned must have the opportunity for developing experience and consistency in the procedure adopted. Except in cases of great urgency, when the judge would be empowered to issue an *ex parte* interdict, the petition would be considered by the judge only when the defenders' reply to the petition had been received. At the first hearing before the court the judge could, depending on the nature of the case and the circumstances, decide the issues summarily, appoint a date for legal argument, ask for full pleadings, or appoint a date for trial of specified issues of fact. It would not be appropriate to introduce into Scottish procedure the requirement of leave which forms part of the practice under Order 53, but the procedure proposed would enable a petition that was wholly without merits to be disposed of without delay.

6.46. The proposals put forward by our Scottish Working Group were in large measure adopted by Lord Dunpark's Working Party in their Report on *Procedure for Judicial Review of Administrative Action* submitted in June 1984. The Lord President of the Court of Session in turn accepted the Dunpark Working Party's recommendations (though not in relation to three particular statutes as to which the Working Party thought that the position was anomalous and that the new procedure should relate to applications to the court under such statutes). A new Rule of Court (rule 260B) was introduced the following year by the Act of Sederunt (Rules of Court Amendment No. 2) (Judicial Review) 1985, SI 1985 No. 500 (s. 48). Certain features are of particular significance. Thus:

1. A new procedure in the Court of Session has been provided. It is called 'the application for judicial review' (paragraph 1). The application is by way of petition (paragraph 5).

2. Any party wishing to invoke the supervisory jurisdiction of the court is bound to use the new procedure.

3. The court is given wide powers to make any appropriate orders for expediting the process together with a broad jurisdiction as to the remedies that may be granted. They include declarator,

reduction, suspension, interdict, implement, restitution, and payment (whether of damages or otherwise) (paragraph 4).

4. A first hearing and a second hearing are provided for, but the court may on the first hearing summarily determine the application. This enables the judge to dismiss a hopeless case without further ado or to grant relief if there is no substantial defence to a good claim (paragraphs 15–17 and 20).

5. In accordance with the Working Party's recommendations the rule omits the words 'in respect of which no right of appeal is available', which formed part of the Working Party's terms of reference (see paragraph 6.43 above). The new procedure could not be applied to cases where the legislature had granted a right of appeal to the Court of Session (for such appeals are determined by the Inner House).

6. Applications are made to a judge nominated by the Lord President (paragraph 6).

7. There is no requirement for the petitioner to obtain the leave of the court.

8. There is no time-limit.

6.47. In general our Scottish Working Group welcomed the new rule 260B. They did, however, have reservations about some aspects of the rule. The new procedure is intended to be an exclusive procedure whenever a party wishes to invoke the supervisory jurisdiction of the Court of Session at common law in respect of the decisions of inferior courts, tribunals, public authorities, and officials. This is a curtailment of rights which could cause practical difficulties and unfairness. It is indeed desirable that there should be a speedy procedure in many such cases, but English experience since *O'Reilly* v. *Mackman* and *Cocks* v. *Thanet District Council* has shown that it is difficult to draw a clear demarcation line between litigation that primarily seeks judicial review of administrative decisions and litigation in which such review is merely incidental to other forms of relief (for example, an action for damages). The Working Group also see difficulty in cases in which the litigant wishes to invoke the supervisory jurisdiction of the court by way of defence to normal proceedings. (The English case of *Winder* referred to in paragraph 6.19 above illustrates the possible problem.) Finally, it was disappointing that the Dunpark Working Party remit was confined to procedure before the Court of Session and so did not address the proposal mentioned in paragraph 6.44 above that the Housing (Homeless Persons) Act, 1977 should be amended so as to confer on sheriff courts powers to review decisions taken by housing authorities under that Act.

6.48. It appears that Scotland has wisely borrowed from England the best features of the application for judicial review and succeeded in avoiding two aspects which we have strongly criticized, namely the need for leave and the short time-limit. Definitional problems may sometimes arise in Scotland; the court still has to decide whether the application invokes the supervisory jurisdiction of the Court of Session.

CHAPTER 6. RECOMMENDATIONS

1. An early opportunity should be taken by the House of Lords to reconsider the decision in *O'Reilly* v. *Mackman* [1983] 2 AC 237. It should be left to Parliament to decide, after appropriate consultation, whether there are any circumstances in which a plaintiff should be obliged to use the Order 53 procedure and be debarred from proceeding by action or originating summons (paragraphs 6.15–6.19).
2. The term 'public law' should cease to be used as the key to identifying those cases which can appropriately be dealt with by the Order 53 procedure (paragraphs 6.20–6.22).
3. The requirement that an applicant must obtain the leave of the court before proceeding under Order 53 should be abandoned. Consideration should be given to amending the rules so as to provide expressly for the striking out of hopeless or bogus applications. Alternatively, consideration should be given to adopting the two 'hearings' of the Scottish procedure (paragraphs 6.23–6.26 and 6.46).
4. If the leave requirement is retained, jurisdiction should be conferred on the House of Lords to entertain an appeal from a decision of the Court of Appeal refusing to grant leave to apply for judicial review (paragraph 6.27).
5. Rule 4 of Order 53 (which lays down a three months' limitation period for applications under Order 53) should be repealed and the matter should be left on the more general basis set out in section 31(6) of the Supreme Court Act, 1981, namely, that undue delay should be a barrier only in so far as it causes substantial prejudice or hardship to others or would be detrimental to good administration (paragraphs 6.28–6.30).
6. Discovery of documents should be permitted more liberally than is currently the case in Order 53 proceedings. The prima facie rule should be that documents which are relevant to contested issues between the

parties should be disclosed. A correspondingly liberal attitude to interrogatories and cross-examination should be maintained (paragraph 6.32).

7. A statutory statement should be enacted of the grounds on which judicial review will lie. Such a list could follow the model in the Australian statute (the Administrative Decisions (Judicial Review) Act, 1977, section 5 with appropriate modifications) (paragraphs 6.33 and 6.34).

8. Provision should be made enabling the court to order that proceedings which have been wrongly commenced by writ should continue as if they were an application for judicial review (paragraph 6.10).

9. In its application to Scotland, Part III of the Housing Act, 1985 (formerly the Housing (Homeless Persons) Act, 1977), should be amended so as to confer on sheriff courts powers to review decisions taken by housing authorities under that Act (paragraphs 6.44 and 6.47).

7

The Courts and the Law

SUMMARY OF ARGUMENT. The chapter falls into two parts. First, there is a consideration of the existing court structure and the manner in which administrative law cases are handled. Reference is made to two possible models which might be adopted—an Administrative Court (on the lines of the French Conseil d'Etat) and an Administrative Division of the High Court of Justice. It is concluded that the case for change is not made out. The limitations on the power of the court to interfere with the decisions of administrators are noted. In special cases it seems that the courts can go behind the facts found by an administrator; they can also intervene where the inferences which he draws do not follow logically from the primary facts.

In the second half of the chapter, the discussion turns to deficiencies in the substantive law as currently applied by the courts. Apart from the topics fully discussed in chapters 3 and 11—the duty to give reasons and compensation for unlawful acts—criticism is directed to three matters: the absence of liability where loss is caused by wrong advice given by officials; the rule that a compulsory purchase order, even if obtained by fraud, cannot be set aside after six weeks; and the doctrine that error of law must appear on the face of the record.

7.1. In this chapter we address ourselves to two questions. The first question is whether there is a need to create a new court or to restructure the existing courts system so as to deal more efficiently with administrative law cases. We add some comments about the powers of the court. Second, we ask whether the substantive law as applied by the courts in such cases is in need of reform.

An Administrative Court?

7.2. Until recently there was a body of opinion which advocated fundamental change in the courts system to deal with the growing volume of disputes between citizens and public authorities. One possibility which was much discussed was the creation of an Administrative Court, on the lines of the French Conseil d'Etat. This court would have been separate from the High Court and might have had investigatory powers. It could have been composed of both judges and laymen. Its jurisdiction would have extended not only to legal disputes of the kind which courts are used to handling in the administrative field but also to allegations about the malfunctioning of the public service. An eloquent proponent of this view was the late Professor J. D.B. Mitchell. Another, less radical proposal which was mooted was the creation of a distinct Administrative Division of the High Court to which could be directed all cases which raised issues involving the administration.

7.3. Since the time when these proposals were first actively considered the position has changed. There has been the procedural reform discussed in chapters 1 and 6 above, namely, the new Order 53 providing for the application for judicial review. We have made clear our view that this has proved a significant advance enabling cases against public authorities to be brought on for hearing before a single judge with great expedition. While we have also made it clear in chapter 6 that there are various aspects of the rules which stand in need of amendment, we do not support any proposal for the creation of a completely new Administrative Division of the High Court along the lines earlier proposed. There is nothing that such a division could achieve that cannot be achieved through existing machinery. In practice, though not in name, there is already a functional segregation of administrative law cases and they are generally tried by specialist judges. There seems to us to be no need to amend the Judicature Acts so as to replace the flexibility of the present system with the rigidity of a separate division.

7.4. For much the same reasons we find ourselves opposed to the introduction of anything on the lines of a Conseil d'Etat. There are, however, some additional objections. It has to be appreciated that in the wake of a revolution the Conseil d'Etat was created to discharge specific tasks. In the course of its life it has undergone considerable change and development. It is not possible, as it were, to pick up such an institution, set it down in alien soil, and expect it to flourish. The membership of the Conseil is composed in large part of administrators who were trained as lawyers. It would be difficult to recruit such a category from the departments here. If a Conseil d'Etat were to be introduced, questions would arise as to whether it was to be given an exclusive area of jurisdiction as in France. If so, it might be necessary to follow the French precedent and to have a separate court or tribunal to decide whether borderline cases should be dealt with by the ordinary courts or by the Conseil. Our view is that the courts are now acting so vigorously and effectively that there is no case for undertaking a novel experiment for which the nation's constitutional history has not prepared it. If there are particular doctrines of law applied by the Conseil d'Etat which would be an improvement on English law, then these should certainly be considered with a view to their adoption, but further than that it seems both unnecessary and undesirable to go.

Powers of the court

7.5. The powers of the court on judicial review are more circumscribed than they are on an appeal. The court cannot substitute its own opinion for the opinion formed by the decision-maker—so long, that is, as he has applied the law correctly and followed the correct procedure. In *Chief Constable of the North Wales Police* v. *Evans* [1982] 1 WLR 1155, 1161 the Lord Chancellor, Lord Hailsham of St Marylebone, said: 'The purpose of judicial review is to ensure that the individual receives fair treatment, and not to ensure that the authority, after according fair treatment, reaches on a matter which it is authorised by law to decide for itself a conclusion which is correct in the eyes of the court.' This means that there remains a wide area within which the decision-maker is not open to challenge. This covers such matters as finding the primary facts on evidence fairly admitted and making the critical appreciation, for example, as to whether, in the light of all relevant planning considerations, the applicant should be granted planning permission.

Judical review and fact-finding

7.6. While the overall position is as we have stated it above, we must draw attention to two decisions which may indicate that the courts in certain (possibly very rare) cases will be willing to go behind the facts found or the inferences drawn by the decision-maker. We refer to the House of Lords decision in *R.* v. *Secretary of State for the Home Department*, ex parte *Khera* and *Khawaja* [1984] AC 74 and the Privy Council decision in the Mount Erebus disaster case (*Mahon* v. *Air New Zealand Limited* [1984] AC 808).

Khawaja

7.7. All the Law Lords who took part in the decisions in *Khera* and *Khawaja* held that the court could re-examine the factual question whether in each case the applicant for judicial review was an 'illegal entrant' within the meaning of the Immigration Act, 1971. On this re-examination further evidence could be looked at and the court was not confined to the material which was before the immigration officer. Four of their Lordships proceeded on the basis that proof that the applicant was an illegal entrant was a 'precedent fact' which had to be established before the immigration officer had any power to exclude or deport. Other terminology used in the case is 'collateral question' or 'jurisdictional fact'. The theory underlying this approach is that the decision-maker has no power to act unless a certain state of facts exists. Thus, a rent tribunal only has jurisdiction if the premises are, in the view of the court, a dwelling house (*R.* v. *Hackney Rent Tribunal* [1951] 2 KB 15). So in *Eleko* v. *Government of Nigeria* [1931] AC 662, the Governor only had power to order deportation if the applicant was a 'native chief'. The rent tribunal in the first of these cases and the Governor in the second could not confer jurisdiction upon themselves by erroneously believing certain facts to exist which did not exist.

7.8. In the *Khawaja* case great emphasis is laid (and properly laid) on the fact that the case concerned the liberty of the subject and this made it especially important for the court to be vigilant to see that no deportation order was made if the facts did not justify the order. But, although four of their Lordships justified their re-examination of the facts and receipt of further evidence on the basis of 'precedent fact', it seems that Lord Wilberforce expressly rejected this theory. He, nevertheless, thought that it was open to the court to go into the question whether on the facts it had been established that the applicants were illegal entrants. He said (p. 105):

The court's investigation of the facts is of a supervisory character and not by way of appeal . . . It should appraise the quality of the evidence and decide whether that justifies the conclusion reached, e.g., whether it justifies a conclusion that the applicant obtained permission to enter by fraud or deceit. An allegation that he has done so being of a serious character and involving issues of personal liberty, requires a corresponding degree of satisfaction as to the evidence. If the court is not satisfied with any part of the evidence, it may remit the matter for reconsideration or itself receive further evidence. It should quash the detention order where the evidence was not such as the authorities should have relied on or where the evidence received does not justify the decision reached or, of course, for any serious procedural irregularity.

7.9. Taking Lord Wilberforce's language, the power of a reviewing court to 'appraise the quality of the evidence' and to 'receive further evidence' seems to be moving very close to a power to re-examine the primary facts. We do not at all dissent from the proposition that a case involving personal liberty should make the court vigilant to ensure that deportation orders and the like are only made when the facts justify them, but, if the underlying principle is sound, we think that there are other classes of case where the reviewing court should be equally vigilant in its scrutiny of the facts. By way of illustration we would cite cases involving a man's livelihood or his reputation.

The Erebus case

7.10. The Privy Council case *Mahon* v. *Air New Zealand Limited and others* was just such a case involving reputation. The Royal Commissioner who had been appointed to investigate an air disaster in Antarctica included in his report highly critical passages which were seriously damaging to the reputations of the airline and of named individuals. The Privy Council said that a Commissioner conducting such an inquiry must base his decision upon evidence that has some probative value. They defined this as meaning that 'the finding must be based upon some material that tends logically to show the existence of facts consistent with the finding and that the reasoning supportive of the finding, if it be disclosed, is not logically self-contradictory'. (Similar language was used by Diplock LJ, as he then was, in *R.* v. *Deputy Industrial Injuries Commissioner*, ex parte *Moore* [1965] 1 QB 456, 488.) After a lengthy consideration of the evidence their Lordships concluded that certain critical findings of fact were arrived at by a process of reasoning that was self-contradictory. (The judgment also proceeded on the ground that the Royal Commissioner had failed to observe the rules of natural justice.)

7.11. The double use of the adverb 'logically' in this quotation ('... material that tends logically to show the existence of facts consistent with the finding ...' and '... reasoning supportive of the finding ... not logically self-contradictory') appears to open the door to the judges of the reviewing court substituting their own conclusions on fact and inferences for those of the decision-maker if they are unconvinced by the route which he has followed.

Further developments in judicial review of fact-finding

7.12. It is impossible to forecast how the courts will utilize these new tools for getting behind the facts found by the decision-maker. Perhaps both cases should be treated as special and as not laying down any general rule. The only comment that we can safely make is that if these cases were to be generally applied the gap between judicial review and appeal would be narrowed notwithstanding repeated judicial pronouncements (to be found in the *Erebus* case as elsewhere) to the effect that review is a very different process from appeal. There is, we believe, a risk that if reopening the facts became a common practice, judicial review itself might come under attack.

The substantive law

7.13. In our Discussion Paper (section G) we drew attention to the change of attitude of the courts towards judicial scrutiny of the activities of the administrator. This has manifested itself over the last thirty years and has ended an era styled by Professor Sir William Wade *Constitutional Fundamentals* (Hamlyn Lectures), 1980, p. 63) as the courts' 'period of amnesia'. There are many decisions which demonstrate the positive attitude which the courts currently adopt. We have given an account of these trends in other chapters in this Report, in particular chapters 6, 8, and 10.

7.14. We have asked ourselves in what respects the existing substantive law is inadequate. By way of answer we single out specific instances in the following paragraphs. The first two topics are dealt with fully in separate chapters of this Report, but it is convenient to marshal them together with our other selected topics.

Reasons

7.15. As we have argued in chapter 3 of this Report, we think that there should be a statutory obligation to give reasons on request for administrative decisions. Although the Donoughmore Committee in 1932 called the giving of reasons the third principle of natural justice, the courts have not taken that view and (with fairly rare exceptions) have allowed administrators to decide without giving any indication of their thought processes.

Compensation

7.16. We think that there should be compensation for the citizen who suffers loss as a direct result of unlawful administrative action.

The law already covers cases of negligence and other recognized torts but there is a wide area, as we demonstrate in chapter 11, where no compensation is available even though financial loss can be shown to have followed directly from wrongful action of an administrative character.

Bad advice by officials

7.17. There should be some protection for the citizen where erroneous advice or a misleading assurance has been given by a public official. The law already covers cases where negligent advice can be shown to have caused financial loss. Sometimes liability can be established in contract where a public official was able to, and did, bind his employer. Cases do, however, arise which are not so covered. For instance, an official may, without personal negligence, give an assurance that planning permission for a certain use of land is not needed. The individual relies upon that assurance and later discovers that the assurance is incorrect. He then seeks planning permission and it is refused. Apparently the individual is without a legal remedy in this situation. He cannot even assert that the local authority is estopped from enforcing the planning law against him, since the Court of Appeal's decision in *Western Fish Products Ltd.* v. *Penwith DC* [1981] 2 All ER 204 comes close to excluding for all practical purposes the law of estoppel from the realm of the exercise of statutory powers. The subsequent House of Lords decision in *R.* v. *Inland Revenue Commissioners*, ex parte *Preston* [1985] AC 835 is to the same effect. In *A.-G. of Hong Kong* v. *Ng Yuen Shiu* [1983] 2 AC 629, the Judicial Committee of the Privy Council held that the Hong Kong government was bound by an undertaking given that an illegal immigrant's case would be considered on its merits. In that case, the court was able to give due protection to the individual against unfair treatment, but there was no overriding statutory duty to be surmounted. In cases where the court is unable to provide an adequate remedy, it will be within the purview of the ombudsmen (both parliamentary and local) to investigate and report on the circumstances, and if justified to recommend the payment of compensation. We accept that, if public authorities are to be held liable for incorrect or misleading statements, a possible reaction to this would be that officials will be instructed not to offer any advice, or will in any event be reluctant to give advice. But we cannot accept that the administration should be able inadvertently to cause loss or injustice and not be required to alleviate the consequences for the individual.

Late challenge to compulsory purchase orders on the ground of fraud

7.18. We think that the rule in *Smith* v. *East Elloe RDC* [1956] AC 736 and *R.* v. *Secretary of State for the Environment*, ex parte *Ostler* [1977] QB 122 (that a compulsory purchase order (CPO) cannot be questioned on the grounds of fraud or bad faith once the statutory time-limit for challenge—normally six weeks—has expired) should be reversed by legislation. While we recognize the very strong arguments of certainty and convenience in support of not disturbing an act that has such consequences as a CPO, it seems to us quite fundamental to our law that fraud or bad faith vitiates any transaction, and it is dangerous to protect the administration from investigation by the courts in such cases. The remedy in damages against the individual guilty of fraud or bad faith (recognized in *East Elloe*) is not enough. In principle a CPO and any similar order or scheme procured by fraud should be capable of being set aside by the court notwithstanding the expiry of the statutory time-limit. The circumstances may, of course, be such that the powers of the court are invoked at so late a stage that any attempt to set the CPO aside would be a *brutum fulmen* or work injustice to innocent third parties. In such a case, the successful plaintiff who has established fraud should be allowed to recover damages from the local authority or other public body for provable loss inflicted on him in excess of the compensation (if any) already awarded to him for the taking of his land. It may well be that in many cases damages would suffice, and it would only be in rare cases that the CPO itself would need to be set aside.[1]

Error of law which does not appear on the face of the record

7.19. We think that the old rule that a decision can only be quashed by certiorari for error of law where the error appears on the face of the record can no longer be justified. Where it can be demonstrated that the decision was actually vitiated by an error of

---

[1] One of the Committee, Sir John Boynton, dissents from the view expressed in paragraph 7.18. He believes that in the interests of finality and certainty the CPO should not be open to any attack after the statutory period has elapsed.

law the court should not be prevented by any technical rule from striking down the decision. We believe that if our recommendation about the obligation to supply full reasons on request were to be implemented the occasions when the 'record' would fail to reveal the error would be much rarer, especially if our further recommendation is adopted that the statement of reasons and findings should be deemed to form part of the record. But even without this reform we consider the old technical rule to be indefensible. That this now seems to be the opinion of the House of Lords appears from Lord Diplock's speech in *O'Reilly* v. *Mackman* [1983] 2 AC 237 (the other Law Lords concurred and did not deliver separate judgments). The view is there expressed that as a result of the *Anisminic* case ([1969] 2 AC 147) the distinction between errors of law within and without the jurisdiction has virtually to be disregarded.[2] In the section of the Australian statute referred to in paragraph 6.33 above (which gives a statutory list of the grounds for judicial review) the relevant head is expressed as follows: 'that the decision involved an error of law, whether or not the error appears on the record of the decision'. It is to be hoped that the English courts will now act on the same basis by following Lord Diplock's guidance.

CHAPTER 7. RECOMMENDATIONS

1. Where erroneous advice or a misleading assurance is given by a public official and loss is thereby caused to a person who reasonably acts on the advice or assurance, that person should have a remedy for his loss without having to prove that the official acted negligently (paragraph 7.17).

2. Where a compulsory purchase order is procured by fraud the court should have jurisdiction to set aside the order notwithstanding the lapse of the six-week period which in all other cases would render the order unimpeachable. The discretion to set aside should only be capable of exercise where the application was made sufficiently promptly and

---

[2] It is difficult to reconcile this *obiter dictum* with authorities to the contrary, in particular the Privy Council decision in the *South East Asia Fire Brick* case [1981] AC 363. The cases are collected in Wade, *Administrative Law*, 5th edn., pp. 264–7 and to them we would add *Stevenson* v. *Barham* [1977] 163 CLR 190, 201 (per Mason and Jacobs JJ. in the High Court of Australia) and *Glenvill Homes Pty. Ltd.* v. *Builders Licensing Board* (1981) 2 NSWLR 608; 4 ALD 358, 359 (per Hope and Samuels JJA in the Court of Appeal of New South Wales).

innocent third parties would not suffer. (One member of the committee dissents from this recommendation.) (Paragraph 7.18.)

3. The rule that certiorari will lie only for an error of law which appears on the face of the record should be abolished. It should be legitimate to establish the error by any appropriate means (paragraph 7.19).

8

Standing

SUMMARY OF ARGUMENT. There are many instances where illegal conduct by persons in positions of power is not subject to the ordinary checks of civil action or criminal prosecution. Before moving the court for a remedy against such conduct an applicant must show that he has 'standing to sue', that is, that he has a sufficient connection with the matter in issue to qualify him to pursue the remedy. A variety of tests, different with the nature of the remedy sought, have been developed to determine whether an applicant has standing. Recent cases suggest some assimilation of approach. The New Zealand case of *Finnigan* v. *New Zealand Rugby Football Union* provides an important precedent by adopting a check-list of factors pointing in favour of standing and by rejecting a hard and fast line of distinction between public and private law. Restrictive rules about standing are, in general, inimical to the healthy state of administrative law.

The test now laid down in England and Wales, which is based on a recommendation of the Law Commission, is that an applicant must satisfy the court that he has a sufficient interest in the matter to which the application relates. However, this question is not necessarily a threshold question and the legal and factual merits of the substance of the application may have to be examined before it can be decided. A private person who lacks a sufficient interest to sue in his own name may invite the Attorney General to do so. If the Attorney General agrees (by granting his fiat) the action is brought in his name 'at the relation' of the true plaintiff. This role of the Attorney General is anachronistic and unsatisfactory. The Attorney General requires to be satisfied that the relator is competent to answer for the costs of the action whereas no such requirement forms part of the ordinary action or application for judicial review. The Attorney General's decision in the matter is unreviewable. The Attorney General never brings proceedings against a minister or a government department; this casts doubt on the universality of his role as protector of public rights. The Attorney General is a member of the Government and his decisions are inevitably seen as being influenced by political considerations—not without reason, as emerged very clearly in a case where the Attorney General of Tasmania announced that he would grant his fiat for proceedings to restrain the building of a dam and the

Cabinet instructed him not to do so. The Attorney General resigned; the Premier took his place and refused a fiat.

In Scotland the provision of remedies in administrative law is very different from that in England and Wales. Reliance has always been placed on general remedies, applicable equally to public and private law, and relator actions are unknown. A litigant must be prepared to show that he has 'title and interest' to sue, that is, that he is the proper person to sue and has a real interest in the outcome of the action. But a Working Party under the chairmanship of Lord Dunpark has recommended legislation to widen the common law rules of title and interest to sue to enable every person directly or indirectly affected by alleged unlawful acts or decisions of the administration to challenge them.

In our view the decision as to standing should be taken by the court. The judge should consider whether the proceedings, be they an action or an application for judicial review, are justifiable in the light of the whole circumstances of the case. Amendments to achieve this should be made by legislation both in Scotland and in England and Wales.

8.1. In ordinary civil litigation between subjects the plaintiff has to have a cause of action which he is asserting against the defendant. He may be asserting a property right, suing for damages for breach of contract or tort, or invoking an express statutory remedy conferred on him. If his pleading does not disclose facts which, if proved, would constitute a cause of action the pleading may be struck out under the Rules of Court or pursuant to the court's inherent jurisdiction to prevent an abuse of its process. If the action goes forward to trial without any application to strike out having been made, it may still be held that the plaintiff has no cause of action. In the field of administrative law the position is not quite the same. The applicant for relief does not necessarily need to have a cause of action in the sense in which that term is used in other areas of the civil law. But he does nevertheless need 'standing to sue'. This is a wider concept than that which underlies the statutory requirement of leave for an application for judicial review, discussed at paragraph 6.23 et seq. above, though the test of standing in such an application is the statutory one of 'sufficient interest', discussed at paragraph 8.42 et seq. below.

8.2. The question of standing may at first sight appear to be a matter of procedure and hence of less importance than issues relating to the substantive law. So to regard standing is, however, to underestimate its central significance. A generous approach by the courts to standing and a willingness by judges to accord standing wherever serious illegality is alleged are, in our view, essential if the rule of law is to be a living precept and not a rhetorical phrase to be rehearsed in ceremonial speeches. As Walsh J. said in the Supreme Court of the Republic of Ireland, it has been observed that 'restrictive rules about standing are, in general, inimical to a healthy state of administrative law' (*The State* (*Lynch*) v. *Cooney* [1982] IR 337, 368).

8.3. To put the matter in concrete form, there are numerous examples of situations where persons in positions of power act illegally. Sometimes the illegality is intentional; sometimes there is a bona fide argument that the conduct is legal. The persons acting illegally (as chronicled in the law reports) include ministers, government departments, local authorities, trade unions, broadcasting authorities, and bodies regulating sport. If the illegal conduct impinges on a clear legal right of a person who has an interest in asserting it and the means to do so, the matter can be brought before the court by an ordinary action. The court will enforce the right and the illegality will be stopped. Similarly, if the authorities responsible for the enforcement of the criminal law are prepared to launch criminal proceedings in cases where the illegality involves a violation of the criminal law a penalty or other sanction can be imposed.

8.4. The decided cases, however, provide many instances of illegal conduct which is not subject to these normal checks by civil action or criminal prosecution. The reasons for this vary with the circumstances and it is not possible here to enumerate a full catalogue. But so far as the civil law is concerned a common reason is that no private right is being infringed and there is no obvious person to bring suit. Furthermore, while there are some situations in which the Attorney General will feel moved to bring civil proceedings to restrain illegality, the Attorney General has never intervened to uphold the law by bringing civil proceedings against ministers or government departments. So far as concerns criminal proceedings, the authorities may have reasons of their own for not wishing to launch prosecutions. In the context of industrial disputes it may, for example, be thought that a prosecution would have a deleterious effect, as by extending or consolidating a strike or by impeding negotiations. A private prosecution may in some circumstances be a satisfactory substitute. In practice, however, private prosecutions are extremely rare. Deterrents include the high standard of proof required, the need to establish *mens rea*, and, for some crimes, the need to obtain the consent of the Attorney General or the Director of Public Prosecutions.

8.5. In all such cases where illegality continues unchecked the rule of law is set at nought and the law is brought into contempt. Where the illegality consists of the breach of a statute or of subordinate legislation made under a power conferred by Parliament, there is the further consideration that unrestrained illegality involves a disregard of the will of the legislature.

8.6. In some of the situations described above where it is manifest that there is no private person with a clear entitlement to sue who is willing or able to intervene and where the public authorities, for reasons of political expediency, timidity, or plain indifference, are standing idly by, individuals or groups have come forward and applied to the court to enforce the law. Depending on the circumstances different remedies have been invoked. Resort has often been had to the public law remedies of certiorari, prohibition, and mandamus. Actions have been brought for injunctions and declarations. Since 1977 applications for judicial review have been made.

8.7. As we demonstrat below, different tests have in the past been applied to determine whether standing should be accorded, the tests varying with the nature of the remedy sought. There are now indications in the recent cases of some assimilation of approach. This is certainly true in relation to applications for judicial review.

8.8. An obstacle commonly put in the path of the plaintiff or applicant has been the allegation that he is not sufficiently involved with the matters in dispute, and is a mere busybody or intermeddler. In some contexts this takes the form of an assertion that the applicant has an 'ulterior purpose' for seeking to have the law enforced.

Topics for discussion

8.9. We will deal with this under five headings.

Part I. Standing in relation to obtaining an injunction or a declaration.

Part II. Standing formerly required for the purposes of the prerogative writs and orders.

Part III. 'Sufficient interest' for the purposes of an application for judicial review.

Part IV. The interpretation of provisions as to standing in statutory rights of appeal.

Part V. Proposals for reform.

We deal separately with the law of Scotland in paragraphs 8.64 to 8.68 below (*Part* VI).

PART I

STANDING IN RELATION TO OBTAINING AN INJUNCTION
OR A DECLARATION

The rule in *Boyce* v. *Paddington Borough Council*

8.10. In the case of actions for an injunction or for a declaration the present law is dominated by the rule that, in general, private individuals have no title to sue to protect the public at large from a wrongful invasion of its rights. The rule may derive from the law of public nuisance, where a private individual can sue only if he can show that the interference with a public right also interferes with his own private right or has caused special damage to him (*Boyce* v. *Paddington Borough Council* [1903] 1 Ch. 109).

8.11. This principle was applied in a case where three ratepayers brought an action against thirty councillors of Camden London Borough Council and against the Council itself alleging that the majority group on the Council had followed unlawful policies which led improperly to increased expenditure and diminished income, thereby adding to the burden on ratepayers. Declarations, accounts, and inquiries were sought. Warner J. struck out the action holding that the plaintiffs lacked standing to sue (*Barrs* v. *Bethel* [1982] Ch. 294). The judge, in so deciding, distinguished *Prescott* v. *Birmingham Corporation* [1955] Ch. 210 (where the Court of Appeal had granted a Birmingham ratepayer a declaration that the Corporation's free travel scheme for the old was *ultra vires*) on the ground that Birmingham Corporation had not in that case put in issue the plaintiff's title to sue. The judge disagreed with the contrary views of Webster J. in *Steeples* v. *Derbyshire CC* (subsequently reported at [1984] 3 All ER 468). He said:

Manifestly local authorities and their members are particularly vulnerable to actions by busybodies and cranks, and I do not think that the law can be criticised for providing, in their case, a filter in the form of a requirement that either the consent of the Attorney General to a relator action or the leave of the court for an application for judicial review should be obtained.

8.12. The Australian courts have followed the traditional English approach. This may be illustrated by three significant decisions over the last fifty years in which actions raising important questions of law were dismissed, not on their merits, but on the ground that the plaintiff in each case lacked standing. (These examples have recently been highlighted by the Australian Law Reform Commission in its Report No. 27 *Standing in Public Interest Litigation* (1985), paragraph 3.) In 1931 the Commonwealth and Queensland governments entered into an agreement concerning sugar marketing. The effect of the agreement was to increase the price of sugar. Mr Anderson, a consumer, sought a declaration that the agreement was unconstitutional. The High Court of Australia held that he lacked standing. In 1961 two companies tendered for the supply of helicopters to an Antarctic expedition. The unsuccessful tenderer sought an injunction on the ground that the contract exceeded the Commonwealth's powers. The New South Wales Supreme Court rejected the claim on the basis that the plaintiff company lacked standing. Finally, in 1983 Mr Everyone sued Tasmania claiming an injunction preventing the construction of Franklin Dam on the ground that the construction would violate a statute. The High Court of Australia held that as Mr Everyone had no special interest in the matter, but only 'a mere intellectual or emotional concern in what is being done to the environment' he had no standing to sue.[1]

8.13. The Courts of New Zealand have generally followed the same approach (*Collins* v. *Lower Hutt City Corporation* [1961] NZLR 250). But in a recent decision a novel approach has been applied.

8.14. In *Finnigan* v. *New Zealand Rugby Football Union* (unreported) which came before the New Zealand courts three times in June and July 1985, the avowed object of the plaintiffs in bringing their action was to halt plans for a tour of South Africa by a New Zealand rugby football team. In law the essence of their case was that the defendant Union was acting contrary to its objects in promoting the tour.

8.15. Sentiment in New Zealand was strongly divided as to the desirability of the tour. In everybody's memory was the 1981

---

[1] The cases are *Anderson* v. *Commonwealth* (1932) 47 CLR 50; *Helicopter Utilities Pty. Ltd.* v. *Australian National Airlines Commission* [1962] NSWR 189; and *Everyone* v. *Tasmania* (1983) 49 ALR 381.

Springbok tour of New Zealand which, in Casey J.'s words,[2] had been 'a disaster both for rugby football and for the community'. There had been unprecedented scenes of violence, with normally law-abiding citizens openly breaching the law. In connection with the proposed South African tour in 1985 by the New Zealand team the Deputy Prime Minister of New Zealand had written to the Rugby Football Union asking it to call off the tour and he attached to his letter a resolution in the same sense passed by a unanimous House of Representatives.

8.16. Two points fell for decision by the New Zealand courts in the early stages of the action:

(*a*) whether the plaintiffs had the necessary standing to bring the action; and

(*b*) whether they were entitled to an interlocutory injunction which would have the effect of barring the defendant Union from proceeding with the planning of the tour until after the trial of the action.

The plaintiffs prevailed on both points.

8.17. For present purposes it is the decision of the Court of Appeal of New Zealand on the first point which is most material. Davison CJ, at first instance, had held that the plaintiffs had no standing to sue; they were not themselves members of the defendant Union, nor were the rugby clubs to which they belonged members of that Union. A five-judge Court of Appeal headed by Cooke J. reversed the Chief Justice's decision. In holding that the plaintiffs had standing the Court of Appeal had regard to some eight factors including: the plaintiffs' links with rugby football and indirectly with the defendant Union through a series of interlocking contracts between affiliated clubs; the momentous importance of the decision for the future of rugby football in New Zealand; the prevalence of the opinion held by the plaintiffs; and the fact that if the plaintiffs were not accorded standing it was unlikely that the legal issue would ever be tested. The court did, however, make it plain that standing would not have been accorded to a mere member of the public.

8.18. In a particularly significant passage in its judgment the Court of Appeal refused to approach the problem by applying narrow criteria taken from private law:

[2] Judgment—13 July 1985, p. 9.

While technically a private and voluntary sporting association, the Rugby Union is in relation to this decision in a position of major national importance . . . In truth the case has some analogy with public law issues . . . We are saying simply that [the decision] falls into a special area where, in the New Zealand context, a sharp boundary between public and private law cannot realistically be drawn.

8.19. Subsequently Casey J. granted the plaintiffs the interlocutory injunction referred to above. He held that if, on the *ultra vires* issue, the test to be applied was whether the council members of the defendant Union had honestly and in good faith reached the conclusion that the tour would further the Union's objects, then he was prepared to hold that there was an arguable case that they had closed their minds to the strength of opposition to the tour. But, following on from the reasoning of the Court of Appeal in the passage quoted above, he was prepared to apply a public-law test—did the council members act *reasonably* in reaching their decision? The decision could appropriately be subjected to this test because it operated 'in the public domain' and affected the community at large and New Zealand's relationship with the outside world.

8.20. No appeal was lodged against the grant of the injunction. Later the Rugby Union sought leave to appeal to the Privy Council on the standing decision. They also intended to attack Casey J.'s decision on the second test mentioned in paragraph 8.19 above. The matter had by then become academic since the tour had been cancelled. Leave was refused by the Court of Appeal of New Zealand on 19 December 1985 with separate judgments being delivered by each of the five members of the court. An application for special leave was thereafter refused by the Privy Council in London. As is customary, no reasons were given.

8.21. A critic of this New Zealand decision might perhaps say that the judges allowed themselves to be drawn into the area of policy-making and enforcement and that in doing so they greatly extended the rules on standing as hitherto understood. It might also be said that, judged at least by the standards of English law, the court produced a new *mélange* of public and private law. We for our part would support the pragmatism of the decision and applaud the willingness of the judges to look behind the legal forms to the underlying issues of substance. While much is made in some of the judgments (refusing leave to appeal to the Privy Council) of the uniqueness of the case and of the resulting decision on standing, we think that it represents an important precedent in at least two respects—the adoption of a check list of factors pointing in favour of standing (that is a consideration of all the circumstances of the matter, including the wider national context and the absence of any other protagonist willing to challenge legality) and the rejection of a hard and fast line betwen public and private law.

Relator actions

8.22. Where a private person does not have a sufficient interest to sue in his own name, he must obtain the consent (or fiat) of the Attorney General to the institution of a relator action. Before deciding to grant a fiat the Attorney General commonly takes counsel's opinion. If a fiat is granted the action is then brought in the name of the Attorney General. No personal interest on the part of the relator is required. The relator need not be a crusader seeking to uphold the rule of law. Indeed, the relator may be actuated not so much by a zeal for law enforcement as by a desire to further his own interests. Thus in *Attorney General* v. *Crayford Urban District Council* [1962] Ch. 575 the relator was the Prudential Staff Union, a trade union established with the object of advancing the interests of its members. The defendant Council had, for the benefit of the Council tenants, entered into an arrangement with the Municipal Mutual Insurance for the collective insurance of the tenants' household goods. The premiums were collected weekly by the Council from tenants who joined the scheme, and were forwarded to the insurance company. The relator's contention was that this activity on the part of the Council was *ultra vires* its statutory powers. (Presumably the underlying business objective of the action was to force the defendant Council to drop its insurance scheme, thus opening the market for 'the men from the Pru'.) The Court of Appeal, while expressing some surprise at the nature of the action which had been brought, held nevertheless that they were bound to entertain it and that they could not question the discretion exercised by the Attorney General in lending his name (pp. 585 and 590). As we shall see below, if the case had taken the form of an application by the Prudential Staff Union for an order of mandamus, the court would very probably have rejected it on the ground of the applicants' 'ulterior purpose'.

8.23. A point in connection with costs deserves mention. It is the practice of the Attorney General to satisfy himself, before agreeing to lend his name to the action, that the relator is competent to answer for the costs of the action. The normal mode of doing this is for the relator's solicitor to furnish a certificate on this point. The procedure is described in the Notes to the Rules of the Supreme Court Order 15 rule 11 in the *Annual Practice*. (The Crown is not liable for the costs of either party unless the Attorney General actively participates in the case.) This is a significant difference between the two forms of 'filter' referred to by Warner J. (paragraph 8.11 above). A judge in deciding whether to give an applicant leave to apply for judicial review does not have to be satisfied that the applicant is competent to answer for the costs of the proceedings.

Gouriet's case

8.24. In the case of *Gouriet* v. *Union of Post Office Workers* ([1977] QB 729, CA; [1978] AC 435, HL) an attempt was made to bring an action after the Attorney General had refused to lend his name to the suit. Mr Gouriet applied as a member of the public to the Attorney General for his consent to bring a relator action to seek an injunction against the defendants to restrain them from delaying the mails to South Africa for a week, which they proposed to do as a political gesture of disapproval of apartheid. Delaying the mail is a criminal offence under the Post Office Act, 1953. The Attorney General having refused his consent, the plaintiff proceeded to issue a writ in his own name and applied for an injunction. At one stage in the proceedings he amended his writ to add the Attorney General, claiming originally a declaration that he had acted improperly in refusing his fiat and subsequently (in substitution for that) claiming a declaration that the plaintiff was entitled to proceed in the absence of the fiat.

8.25. A strong difference of view emerged between the Court of Appeal and the House of Lords. The Court of Appeal held that there was jurisdiction to grant a declaration and an interlocutory injunction. Lord Denning MR was prepared to go further and to hold that it was possible for the court to review a refusal by the Attorney General to lend his name to an action, though he admitted that the grant of a fiat was unreviewable (citing Lord Halsbury LC in *LCC* v. *Attorney General* [1902] AC 165, 168–9).

8.26. A unanimous House of Lords reversed this decision, holding that as the plaintiff could establish no injury to himself as a result of the proposed action by the Post Office workers, the court had no jurisdiction to entertain his claims for either a declaration or injunction (whether interim or final). They took the opportunity to stress that the exercise of the Attorney General's discretion was alike unreviewable whether it led to the grant or refusal of a fiat. The House of Lords also condemned the frequent use of civil proceedings as an indirect method of securing compliance with the criminal law.

8.27. We very much agree with the last point. In principle it is right that where a breach of the criminal law is alleged the defendant should have the benefit of all the safeguards afforded by the criminal law. We have in mind such matters as the right to trial by jury, the strict rules of evidence applicable in criminal trials, and the requirement that the charge be proved beyond all reasonable doubt. These safeguards would be undermined if criminality could as easily be established in civil proceedings.

8.28. We are, however, dissatisfied with the rule reaffirmed in *Gouriet* that (to quote Lord Wilberforce's words [1978] AC at 484) 'only the Attorney General—either *ex officio* or *ex relatione*—can apply to the civil courts for injunctive relief against threatened breaches of the law'. We have already pointed out that the Attorney General never brings proceedings *ex officio* or allows them to be brought *ex relatione* against a minister or government department. This removes an enormous area of administrative activity (and hence of potential breaches of the law) from the scope of a relator action. The fact that the Attorney General has never sanctioned proceedings *ex relatione* or brought them himself *ex officio* against ministers or government departments must cast doubt on the universality of his role as protector of public rights. There must have been many cases when the Attorney General of the day formed the view that a minister or department was proposing to act illegally. No doubt in a percentage of cases the Attorney General was able to intervene and persuade a colleague to accept his view. But there must have been other cases in which the illegality (as perceived by the Attorney General) continued without check. It would be easy to explain this phenomenon if one could say that the Attorney General was so closely identified with the Government (of which he formed part) that it would be inappropriate for him to bring suit. But the justification always given for the Attorney General's role in the accepted sphere of relator actions, namely suits against non-governmental persons and bodies, is that he is independent of

Government and stands aside from political considerations in forming an impartial view as to whether it is in the public interest that a proposed action should be brought.

8.29. Over and beyond this limitation in scope of the relator action, we think that it is unfair to the Attorney General and unsatisfactory from the public viewpoint to place in his hands the sole discretion whether to sanction civil proceedings which may have political overtones. The holder of the office of Attorney General has to discharge many different duties and, while we do not doubt the scrupulous fairness with which he endeavours to decide whether the case is one to which to lend his name, the plain fact is that the public tend to identify him with the Government which he serves and his decision is widely regarded as being influenced by political considerations. The fact that it is the practice of the Attorney General to give no reasons when refusing a fiat naturally tends to increase public suspicion. An extreme example of the difficulties that can arise is given by the Australian Law Reform Commission in their Report *Standing in Public Interest Litigation* (1985). The Commission recounts (p. xix) how in 1972 a major controversy arose over proposals put forward by the Tasmanian Hydro-Electric Commission to flood Lake Peddar. Conservationists, who claimed that the construction would be illegal, sought the fiat of the Tasmanian Attorney-General for proceedings to restrain the building of the dam. The Attorney-General announced that he would grant his fiat. The Cabinet intervened and instructed him not to do so. The Attorney-General resigned, making it clear that he treated the intervention of the Cabinet as an improper form of political interference in the administration of justice. The Premier took his place and refused a fiat. As we have said, that is an extreme case, but it serves to illustrate how awkward the role of the Attorney General is in a situation where the policy of his Government is strongly opposed to the legal argument which the relator is putting forward and where the relator's ultimate success could have damaging political implications for the government. In the words of Ormrod LJ in the Court of Appeal in *Gouriet* ([1977] QB 729, 778—a judgment subsequently criticized in the House of Lords)—if a fiat is refused the Attorney General appears to be standing between the private citizen and the court.

An exception to the relator action rule—Local Government Act, 1972, section 222

8.30. By various enactments Parliament has from time to time sought to give to local authorities a power to enforce the law by taking proceedings themselves against law-breakers. Judicial interpretation repeatedly gave a restricted scope to such provisions when local authorities tried to sue in their own name instead of proceeding by way of relator action. The history is recounted by Lord Templeman in *Stoke-on-Trent Council* v. *B. &Q. Ltd* [1984] AC 754, 772–3. The principal statutory provision now in force is section 222(1) of the Local Government Act, 1972, which provides:

(1) Where a local authority considers it expedient for the promotion or protection of the interests of the inhabitants of their area

    (a) they may prosecute or defend or appear in any legal proceedings *and, in the case of civil proceedings, may institute them in their own name*
    ...

8.31. Notwithstanding the emphatic wording in the passage italicized, in the *Stoke-on-Trent* case it was nevertheless argued for the appellant shopkeepers that this statutory provision did not alter the basic rule that only the Attorney General could bring proceedings to restrain breaches of the criminal law. The House of Lords rejected this argument and refused to 'emasculate' the statutory language, holding that the section conferred on a local authority a power additional to the powers constitutionally vested in the Attorney General to enforce obedience to public law.

8.32. Two other points on the decision may be noted. The Law Lords emphasized that although local authorities had, by virtue of the statute, *locus standi* to apply for an injunction, it would only be appropriate for the court to grant such relief where the offender was deliberately and flagrantly flouting the law. Persistent trading on Sunday in violation of section 47 of the Shops Act, 1950, satisfied this requirement in the *Stoke-on-Trent* case and other cases. Secondly, the House of Lords commented that a local authority was entitled to have regard to the expense involved in bringing legal proceedings when deciding to exercise its discretion under section 222. There is a similar provision to section 222 of the Act in the Local Government (Scotland) Act, 1973, but it has never been used in the way it has been in England.

STANDING FORMERLY REQUIRED FOR THE PURPOSES OF THE PREROGATIVE WRITS AND ORDERS

Certiorari and prohibition

8.33. Both could be applied for at the suit of 'strangers'. The underlying theory was that the King's Court was intervening to ensure that an inferior tribunal or decision-making body was confined within the limits of its jurisdiction. For this purpose it did not matter how the matter came to the attention of the court. *Worthington* v. *Jeffries* (1875) LR 10 CP 379 is an example of prohibition being granted at the suit of a stranger to prevent the mayor's court from exceeding its jurisdiction. The same was stated to be the law as regards certiorari by Parker LJ (as he then was) in *R.* v. *Thames Magistrates Court*, ex parte *Greenbaum* (1957) 55 LGR 129: 'If the application is made by what for convenience one may call a stranger, the remedy is purely discretionary. Where, however, it is made by a person who has a particular grievance of his own, whether as a party or otherwise, then the remedy lies *ex debito justitiae*.'

8.34. Another example of the application being made by a stranger is furnished by the remedy formerly known as an information in the nature of a *quo warranto* (the successor of the ancient writ of *quo warranto* and the precursor of section 30 of the Supreme Court Act, 1981). A stranger was entitled to apply to the court for the purpose of securing that usurpers of public offices be restrained. In *R.* v. *Speyer* [1916] 1 KB 595, 613 Lord Reading CJ said:

[The applicant] appears to have brought this matter before the Court on purely public grounds without any private interest to serve, and it is to the public advantage that the law should be declared by judicial authority. I think the Court ought to incline to the assistance, and not to the hindrance, of the applicant in such a case if the Court has power, which I think it has.

Lush J. (p. 628) said that any subject had 'an interest in securing that public duties shall be exercised only by those competent to exercise them . . .'.

Mandamus

8.35. For some reason the law followed a different route in mandamus cases. It was affirmed as a well-established rule that an applicant for mandamus 'must first of all show that he has a legal specific right to ask for the interference of the court' in *R.* v. *Lewisham Union Guardians* [1897] 1 QB 498, 500, per Wright J. In that case Bruce J. said: 'This Court has never exercised a general power to enforce the performance of their statutory duties by public bodies on the application of anybody who chooses to apply for a mandamus' (p. 501). This approach was followed and we find judges saying that the court proceeded 'on a very strict basis' and that 'a far more stringent test had to be applied'. The judges also evoked 'the ulterior purpose' ground as a reason for dismissing the application.

8.36. In *R.* v. *Commissioners of Customs and Excise*, ex parte *Cook* [1970] 1 WLR 460 two bookmakers tried to get the Divisional Court to make an order requiring the Commissioners of Customs to comply with the statute which imposed excise duty on off-course betting premises. The statute required that the duty should be paid by an annual sum or by two half-yearly instalments. There was no power to vary or waive this provision. The Commissioners had, nevertheless, in response to representations from the trade, allowed bookmakers to pay by twelve cheques, eleven of which could be post-dated. One might have supposed that as soon as this illegal conduct was drawn to the attention of the Divisional Court an order of mandamus would have issued as of course requiring the Commissioners to collect the duty in the manner required by law. The decision in fact went the other way. The applicants failed for two reasons. First, they had no specific right or duty owed to them to enforce; they stood in the same position as any member of the public. Second, they had an ulterior purpose. They wanted the Commissioners to collect duty in accordance with the letter of the law. The effect would be to impose a severe financial burden on some of their competitors, who would go out of business. The court called in aid the following passage from Halsbury's *Laws of England* (3rd edn. (1955), Vol. 11, p. 105, paragraph 196):

But the mere fact that a person is interested in the performance of a duty as a member of a class of persons, all of whom may be regarded as equally interested, but himself having no particular ground for claiming performance, or that he has some ulterior purpose to serve, but no immediate interest on his own or any other person's behalf, will not be sufficient grounds for granting a mandamus.

8.37. We would make two comments. It is hard to see how any person could have been bothered to launch proceedings in the foregoing case except bookmakers who thought that enforcement of the law would benefit their business. The average law-respecting citizen, even if aware of the illegal concession granted by the Commissioners, would probably have thought it was a matter of little moment, certainly not an issue on which to risk legal costs. For reasons already explained it would have been vain to ask the Attorney General to enforce the law against a government department. So in effect the court castigated as 'an ulterior purpose' the only motive that would mobilize anyone into seeking to enforce the law.

8.38. Our second comment is directed to the scale of values implicit in the court's approach. Disapproval of the applicants' business motivation was given pride of place; securing compliance with the law by a government department was placed second.

8.39. Although as we have said there is a line of cases requiring the applicant in mandamus proceedings to show a specific legal right, it is possible to point to other cases in which token respect was paid to this principle but in which mandamus was granted to persons lacking a specific legal right. Cases in which ratepayers obtained orders of mandamus are examples of this. *R. v. Hereford Corporation*, ex parte *Harrower* [1970] 1 WLR 1424 is such a case. There, although some of the applicants satisfied the technical requirement of being ratepayers, their real interest was as electrical contractors on the Corporation's approved list who had not been invited to tender for an important contract. The failure to invite them was a breach of standing orders on the part of the local authority.

8.40. By 1976 the test applied in mandamus cases had begun to move closer to that used in *quo warranto*, certiorari, and prohibition. In one of several cases brought by Mr Raymond Blackburn or his wife with the object of forcing the police or some other public authority to comply with their duty, Lord Denning MR said this:

I regard it as a matter of high constitutional principle that if there is good ground for supposing that a government department or a public authority is transgressing the law, or is about to transgress it, in a way which offends or injures thousands of Her Majesty's subjects, then any one of those offended or injured can draw it to the attention of the courts of law and seek to have the law enforced, and the courts in their discretion can grant whatever remedy is appropriate. (*R. v. GLC*, ex parte *Blackburn* [1976] 1 WLR 550, 559.)

PART III

'SUFFICIENT INTEREST' FOR THE PURPOSES OF AN APPLICATION FOR JUDICIAL REVIEW

8.41. In 1975 the Law Commission published its *Report on Remedies in Administrative Law* (Law Com. No. 73 Cmnd. 6407). As we note elsewhere, this report led to the introduction into English law in 1977 of the application for judicial review. When first introduced the matter was regulated by a new Order (Order 53) inserted into the Rules of the Supreme Court. In 1981 Parliament passed the Supreme Court Act, section 31 of which was designed to set at rest any question which might have been raised as to whether Order 53 was *intra vires*. As regards standing, the Law Commission recommended a uniform formula, but recognized that this could be applied flexibly to meet new situations. In the Working Paper and in the Report they commented on the different tests which the courts had used in defining standing for the purposes of the various remedies and concluded that both the uncertainty and the variety of the tests applied were unsatisfactory. The material passage in their Report (paragraph 48) stated:

The predominant view expressed in the consultation on our Working Paper No. 40 [published in October 1971] was that any attempt to define in precise terms the nature of the standing required would run the risk of imposing an undesirable rigidity in this respect. We appreciate this danger, and think that what is needed is a formula which allows for further development of the requirement of standing by the courts having regard to the relief which is sought. Our recommendation is therefore that the standing necessary to make an application for judicial review should be such interest as the Court considers sufficient in the matter to which the application relates.

8.42. The test laid down in section 31(3) of the 1981 Act is as follows:

(3) No application for judicial review shall be made unless the leave of the High Court has been obtained in accordance with rules of court; and the court shall not grant leave to make such an application unless it considers that the applicant has a sufficient interest in the matter to which the application relates.

This test applies to applications for judicial review in which the applicant seeks an order of mandamus, prohibition, or certiorari, a declaration or injunction pursuant to section 31(2), or an injunction under section 30 restraining a person not entitled to do so from acting in an office to which that section applies (that is the old *quo warranto* type of case).

The *National Federation of Self-Employed* case

8.43. The leading authority on the meaning of 'sufficient interest' is *R.* v. *Inland Revenue Commissioners*, ex parte *National Federation of Self-Employed* [1982] AC 617. Tax evasion on a massive scale had been going on for years in Fleet Street. Wage sheets had been made out to casual workers bearing names like 'Mickey Mouse of Sunset Boulevard'. The Revenue finally made an arrangement with the unions and the employers under which, for the future, matters were to be regularized, some back tax was to be paid, but no further inquiry into the past would be pursued. The applicant Federation, which represented self-employed persons and the proprietors of small businesses, alleged that the arrangement amounted to an illegal 'amnesty' and had been procured by wrongful pressure exerted on the Revenue by the unions. The House of Lords, reversing the Court of Appeal, held that the Federation lacked standing. Their Lordships took the view that in some cases, of which the instant case was an example, standing could not be treated as a threshold question but had to be viewed against the legal and factual merits of the substance of the application. Lord Diplock declined to decide against the Federation on the basis of lack of standing. It is noteworthy that he expressly approved (at p. 641) the passage from Lord Denning's judgment in the *Blackburn* case which we have cited in paragraph 8.40 above. Lord Diplock held, on the merits, that the Revenue had acted perfectly lawfully in the bona fide exercise of its managerial discretion in entering into the arrangements which it had made. On this ground the application for judicial review should have been rejected. Lord Scarman held that the Federation lacked standing because on the merits they had failed to show reasonable grounds for believing that the Revenue had abused its managerial discretion or that there was a case to that effect which merited investigation and examination by the court. The other three Law Lords, in holding that the Federation lacked standing, did so on the basis that an individual taxpayer has no standing to challenge the way in which the Revenue has handled the affairs of another taxpayer and that the Federation could not acquire standing merely because it represented many individual taxpayers. With this approach may be contrasted Lord Diplock's words (p. 645):

It would, in my view, be a grave lacuna in our system of public law if a pressure group, like the federation, or even a single public-spirited taxpayer, were prevented by outdated technical rules of locus standi from bringing the matter to the attention of the court to vindicate the rule of law and get the unlawful conduct stopped. The Attorney General, although he occasionally applies for prerogative orders against public authorities that do not form part of central government, in practice never does so against government departments.

8.44. The *National Federation of Self-Employed* case cannot, however, be treated as a decision that a public interest suit can never be brought against the Revenue. There are dicta in the speeches in that case which recognize that the possibility of a public interest suit exists if the facts are serious enough to justify it. We have already noted Lord Scarman's view (p. 654) that the Federation failed on standing because it established no reasonable grounds for the belief that its case was right or merited investigation. The other relevant dicta are:

1. Lord Wilberforce (p. 633): 'That a case can never arise in which the acts or abstentions of the Revenue can be brought before the court I am certainly not prepared to assert, nor that, in a case of sufficient gravity, the court might not be able to hold that another taxpayer or taxpayers could challenge them.'

2. Lord Fraser (p. 647): 'It may be that, if he [the taxpayer] was relying upon some exceptionally grave or widespread illegality, he could succeed in establishing a sufficient interest.'

3. Lord Roskill (p. 662): 'Theoretically, but one trusts only theoretically, it is possible to envisage a case when because of some grossly improper pressure or motive the appellants have failed to perform their statutory duty as respects a particular taxpayer or class of taxpayer. In such a case, which emphatically is not the present, judicial review might be available to other tax payers.'

8.45. According to these dicta standing is made to depend upon the degree of illegality alleged by the applicant. This seems to us to be fundamentally unsound. No doubt there is room for the application here, as elsewhere, of some sort of *de minimis* principle, but, subject to that, if a public authority can be shown to be breaking the law, the courts ought to be prepared to act when the breach is drawn to their attention. We recognize, however, that the Revenue context may have provoked these restrictive formulations of standing and that other types of public interest suit may fare better.

8.46. A further point of interest in the case is, as Lord Wilberforce explained, that the statutory formula 'sufficient interest' need not be given a uniform interpretation covering all forms of remedy sought by way of judicial review. Reference back to earlier authorities is still legitimate and the meaning of 'sufficient interest' may vary depending upon the nature of the remedy sought.

Subsequent cases

8.47. It is obviously not possible to do more than to give illustrations of cases in which the standing issue has arisen. We will take cases which severally involve traders, a pressure group, and a public-spirited citizen. In *R. v. Braintree District Council*, ex parte *Willingham* (1982) 81 LGR 70 a group of shopkeepers applied for an order of mandamus requiring the local authority to comply with its statutory duty under section 7(1) of the Shops Act, 1950, and to take steps to stop the Sunday trading which rival traders continued to carry on in defiance of the law. The application also involved reviewing the considerations which the Council had had in mind in reaching the decision not to prosecute. The applicants were accorded standing and an order of mandamus issued. This case may be contrasted with the *Cook* case referred to in paragraph 8.36 above which was decided before the new Order 53. Applying what was said in *Cook*, it would seem that the applicants in the *Braintree* case had what would have been called an 'ulterior purpose' of their own to promote. This, however, was not allowed to affect the result—and rightly so in our opinion.

8.48. In *R. v. Secretary of State for Social Services*, ex parte *Child Poverty Action Group* (*The Times* 16 August 1984, Woolf J.; and 8 August 1985, Court of Appeal) standing was accorded to CPAG to challenge the way in which the Secretary of State was administering the law, to the detriment (so it was alleged) of impoverished claimants of social benefits.

8.49. In *R. v. Her Majesty's Treasury*, ex parte *Smedley* [1985] 1 QB 657 the applicant was a taxpayer seeking to establish that an Undertaking entered into by the Government to finance a supplementary EEC Budget contravened the Council's Own Resources Decision and was not 'a treaty ancillary to any of the Treaties' within the meaning of section 1(2) of the European Communities Act, 1972. If these contentions were right the applicant further contended that a draft Order to be laid before Parliament giving statutory backing to the Undertaking was *ultra vires*. The case failed on the merits. For present purposes what matters is that a challenge was made, albeit not strongly pressed, to Mr Smedley's standing to apply for judicial review. It was contended that he lacked a 'sufficient interest'. Slade LJ dealt with the contention in his judgment and rejected it. He thought that Mr Smedley had raised a serious question as to the power to make the Order in Council. If made, the Order would lead to substantial expenditure of monies out of the Consolidated Fund. He said (p. 670): 'I do not feel much doubt that Mr. Smedley, if only in his capacity as a taxpayer, has sufficient locus standi to raise this question by way of an application for judicial review; on the present state of the authorities, I cannot think that any such right of challenge belongs to the Attorney General alone.'

8.50. The trend of these cases is in the right direction. In 1985 Woolf J. expressed the view that it 'would be regrettable if a court had to come to the conclusion that in a situation where the need for the intervention of the court had been established that intervention was prevented by rules as to standing' (*R.* v. *Attorney General*, ex parte *ICI, The Times* 12 February 1985). Regrettable though it might be there must, we think, still be a risk of this happening in view of the stress, in section 31(3) of the Supreme Court, 1981 (and in the corresponding provision of Order 53) on the sufficient interest *of the applicant* and in the light of the reservations expressed by the majority of the House of Lords in the *National Federation of Self-Employed* case.

PART IV

THE INTERPRETATION OF PROVISIONS AS TO STANDING IN STATUTORY
RIGHTS OF APPEAL

8.51. Some statutes in conferring a right of appeal lay down a test of standing which has to be satisfied. A phrase commonly used is 'person (or party) aggrieved'. This phrase has in the past often been interpreted by the courts as requiring the applicant to show that a common law right of his is in question. In the well-known *Chalkpit* case, a neighbouring landowner was held not to be a person aggrieved even though he was complaining about the legality of departmental procedures which followed a public inquiry in which he had taken a leading part: *Buxton* v. *Minister of Housing* [1961] 1 QB 278). A subsequent decision allowing standing in such a case to a local residents' association is greatly to be preferred (*Turner* v. *Secretary of State for the Environment* (1973) 72 LGR 380). A local planning authority was held not to be a 'person aggrieved' when an enforcement notice which it had served was quashed by a magistrates' court (*R.* v. *Dorset Quarter Sessions Appeals Committee*, ex parte *Weymouth Corporation* [1960] 2 QB 230). In a Privy Council case, it was held that the words 'persons aggrieved' should be interpreted broadly to include 'a person who has a genuine grievance because an order has been made which prejudicially affects his interests' (*A.-G. of the Gambia* v. *N'Jie* [1961] AC 617, 634). We would strongly support the broad approach suggested in the *N'Jie* case. Decisions such as the *Buxton* and *Dorset Quarter Sessions* cases appear to be unnecessarily restrictive.

PART V

PROPOSALS FOR REFORM

Barbados

8.52. As we have seen, when the Law Commission for England and Wales proposed the 'sufficient interest' test which was subsequently adopted for the purposes of the new Order 53, it handed to the courts the task of developing the law of standing for the purposes of judicial review and gave them a new formula on which they could elaborate. The Commission took no view as to what types of interest should be regarded as sufficient for particular remedies. In particular they offered no guidance as to how the courts should handle so-called 'public interest' suits or the cases in which a citizen seeks to secure that a public authority complies with its legal obligations. This approach may be contrasted with that subsequently adopted in the Barbados Administrative Justice Act 1980. (This Act, which was drafted by Professor Sir William Wade, was proclaimed in July 1983; see Appendix 9.) The problem is specifically addressed in section 6 of the Act:

The Court may on application for judicial review grant relief in accordance with this Act

(a) to any person whose interests are adversely affected by an administrative act or omission;
(b) to any other person if the Court is satisfied that that person's application is justifiable in the public interest in the circumstances of the case.

The merit of head (*b*) in this section is that the applicant does not have to establish that he personally has sufficient interest. It is enough to show that there is *a* public interest sufficient to justify the application. This is a salutary reminder of the fact that historically certiorari, prohibition, and mandamus were public law remedies whereby the sovereign through his courts controlled and supervised the activities of inferior courts, tribunals, justices, and administrative authorities and ensured that they did not exceed their jurisdiction or usurp functions and poewrs which were not properly theirs.

Canada

8.53. In 1980 the Law Reform Commission of British Columbia published its Report on *Civil Litigation in the Public Interest*. Their concern was not so much with judicial review as with actions brought by individuals raising public interest issues. They discuss the English cases which we have noted (such as *Boyce* v. *Paddington Borough Council*; paragraph 8.10 above) and relator actions in general. The special feature of Canadian jurisprudence on which they comment is a line of constitutional law cases stemming from *Thorson* v. *Attorney General of Canada* (1974) 43 DLR 3d. 1 in which the Supreme Court of Canada has allowed individual taxpayers to bring suit to establish that particular enactments are in whole or in part unconstitutional. The following passage from the judgment of Laskin J. deserves quotation: 'Where all members of the public are affected alike, as in the present case, and there is a justiciable issue respecting the validity of legislation, the court must be able to say that as between allowing a taxpayer's action and denying any standing at all when the Attorney General refuses to act, it may choose to hear the case on its merits.'

8.54. Influenced no doubt by this judicial attitude, the British Columbia Law Reform Commission recommended a wider rule on standing. Subject to two qualifications, they proposed that any member of the public should have the right to bring proceedings in respect of actual or apprehended violation of a public right whether the violation relates to public nuisance, to repeated infraction of a statute enacted for the benefit of the public, or to a public body exceeding its powers. The applicant would have to give notice to the Attorney-General of the proposed action. It would be open to the Attorney to decide within ten days whether to sue himself or consent to the use of his name in relator proceedings. If, however, he remained inactive or refused his consent, the applicant would be allowed to proceed in his own name but subject to obtaining the leave of the court. The court would be expected to give its leave automatically unless the case raised no justiciable issue.

8.55. In a separate recommendation relating to suits raising questions as to the constitutionality of a statute the Commission recommended that the relevant British Columbia enactment (the Constitutional Question Act, RSBC 1979 c. 63) be amended by adding a new section in the following terms: '11. Any person may commence a proceeding in the Supreme Court for a declaration that an enactment of the Province or of Canada is invalid whether or not consequential relief is or could be claimed and whether or not the person has an interest in or is affected by the enactment.' Clearly for this type of case the mandatory requirement to apply to the Attorney-General for leave to use his name has been dispensed with and no substitute 'leave of the Court' is interposed. The recommendations have not yet been implemented.

Australia

8.56. In 1985 the Australian Law Reform Commission published its Report No. 27 *Standing in Public Interest Litigation*. They did not favour the British Columbian approach and criticized it essentially on two grounds (p. 143). They did not believe that 'any person' should be allowed to launch a public interest suit; second, they considered that the requirement to refer the prospective claim to the Attorney-General, and the consequent necessity to wait for ten days while he made up his mind, would introduce a possibly detrimental delay in any case where swift action was necessary either in the interests of the plaintiff or in the public interest.

8.57. Instead, the Australian Law Reform Commission came forward with a proposal of their own. Under their proposed procedure no reference to the Attorney-General would be required. Any person would be allowed to commence a public interest suit if *either* he had a personal stake in the subject-matter of the litigation *or* he had the ability to represent the public interest. The presumption would be in favour of standing unless the court was satisfied that the person was 'merely meddling'. They summarize their philosophy in the phrase 'An "open door" but with a "pest screen" ' (p. xxi). The screen would catch those who were 'merely meddling', a phrase which they would define as covering not just the 'dilettante' plaintiff, but also those 'whose manner of presenting the issues betrays a clear incapacity or unwillingness to represent the public interest adequately in conducting the case'. Those who, 'despite the best will in the world', proved incapable of presenting the issues satisfactorily would be denied standing (p. 138).

8.58. We confess that we have great difficulty in seeing how this proposal would work satisfactorily in practice. At the early stages of an action the court is not really in a position to tell how well the case is going to be presented at the trial. A pressure group who launch a public interest suit, for example to protect part of the environment from destruction, may have to spend a lot of time in preparation for the trial fund-raising and gathering support and evidence from interested parties. Must they wait until they are fully armed before launching an action? If so, they may be too late and may, for example, be refused an injunction on the ground of delay. When the case gets to trial the judge can, of course, assess whether the plaintiffs demonstrate a clear incapacity to represent the public interest adequately. But suppose, notwithstanding that incapacity, the judge can clearly see that their point of law is a good one—and that the evidence, including documents disclosed by the defendants, proves the case, why should he not grant the relief claimed? Judges frequently have the task of arriving at a just result though denied adequate assistance by one side or the other. If, of course, in the hypothetical public interest suit which we have been considering, the plaintiffs fail to call the necessary evidence or cannot mount effective cross-examination of the expert witnesses called for the defence, then necessarily the judge will be obliged to give judgment for the defendants. But that would be on the merits, not on a technical requirement about standing.

8.59. A further anomaly involved in the Australian proposal is that a plaintiff with 'a personal stake' will not be subjected to the regime which applies to a mere meddler. It follows that he will be accorded *locus standi* even if he betrays a clear incapacity or unwillingness to present the case adequately. The phrase 'a personal stake' presumably means something other than a legal right, so we are talking about somebody who does not have a cause of action in the traditional sense. It is difficult to see why, on the one hand, a competence test is irrelevant to a 'personal stake' plaintiff, but, on the other hand, essential to the definition of a 'mere meddler' plaintiff.

Our own proposal

8.60. We agree with the British Columbian and the Australian Law Reform Commissioners in their objections to relator actions. For the reasons given in paragraphs 8.28 and 8.29 above we think that it is unsatisfactory to involve the Attorney General in this way. There should be direct access to the courts for litigants who wish to raise public interest issues. Assuming, as we do, that it is desirable to have some sort of filter to control possible abuse of an extended right of access, the question arises as to whether cases should be filtered out by reference to the characteristics and capabilities of the plaintiff (which is essentially what is involved in the Australian proposal) or whether prime importance should be attached to the nature of the issue that is to be raised. We think that the second approach is correct and that the court in deciding whether or not to accord standing should have regard to the whole circumstances of the case and should ask itself the question whether the action is justifiable in the public interest in the light of those circumstances. That was essentially the approach of the New Zealand Court of Appeal in the 1985 case about the All Blacks' proposed tour to South Africa (discussed in paragraphs 8.14–8.21 above) and represents the effect of section 6(b) of the Barbados Administrative Justice Act in the context of judicial review (paragraph 8.52 above).

Relevant factors

8.61. 1. Prominent among the factors to be considered would be the nature and importance of the legal point to be decided.

2. The plaintiff's link with the subject matter of the case would also be relevant but should not be controlling. To revert again to the All Blacks case, we do not see why standing could not have been granted to any public-spirited citizen who, though not a member of any rugby club, was nevertheless a follower of the game and felt concern both about law and order in New Zealand and the country's

international relations. Such a plaintiff would have been able to rely upon seven out of the eight factors which enabled the actual plaintiffs to win the standing issue in that case.

3. Another material consideration must be whether there is any real prospect of the legal point being raised and decided if the action is not allowed to proceed.

4. The status of the plaintiff and the support which his cause enjoys could be a material matter in some cases, though in saying that we would not wish to discourage the court from granting standing to a single individual who had, unaided and unsupported, brought a serious matter before the court. In that connection the names Blackburn, McWhirter, Congreve, Gillick, and Smedley spring to mind!

8.62. The change which we are advocating as regards relator actions would require legislation. At the same time the opportunity should be taken to bring the law relating to judicial review into accord with this change. This could be achieved by amending section 31(3) of the Supreme Court Act, 1981, so as to insert at the end of the subsection the additional words 'or that his application is justifiable in the public interest in the circumstances of the case'. A corresponding change would be needed in Order 53.

8.63. We have considered the point made by Lord Wilberforce in *Gouriet* ([1978] AC 435, 482) to the effect that the court is not in a position to judge whether it is in the public interest for an action to be brought. 'The very fact that, as the present case very well shows,' he said, 'decisions are of the type to attract political criticism and controversy, shows that they are outside the range of discretionary problems which the courts can resolve.' Since those words were spoken, however, we have the dicta of the Law Lords in the *National Federation of Self-Employed* case indicating that the judges would be able to recognize the type of case (grave in its implications) in which a taxpayer would be granted standing to sue the Revenue and we have seen many cases in which judges have accorded standing by applying a test, explicit or implicit, very close to a public interest test. We have given instances in paragraphs 8.47–8.50 above. In any event a vigorous law of judicial review of administrative action inevitably means that from time to time the courts are exposed to political criticism and controversy. There is no longer any safe judicial harbour free from the stormy blasts (if indeed there ever was one).

PART V

THE LAW OF SCOTLAND

Remedies and 'title and interest' to sue

8.64. In Scotland, apart from statutory remedies such as the six-week right to seek judicial review of compulsory purchase orders and town planning decisions (where essentially the same legislation applies as in England), the provision of remedies in administrative law is very different from that in England (see *Stair Memorial Encyclopaedia*, *The Laws of Scotland* (1987), vol. 1, 'Administrative Law', pp. 147–66). In particular the remedies of certiorari, prohibition, and mandamus were never available in Scotland; reliance was placed upon general remedies (an action of reduction, declarator, or interdict), themselves as much private law as public law remedies. As we have explained in chapter 6 above, a procedural change was introduced in 1985 enabling litigants applying to the supervisory jurisdiction of the Court of Session to apply by way of judicial review. When seeking a remedy in the courts, a litigant must be prepared to show that he has the requisite 'title and interest' to sue, that is, that he is the proper person to sue and has a real interest in the result of the action. In respect of public rights, relator actions are unknown and it is well established that any person who is within the class of those entitled to enjoy a public right has title and interest to enforce it. Thus, anyone who may wish to use a public highway has title and interest to proceed against obstruction of that highway and is not required to show that he has suffered special damage or that a private right of his own has been infringed (*Duke of Athol* v. *Torrie* (1852) 1 Macq. 65; *Ogston* v. *Aberdeen Tramways Co.* (1896) 24 R (HL) 8).

A restrictive approach

8.65. In respect of the enforcement of the statutory duties of public authorities, Scots law does not, however, invariably grant title and interest to any individual even if his interests are closely affected by the acts of the public authority. A neighbouring owner has been held to have no title and interest to challenge the legality of a town planning permission (*Simpson* v. *Edinburgh Corporation* 1960 SC 313); a taxi-licensing scheme has been held to create no title and interest in the licensed taxi-drivers to sue to ensure the proper enforcement of the scheme (*Reid* v. *Mini-cabs* 1966 SC 137); and a shipping firm has been held as a competitor to have no title and interest to challenge the *ultra vires* activities of a statutory harbour authority (*D. &J. Nicol* v. *Dundee Harbour Trustees* 1915 SC (HL) 7), though as a ratepayer it was held entitled to make the challenge by virtue of the legal relation subsisting between it and the rating authority. This gave rise to a fiduciary duty on the one hand and a legitimate interest in the administration of the funds on the other.

Wilson v. *IBA*

8.66. In this case, leading members of a group campaigning for a 'No' vote in the referendum on devolution in 1979 were held to have title and interest to sue for an interdict to restrain the Independent Broadcasting Authority (IBA) from showing on television a series of party political broadcasts. Their complaint was that the programmes did not maintain a proper balance between the 'Yes' and 'No' campaigns. The action sought to enforce the IBA's statutory duties. The judge, Lord Ross, stated that he could 'see no reason in principle why an individual should not sue in order to prevent a breach by a public body of a duty owned by that public body to the public. It may well be that the Lord Advocate could be a petitioner if the interests of the public as a whole were affected . . . but I see no reason why an individual should not sue provided always that the individual can qualify an interest'. (*Wilson* v. *IBA* 1979 SLT 279, 282.) He considered the petitioners to have sufficient interest in the matter since they were registered electors, being entitled to vote in the referendum and belonging to a group which was campaigning for a 'No' vote. It remains an open question whether in Scotland the statutory duties of the IBA can be enforced in court at the request of any person who is merely a television viewer (see *Attorney General, ex rel. McWhirter* v. *IBA* [1973] QB 729). By contrast, in English law the effect of the *Gouriet* decision is that any individual challenging the IBA's decisions would require the Attorney General's consent to relator proceedings unless, in some way or other, he could prove an infringement of his own private rights. If the action concerned the legality of political broadcasts, as in the *Wilson* case, it seems to us particularly inappropriate (for reasons which we have already given) that the Attorney General should be the person to decide whether a would-be plaintiff should be enabled to launch an action.

Parallels with English decisions

8.67. The town planning case mentioned in paragraph 8.65 above (*Simpson* v. *Edinburgh Corporation*) produces a result curiously similar to the English decision in *Gregory* v. *Camden LBC* [1966] 1 WLR 899 where it was held that a landowner had no standing in an action to seek a declaration to the effect that an unlawful planning permission had been given for development on neighbouring land which closely affected his own property; in each case the pursuer or plaintiff was treated as a third party without rights. Yet planning legislation has been steadily advancing and doing more to protect the position of third parties. Examples are public participation in the development plan process, the requirement to notify the neighbours of development, the right to have representations about 'bad neighbours' development taken into account, and limited third-party rights to appear at inquiries. Today, Mr Gregory could probably establish sufficient interest for the purposes of an application for judicial review.

A possible approach to reform

8.68. The case for reform of the law in Scotland rests in part on the proposition that, notwithstanding the ability of private individuals to enforce certain public rights (such as the right to use the highway), the concept of 'public right' for this purpose is not broad enough to include all the situations in which an individual has a definite interest in challenging the acts of public authorities. This is especially so where an individual's interests might be directly affected by the manner in which a public authority exercises regulatory functions. Over and beyond this is the question whether it is satisfactory that the insistence on title and interest inhibits the possibility of public interest suits. When the Working Party under the chairmanship of Lord Dunpark was set up in 1983 to consider possible reform of the procedure used in administrative law cases (as to which see chapter 6, paragraphs 6.43–6.46 above), the Faculty of Advocates urged the Working Party to recommend the liberalizing of established common-law rules of title and interest. This, they suggested, could be done by subordinate legislation, namely an amendment to the Rules of Court affected by an Act of Sederunt made pursuant to powers conferred by section 16 of the Administration of Justice (Scotland) Act, 1933. The Working Party agreed with the Faculty that it would be desirable to extend the common law by incorporating the phrase 'sufficient interest', which is to be found in section 31(3) of the Supreme Court Act, 1981 (applicable in England and Wales only), but they were of the opinion that this would involve an alteration of substantive law which could not be achieved by Act of Sederunt. After referring to *Nicol* v. *Dundee Harbour Trustees* and *Reid* v. *Mini-cabs*, the Working Party said (Report, paragraph 8):

We consider that every person who relevantly claims to have been commercially prejudiced by an unlawful act or decision should have the right to challenge it. There is, in our opinion, a strong case for the extension by the legislature of our common law rules of title to sue to enable every person who is directly or indirectly affected by alleged unlawful acts or decisions competently to challenge them.

It is therefore disappointing that in the first reported case dealing with title and interest to sue under the new procedure the petitioners were held not to qualify in a case challenging social security regulations affecting old people in Scotland: *Scottish Old People's Welfare Council (petitioners)* 1987 SLT 179. If the proposals for reform which we have made in relation to English law were to find favour, it might be thought to be anomalous if the law of Scotland provided less ample opportunity for challenge.

CHAPTER 8. RECOMMENDATIONS

1. The law in connection with relator actions should be changed. The requirement to obtain the *fiat* of the Attorney General in a 'public interest' suit should be dropped. The decision to accord standing should be taken by the court. The judge should have regard to the whole circumstances of the case and ask himself whether the action is justifiable in the public interest in the light of these circumstances (paragraphs 8.24–8.29 and 8.60).
2. Relevant factors for the Court to take into account should be:
    (a) the importance of the legal point;
    (b) the plaintiff's links with the subject matter of the case;
    (c) the chances of the issue being raised in any other proceeding;
    (d) the extent to which there is public interest or support for the issue being raised.

(Paragraphs 8.17 and 8.61.)

3. A corresponding change to that involved in Recommendation 1 above should be made to the law relating to judicial review. This could be achieved by amending Section 31(3) of the Supreme Court Act, 1981, by adding the words 'or that his application is justifiable in the public interest in the circumstances of the case'. A corresponding change in Order 53 would be required (paragraph 8.62).

4. If reforms are to be made in the law of England and Wales along the lines proposed in Recommendations 1 to 3 above, consideration should be given to bringing the law of Scotland into harmony by relaxing the rigour of the 'title and interest' rules. At least the amendment favoured by Lord Dunpark's Working Party should be introduced and the concept of 'sufficient interest' should be added to the scope of title and interest as currently understood (paragraph 8.68).

9

Tribunals

SUMMARY OF ARGUMENT. Tribunals resemble courts in their independence, openness, and form, but their concern, unlike that of the courts, is commonly with the merits of administrative decisions. The majority of tribunals deal with differences between citizens and state, but some deal with disputes between citizens and then their role more closely resembles that of the courts. The existence of every tribunal is the result of deliberate parliamentary choice based on a variety of reasons which, when examined, disclose no consistent principle. The general objective, however, has been to make adjudication on administrative decisions cheap and accessible.

The report of the Franks Committee on tribunals and inquiries in 1957 was a watershed for tribunals because it anchored them firmly within the machinery of justice rather than of administration. Haphazard though the establishment of tribunals has been the system that now exists is generally sensitive to the needs of those affected and, broadly speaking, it achieves a reasonable balance between the demands of justice, the practicalities of administration, and the imperative of cost.

The Council on Tribunals, established in 1958 on the recommendation of the Franks Committee, have performed the necessary function of supervising the performance of the tribunals, but their effectiveness has been impaired in various ways: their jurisdiction does not extend to all tribunals; they lack the resources to provide continuous and widespread observation of tribunals under their aegis: and their powers are limited.

What has caused us the most concern is the matter of access to tribunals. Informed opinion, notably the Lord Chancellor's Advisory Committee, has for many years called for improvement in the provision of assistance for persons involved in tribunal proceedings, but the Government's response has been unhelpful. Recently however, the Government has issued a White Paper outlining a new framework for legal aid in England and Wales (Scotland already has one) that contains far-reaching proposals. The three problem areas of initial advice, co-ordination of advisory services, and tribunal representation call for greater attention than they receive in the White Paper, and the future of the Advisory Committee needs to be assured.

A notable Commonwealth development has been the creation of the

Administrative Appeals Tribunal in Australia which centralizes the process of considering the merits of a wide range of statutory decisions and which harnesses the expertise of judges, administrators, and private persons. In our view, however, in this country, effort should be directed rather towards the improvement of existing institutions than to their wholesale replacement.

The provisions of the European Convention on Human Rights impinge on the process of re-examining administrative decisions and are likely to lead to more administrative decisions being brought within the jurisdiction of tribunals, as well as to changes in the procedure of some tribunals.

Courts are restricted to review of legality

9.1. As we indicated in chapter 7 the task of the court in the administrative law field is essentially to supervise the legality of administrative action. Where the administrator is vested with power to assess the facts and to make a discretionary decision, it is not for the courts to take the decision afresh and thereby to provide a full right of appeal against all aspects of the decision. But an individual is entitled to expect that administrators should stay within their legal powers and should observe the requirements of the law in the decisions they take. Where an individual is claiming the benefit of rights that have been created by legislation, he will not readily accept that he can be denied them by the decision of an official. In practice the courts' power to review the legality of administrative decisions may require the court to lay down the correct interpretation of a statute or other legal instrument. The court may have to decide whether in the exercise of discretion it was legitimate for the decision-maker to have regard to a particular matter. So too the court may conclude that there was only one category under which the individual's claim could reasonably be fitted. In each such case a judge would say that a question of law was involved and there would be scope for judicial review of the challenged decision. In theory the judge could not substitute his own decision as the effective decision, though the practical effect of his judgment might be that the decision-maker would decide for a second time but on this occasion in accordance with the intimation given by the judge.

Tribunals have a different function

9.2. It remains, nevertheless, broadly correct to say that the true role of the courts is restricted to a review of legality and the judges are not concerned with the merits in the sense of the rightness (or wrongness) of the decision. Tribunals, on the other hand, are given a different role. Very commonly they are concerned with the merits of the decision and typically they will be given the task of deciding, as between citizens and the state, whether an official has dealt correctly with a claim or application. Tribunals thus provide a means whereby the citizen can appeal from a decision made by a government department or other public authority. The tribunal hearing may provide opportunity for a complete rehearing of the matter, and the applicant/claimant will not be restricted to the evidence which was first submitted to the original decision-maker.

The work load

9.3. The proliferation of tribunals is a phenomenon of the present century. Many, but by no means all, tribunals form part of the apparatus of the welfare state. The spreading jurisdiction which has been conferred on tribunals by Parliament might have been conferred on the courts, but the statistics demonstrate that the existing courts would have been totally engulfed by the flood of cases. Tribunals handle well over a quarter of a million cases annually (Council on Tribunals, Annual Report 1985–6, HC 42, paragraph 2.19). But Parliament's choice of a tribunal in preference to a court has been based on more than a desire to spare the courts from an insupportable burden. The intention has been that tribunals should be cheap and accessible. A tribunal will commonly be made up of three persons—a legal chairman and two laymen. These laymen may be chosen so as to represent different elements in society. For example, one may come from the employers' side and the other may be a trade union representative. The lay members (or wing men) of the tribunals are expected to take an active part. The evidence suggests that this involvement is welcomed by persons appearing before tribunals. What is not liked is an appearance that the legal chairman totally dominates the proceedings.[1]

The need for independence

9.4. The Franks Committee[2] could detect no coherent principle on the basis of which Parliament provided tribunal facilities in some

---

[1] See Professor Kathleen Bell, 'Social Security Tribunals—A General Perspective', 38 Northern Ireland Legal Quarterly (1982) 132, 145.
[2] *Report on Administrative Tribunals and Enquiries* (1955), Cmnd. 218, para. 30.

cases and in other cases left the final decision to the Minister and his departmental officials. The existence of every tribunal is the consequence of parliamentary allocation of its subject matter to that form of judicial supervision rather than to the ordinary courts. A political decision is involved. Instances of this parliamentary preference for removing particular issues from the jurisdiction of the courts may be found in the eighteenth century. The extension of this in the nineteenth century was associated with technical advances, notably in the field of transport, and in the early twentieth century with developments in social welfare, which is now the most numerically significant area. This preference is based on a variety of reasons, the declared importance of which, relative to one another, has varied also at different times.

9.5. As a matter of general principle the Franks Committee preferred tribunals to ministers and courts to tribunals. But it saw in the appointment of a tribunal a deliberate choice that the decision should be rendered independently of the minister, hence their conclusion, 'We consider that tribunals should properly be regarded as machinery provided by Parliament for adjudication rather than as part of the machinery of administration' (paragraph 406). At the time of the Franks Committee's deliberations it was still possible for tribunals to be seen in a light that would be impossible today. 'Much of the official evidence, including that of the Joint Parliamentary Secretary to the Treasury, appeared to reflect the view that tribunals should properly be regarded as part of the machinery of administration, for which the Government must retain a close and continuing responsibility' (Franks, paragraph 40). The Franks Report firmly rejected this view and concluded that 'the intention of Parliament to provide for the independence of tribunals is clear and unmistakable' (ibid.). This is now accepted by the administration. Thus, the (Pliatzky) *Report on Non-Departmental Public Bodies* (1980, Cmnd. 7797) says of tribunals: 'their functions, like those of the ordinary courts of law, are essentially judicial in that, independently of the executive, they decide the rights and obligations of private citizens towards each other or towards a Government Department or other public authority' (p. 24).

9.6. We share the general opinion that the Franks Report was a watershed for tribunals. It securely settled them within the judicial rather than the administrative framework, and it led to the provision of a special institution, the Council on Tribunals, the purpose of which was to improve standards by reviewing performance, exerting a unifying influence on procedure, and proposing improvements in the system generally. The Council themselves believe that:

Our most important contribution over the years has been our constant effort to translate the general ideals of the Franks Committee into workable codes of principles and practice, accepted and followed by all those who are responsible for setting up administrative tribunals, devising their manner of operation and, indeed, serving upon them as chairmen and members. (Special Report, *The Functions of the Council on Tribunals*, 1980, Cmnd. 7805, paragraph 6.3.)

However, the Council are also aware that since Franks other standards than 'openness, fairness and impartiality' have become significant, such as efficiency, expedition, and economy. It is by all these standards, and with particular regard to the needs of users, that the Council seek to assess the performance of tribunals (*Annual Report*, 1985–6, paragraph 2.5).

9.7. Franks also recognized that the 'tendency for issues arising from legislative schemes to be referred to special tribunals is likely to grow rather than diminish'. This preference for tribunals rather than courts was to be explained by the general characteristics of tribunals: cheapness, accessibility, freedom from technicality, expedition, and expert knowledge of the particular subject (paragraph 38).

9.8. A recent rare example of the Administration's disenchantment with a tribunal is the provision for a statutory right to a management review, at two levels, rather than an appeal to a tribunal, in regard to the discretionary loans and grants from the new Social Fund that will replace many supplementary benefit payments, especially single payments as from April 1988. The White Paper, *The Reform of Social Security* (1985, Cmnd. 9519), which foreshadowed the Social Security Act, 1986, defended this procedure on the ground that a formal system of adjudication was inappropriate for reviewing the exercise of judgment by Social Fund officers, and that the reasonableness of giving or withholding help in any particular case was not suitable for external assessment. The need for speed of decision was also relied on. The Council on Tribunals regarded this as 'a highly retrograde step' and took the most unusual course of issuing a Special Report (January 1986, Cmnd. 9722) in which they criticized the lack of independence of the new procedure, coupled as it was with the absence of any ministerial accountability.

The Council pointed out that the discretions to be exercised did not differ in principle from those exercised in the system prior to the reforms of 1980, which had been subject to independent, that is, tribunal, appeals, and urged that very good reasons were needed before a right to an independent appeal which had existed for more than fifty years was abolished. The Council pressed for the restoration of such a right of appeal. The Government made no formal response to this, but, at the Report stage of the Bill in the Commons, did substitute a review of the decisions of the local Social Fund officers by Social Fund inspectors outside the local office management hierarchy—thus undermining the argument against tribunals based on the need for swift decisions. In the House of Lords a right of appeal from a Social Fund decision to a Social Security Appeal Tribunal was inserted, but was removed when the Bill returned to the Commons, save in regard to Social Fund payments for funerals and maternity. The Act, which received the Royal Assent in July 1986 (but will not come into force until April 1988), provides for a Social Fund Commissioner who is to appoint Social Fund inspectors and check their work, and who will report annually to the Secretary of State.

9.9. Franks concluded that 'despite the haphazard way in which they have developed, the method of decision works on the whole reasonably well' (paragraph 403). We endorse this conclusion. The piecemeal establishment of tribunals has, over a period of time, produced a system that is generally sensitive to the needs of those affected and it achieves a reasonable balance between the demands of justice, the practicalities of administration, and the imperative of cost. We also share the view of the Franks Committee that 'tribunals as a system of adjudication have come to stay' (paragraph 37). As the *Report on Non-Departmental Public Bodies* points out,

administrative tribunals could not be abolished unless either Parliament was prepared to reverse the policy which has developed since the War and to make the Executive the final arbiter in disputes to most of which it is itself a party, or to transfer the jurisdiction of the tribunals to the ordinary courts of law. Adoption of the former course would require a major change of political direction. Adoption of the latter would have serious disadvantages: not only are the ordinary courts of law already heavily burdened, but their procedure is more formal and expensive and many of the heads of jurisdiction now exercised by administrative tribunals require both expert knowledge of a particular administrative scheme and adjudication by a body some of whose members have personal experience in the relevant field. (p. 25.)

9.10. It was suggeted to us that the technique of entrusting any newly created statutory jurisdiction to a tribunal rather than to the courts has become too prevalent. In particular the Law Reform Committee of the Senate of the Inns of Court forwarded to us the comments of Mr Justice Woolf (as he then was) in which he cogently argued that more selectivity should be exercised before disputes were taken away from the courts and remitted to a tribunal for determination. While we agree that there are clear advantages in letting the courts handle issues which involve serious questions of law and which require trained legal minds to handle them, the reality is that there is a limited supply of skilled legal services. (We refer here both to the judiciary and to the two branches of the legal profession.) If too great a workload were to be pushed on to the lawyers there would either be inordinate delays or a lowering of standards. Nor do we think that the courts of law are normally the right body to undertake many of the tasks. Experience has shown that tribunals are for some issues a better and more effective institution.

9.11. The purpose of tribunals is to provide a source of decision-making independent of the administration. There is a wide spectrum of both type and complexity of subject matter. Thus, in some cases, the character of a tribunal is grafted on to an independent administrative agency, such as the Civil Aviation Authority or the Director General of Fair Trading. The Performing Rights Tribunal is 'the forum for disputes of considerable dimensions and financial implications' (Council on Tribunals, *Annual Report*, 1981–2, p. 10). Tribunals may serve as a substitute or surrogate for the administrative decision-maker; in such cases they are in effect regulatory agencies. More commonly, they provide the first tier of appeal from the administrator's decisions; they provide what the Franks Report called 'the further decision'. There are also second tier tribunals which hear appeals from first tier tribunals. A tribunal can only be as good as its legislative basis and resources allow. Thus, in the case of immigration control the inherent difficulties of obtaining evidence inevitably cause dissatisfaction with the system.

9.12. We have received very little comment on the composition of tribunals. We noted in our Discussion Paper (paragraph 42) the trend for chairmen of tribunals to be legally qualified, and they are appointed either by the Lord Chancellor or by the Lord Advocate. Members, however, are appointed in various ways, the most common of which is by a minister of the parent department. Recommendations for appointments are made by a wide range of bodies. The Council on Tribunals have not had much to say about this matter in their Annual Reports; an instance of their concern is their twice repeated, but unavailing, recommendation that Immigration Adjudicators should be appointed by the Lord Chancellor (*Annual Reports*, 1981–2, paragraph 3.24 and 1985–6, paragraph 4.40). It would be unsafe to conclude from this that all is necessarily well. The Council on Tribunals do not have the resources to provide continuous and widespread oversight; the legal profession is not widely concerned with tribunals; the ombudsmen have no jurisdiction; the courts' supervision of tribunals is random; and few individual appellants are likely to have much experience on which to judge the performance of tribunals or to have much inclination to ventilate dissatisfaction with them effectively.

9.13. The work of tribunals, Franks thought, should be characterized by openness, fairness, and impartiality. Indeed, the visible independence of the tribunals is the cornerstone of the system. In the matter of adjudication appearance is crucial. The Council on Tribunals have done much to press this point and continue to do so in their annual reports and in less formal ways. For the members of a tribunal to be appointed directly by the authority whose decisions are the subject of adjudication by that tribunal inevitably undermines their visible independence. Franks, indeed, advised that members be appointed by the Council on Tribunals (paragraph 49), but this proposal has not been acted upon, no doubt because of the obvious practical difficulties.

9.14. Another potential threat to the independence of tribunals that has caused us concern is the length of term of appointment. Once appointed, a member of a tribunal can only be discharged with the consent of the Lord Chancellor, or, as the case may be, the Lord President of the Court of Session, or the Lord Chief Justice of Northern Ireland. But the commonest term of appointment is for three years. That is a short period and it certainly does raise the possibility that an appointee may have a subconscious, if not conscious, anxiety not to antagonize the appointing minister. On the other hand, in a system under which large numbers of appointments are made and the opportunities for assessment of candidates is limited, a comparatively short initial appointment may be justified. Moreover, part-time members may not wish to serve for a longer period. One way of securing visible independence of members would be to appoint only for a single term. In our view, no appointment should be made for a period of less than three years, subject, of course, to the continuing existence of the tribunal. A consequence of the concern for the independence of tribunals is that the means of complaining about the performance of tribunal members (including chairmen) are limited—as indeed they are in the case of judges and magistrates, but we have little evidence of dissatisfaction with this state of affairs.

9.15. The presidential system, in which a president is appointed to head a group of tribunals of a particular type and to be responsible for their administration and proper working, is an important development. It secures both greater independence and greater efficiency of tribunals. The Council on Tribunals have drawn attention in some of their Annual Reports and their Special Report of 1980 (paragraph 6.8) to the advantages of this system. The system also facilitates the consideration of complaints about the tribunal members. We welcome the extension of the system to the area of Social Security Appeal Tribunals (achieved by the Health and Social Services and Social Security Adjudications Act 1983, s. 25 and Schedule 8, paragraph 8).

9.16. The Council on Tribunals have an essential role to play in supervising the tribunal system and should not be hampered through inadequate resources in obtaining comprehensive and up-to-date information about the working of the tribunals under their aegis. For historical reasons, not all tribunals come under the supervision of the Council. In our view the time has come to end this disparity. The Council makes an important contribution to securing the proper working of tribunals and we can see no reason why the safeguard it provides should not be extended to all of them. The necessary resources for this extended function should be allocated.

9.17. Tribunals depend heavily for staff upon secondment from the departments with which they are associated. The Franks Committee looked at the objections to this system with some care but considered that the advantages outweighed the disadvantages. In our Discussion Paper we referred to the proposal made by Wraith and Hutchesson, *Administrative Tribunals* (1973, pp. 306, 317–

18), that there should be a unified tribunal service for which the Lord Chancellor and the Lord Advocate would be responsible. The object of the proposal was to secure greater independence of the staff of tribunals and to allow for interchange and promotion with beneficial effects on morale and the quality of work. We have received very little comment on this suggestion. The Council on Tribunals have paid particular attention to the means of minimizing the adverse consequences of departmental provision of tribunal staff. We support these efforts and have no further comment to make.

9.18. The Council on Tribunals have concerned themselves with the location of tribunal premises. Here again, it is the appearance of things that matters. The independence of tribunals is emphasized if hearings are held elsewhere than in premises of the department the decisions of which are the subject of adjudication. There are practical difficulties, not the least of which is the question of expense. We recommend that the location of tribunals in premises occupied by the parent department should be regarded as something exceptional and to be avoided if possible. Where it is not possible to arrange this the chairman should always make a point of explaining the position at the commencement of the hearing.

9.19. The Council on Tribunals have over the years campaigned energetically for improved standards of procedure in all tribunals. We certainly support that effort. Some tribunals have no rules at all. Others have only out-of-date and incomplete rules. The need for regular revision is clear. The Council on Tribunals have rendered a most useful service in laying so much emphasis on the necessity for fair procedures in their Annual Reports.

9.20. In general, tribunals have to conform to the requirements of Article 6 of the European Convention on Human Rights and must provide a fair and public hearing. The Convention recognizes that departures from this requirement may be made in the interests of public morals, public order, and national security, in the interests of juveniles and the protection of privacy, and also (to the extent strictly necessary in the view of the tribunal) to avoid prejudice though publicity. Here again the Council have exerted a beneficial influence and have secured the revision of several established practices so as to provide for public hearings. We share the Council's view that a case must always be made out for any departure from the general rule that hearings should be held in public. One anomaly is that whereas hearings before the General and Special Commissioners for Income Tax are heard in private, appeals from the Commissioners are to the High Court and so in public. However, we have received no comment on this.

9.21. Tribunals are not bound by the strict rules of evidence that apply in court and we would not wish to make tribunal proceedings more complex by subjecting their hearings to such rules. Nevertheless, the objectives of consistency of treatment and fairness require that variations in the acceptability or otherwise of evidence be limited to what is unavoidable in the circumstances. We have received no representations about this, but some instances that we have encountered in the course of our review do cause us concern. Immigration appeals are a case in point. In our view this problem calls for further consideration and we hope that it will be included in the review of the procedures of all tribunals which the Royal Commission on Legal Services in England and Wales recommended should be carried out by the Council on Tribunals (recommendation R 15.1, *Final Report*, 1979, Cmnd. 7648). This recommendation was accepted in principle by the Government subject to further consideration being given to timing and the availability of resources (1983, Cmnd 9077, p. 18). The Council report that, unfortunately, they have experienced difficulty in obtaining the necessary resources to carry out this review. As they point out, the aim of the Royal Commission cannot be achieved by the slow process of reviewing tribunals in turn, which would take a very long time to achieve results, or by the review of selected tribunals. What is needed is a comprehensive and concurrent review of tribunals to produce model rules which, with appropriate modifications to meet particular requirements, can be used for any tribunal when the opportunity occurs (*Annual Report*, 1985–6, paragraph 3.77). We hope that the comparatively modest expenditure needed to implement the Royal Commision's recommendation will shortly be authorized. The standard of proof should be included in any comprehensive review. Here too the objectives are consistency and fairness.

9.22. With a large and predominantly part-time service it is difficult to attain uniform standards. The Council on Tribunals have for many years emphasized the importance of training for tribunal members. That there is now much more training in the case of busier tribunals is largely to the credit of the Council. We support the extension of training as a means of securing proper standards of investigation and adjudication. The presidential system can, as we have said, also serve to improve standards. We support the view of the Franks Committee that the publication of selected decisions of appellate or second instance tribunals can contribute to the achievement of consistency (*Report*, paragraphs 102 and 219).

Delay

9.23. One of the advantages of tribunals is supposed to be their ability to dispose of cases quickly. The Council on Tribunals have, therefore, rightly been concerned in recent years about such delays. Their latest report describes measures they have taken to improve their gathering of information about such delays. The Council make two particular points on this matter. The first is that a lack of resources imposes limitations on what they can usefully do to keep track of delays. The second is a more general point:

We are ... concerned that delays should not become a persistent and accepted feature of a tribunal's operation, and that a shortage of essential resources should not normally be allowed to prevent tribunals and ancillary services from carrying out their functions efficiently and expeditiously. (*Annual Report*, 1985–6, paragraph 3.35.)

In recent years the Council on Tribunals have commented adversely on delays in relation to Industrial Tribunals in England and Wales. The year 1985–6 was no exception. In that year only 50 per cent of Industrial Tribunal cases reached a first hearing in less than twelve weeks and 10 per cent did so in not less than twenty-six weeks; 30 per cent of adjourned cases took longer than eight weeks to reach a final hearing. In 25 per cent of cases the issuing of written decisions took longer than four weeks. These times are 5–10 per cent longer than the previous year's. A possible explanation for the lengthening is the nature of the appeals:

The Secretary of the Industrial Tribunals told us that there are indications that cases are becoming more complex and that hearings are taking longer. The proportion of cases heard over more than one day rose from sixteen per cent in 1984/85 to twenty-three per cent in 1985/86 ... it may be that some part of the increased figures for delay reflects a more accurate assessment of the true position. (*Annual Report*, 1985–6, paragraph 4.44.)

At present the statistics are obtained by sampling: the tribunals are considering whether statistics relating to all cases should be collected in future. The Council also note delays in Social Security

Appeal Tribunals. The overall average time for all social security appeals was, at the end of 1985, about 15 weeks though the situation should, the Council point out, change substantially after April 1988 when single payments, which form the bulk of supplementary benefit appeals, are to be administered out of the Social Fund with no right of appeal to Social Security Appeal Tribunals. In the meantime, the Council comment, 'the situation has become increasingly serious and is now extremely unsatisfactory' (ibid., paragraph 4.56).

9.24. The Council were not surprisingly concerned about a case which was listed for hearing before the Mental Health Review Tribunal on 5 November 1985 but which, owing to various difficulties in finding a judge to preside, was not heard until 12 May 1986. As the liberty of the subject may be involved, delays such as this are disturbing. The Council pursued the matter with the Lord Chancellor's Department and were informed that, as there is no scope for a panel of reserve judges, 'on the day everything turned on the court administrator's judgment of priorities in the light of the resources open to him' (ibid., paragraph 4.29). We hope that steps will be taken to impress upon court administrators the importance of prompt hearings in Mental Health Review Tribunal cases.

Access

9.25. Of the various matters that we raised in regard to tribunals in our Discussion Paper the one that has caused us the most concern is that of accessibility. Under that heading we include the awareness of the person concerned of the existence of tribunal remedies, advice about them and assistance and representation at tribunals; and it is in this order that we discuss the subject. A good deal has been written about these topics, notably, among the official bodies, by the Lord Chancellor's Advisory Committee on Legal Aid, the Council on Tribunals, The Law Society, the Law Society of Scotland, and the Law Society of Northern Ireland (in their capacities as administrators of the legal aid schemes), the Royal Commission on Legal Services in England and Wales and the Royal Commission on Legal Services in Scotland.

9.26. The Franks Committee were specific about the basic need: 'The most important requirement at the preliminary stage is that the citizen should be fully aware of and fully understand his right to apply to a tribunal' (*Report* paragraph 67). The first Principle of

Recommendation No. R(81)7 of the Committe of Ministers of the Council of Europe—Measures facilitating Access to Justice, to which the United Kingdom has subscribed, is to the same effect: '1. Appropriate measures should be taken to inform the public of the location and competence of the courts and the way in which proceedings are commenced or defended before those courts' ('court' in this context includes tribunal). Yet, twenty-five years after Franks the Lord Chancellor's Advisory Committee on Legal Aid, which is the Government's constitutional adviser on the subject (the description is the Lord Chancellor's: *Hansard*, HL, 19 March 1984, c. 413) was expressing a high degree of concern about the plight of the unaided applicant in tribunal cases:

261. Receipt of early assistance is the single most important requirement for tribunal applicants . . .

262. . . . according to much of the research conducted within the last decade, there are still many tribunal applicants—and presumably potential applicants—who receive no formal advice whatsoever, despite the availability of advice and assistance under the green form scheme and from other sources such as Citizens Advice Bureaux. As important as taking steps to improve the scope and quality of advice, therefore, must be measures aimed at encouraging applicants to take advantage of the services that are available.

263. We recommend in respect of those tribunals that hear appeals against administrative decisions of Government departments and public officials, applicants should, as a matter of course, not only be informed of their right to appeal to a tribunal but also be advised to seek advice and be informed of the location of the appropriate source of advice. We recognise that some departments and local offices already perform some of these duties, either because of statutory obligation or as a matter of national or local administrative policy. (*33rd Annual Report*, 1982–3, HC 137.)

The Lord Chancellor's Advisory Committee emphasized this recommendation in their *35th Annual Report* (1984–5, HC 156):

130. It remains our view in general that the earlier any tribunal applicant is advised of sources of advice and assistance the better . . . We cannot stress too strongly that early advice is vital.

9.27. Help with where to obtain relevant advice is certainly a necessity in view of the bewildering variety of agencies actively offering it. In 1977 the National Consumer Council pointed out that 'We have at the present time a better and more accessible advice service than ever before, probably better than any other country in

Europe ... We have, albeit in a haphazard and disjointed fashion, the beginnings of a national network of effective advice services.' (*The Fourth Right of Citizenship: A Review of Local Advice Services*, 1977, paragraph 56.) But, the report added, 'There is no coherent national policy towards advice services in the United Kingdom' (ibid., paragraph 63). In his report, *Social Insurance and Allied Services*, 1942 (Cmd. 6404), Sir William Beveridge recommended that there should be an advice bureau in every local security office which would inform the inquirer: 'not only about official provision for social security but about all the other organs—official, semi-official and voluntary, central or local—which may be able to help him in his difficulty' (paragraph 397). The Council on Tribunals, in its report for 1985–6 (HC 42), noted that:

At present SSAT (Social Security Appeal Tribunal) offices tell appellants of the value of seeking advice and suggest seeking out their local citizens' advice bureau, law centre or advice centre. This information is set out on a standard form giving notice of the proposed date of the hearing. However, no names or addresses are supplied (paragraph 3.9). ... The present generalised advice is no substitute for specific localised advice of direct benefit to individual appellants (paragraph 3.12).

In February 1986 the Council issued a memorandum on the subject in which they suggested the solution of a list of local advice agencies compiled by the agencies themselves (with disclaimers as to any recommendation), which would be displayed in tribunal offices, local Department of Health and Social Security and Department of Employment offices, local authority offices, libraries, and CABx, and which would be sent to those giving notice of appeal. The essence of this proposal is that the information should be up to date and not misleading. Both requirements call for a degree of commitment to accuracy that may be difficult to maintain. The National Committee for Social Security Tribunal Assistance, while supporting the proposal of local lists where their compilation is practicable, has suggested that where it is not a 'clearing house' approach should be adopted under which local agencies would nominate one agency to serve as a point of first contact. The nominated agency would refer appellants to the appropriate local agency. The Lord Chancellor's Advisory Committee has suggested that an alternative or additional approach would be a Freefone number and thought that this would probably be the most effective route to good early advice (*35th*

Annual Report, paragraph 132). They urged that consideration be given to the feasibility of tailor-made local schemes.

9.28. A consequence of making advice generally more accessible would be to increase the burden on the advice-giving agencies. The Lord Chancellor's Advisory Committee recognized that 'in many cases such an increase would cause intolerable problems of over-loading unless there were a commensurate increase in resources', and recommended that the Government's financial support should be increased to meet the augmented workload (*35th Annual Report*, paragraph 132).

Legal Aid

9.29. Publicly financed legal aid, first introduced by the Legal Aid and Advice Act, 1949, now takes three forms:

(*a*) provisional (emergency), or full, legal aid for civil court proceedings;

(*b*) legal advice and assistance (commonly known as the green form scheme from the form (LA/REP/6A) on which application for the service is made);

(*c*) assistance by way of representation.

All these forms of legal aid are contributory, and so means-tested, and eligibility for them is restricted by financial limits on both income and capital. Application forms are completed by the solicitor consulted. Not all solicitors undertake legal aid work but the Law Societies advise all their members to consider whether a client would benefit from legal aid facilities and advise their clients accordingly. The Law Society has also organized a voluntary, fixed fee 'diagnostic interview' scheme the purpose of which is to enable a person to approach a solicitor in the knowledge that the initial interview of up to half an hour will not cost more than £5 inclusive of value added tax. The idea is that this should enable persons to ascertain whether or not they qualify financially for green form aid and, if so, what the extent of any contribution may be. Civil legal aid includes assistance preliminary, incidental, and subsequent to proceedings and representation at proceedings. As well as being means-tested it is merit-tested. Financial assessment is carried out by legal aid assessment offices of the Department of Health and Social Security. It is for the applicant to show that he has a reasonable case. The merits of a case are evaluated in accordance with prescribed criteria by the area legal aid office; an application can only be refused by a committee of practitioners (for the position in Scotland see paragraph 9.46 below). A decision on eligibility is reached in about six weeks. There is provision for the issue of emergency certificates. Full legal aid is available for tribunal cases only in the Lands Tribunal and before the Commons Commissioners and the Employment Appeal Tribunal (which is, in fact, a court).

9.30. The green form scheme covers all advice and assistance that a solicitor can give short of representation. It is available for all tribunal cases. There is no formal merits test and financial eligibility is assessed by the solicitor with the aid of a periodically reviewed key card setting out the eligibility limits and the scale of contributions. The limit of solicitor's costs that may be incurred without authorization is £50 exclusive of VAT (in June 1986 solicitor's remuneration was allowed at the rate of £28.50 an hour). Extensions may be applied for to the legal aid area office where they are usually considered by staff who are not solicitors. Assistance by way of representation is an extension of the green form scheme to allow representation in court, but it requires the approval of the legal aid office. An application can only be refused by a committee of practitioners. Assistance by way of representation is available for proceedings in only one tribunal, the Mental Health Review Tribunal (and in such cases an application for assistance must be approved 'unless it appears unreasonable that approval should be granted in the particular circumstances of the case': regulation 17(3) of the Legal Advice and Assistance Regulations (No. 2), 1980 as amended). The Government, in its response to the Royal Commission on Legal Services, stated that 'extensions of assistance by way of representation and legal aid are made when it is shown to be necessary and resources allow' (1983, Cmnd. 9077, p. 18). There has been no such extensions in the case of tribunals since then.

9.31. The Legal Advice and Assistance Act, 1972, contained provisions, to come into force on a day or days appointed, for the employment of solicitors and other staff for the purpose of giving advice and assistance, acting for persons receiving legal aid, and for performing the following services for or in connection with local organizations concerned in the giving of advice or guidance to persons in the locality:

(i) furnishing legal assistance to the organization in its function of giving advice and guidance;

(ii) promoting contacts between the organization and solicitors practising in the locality with a view to enabling applicants to obtain the professional services of those solicitors;

(iii) giving oral advice to applicants, instead of referring them to solicitors.

In England and Wales these provisions are now contained in section 16 of the Legal Aid Act, 1974; in Scotland in Part V of the Legal Aid (Scotland) Act, 1986; the provisions have not yet been brought into force (see paragraph 9.46 below).

The need for representation

9.32. The Franks Committee considered that there was 'a strong argument for extending legal aid to tribunals, particularly since some tribunals have a status equal to the County Court (to which the provision of legal aid had then recently been extended) and involve greater legal costs. We consider that there is a good case for extending the legal aid scheme at once to those tribunals which are formal and expensive and to final appellate tribunals' (*Report*, paragraph 89). In their important *24th Annual Report* (1973–4, HC 20), the Lord Chancellor's Advisory Committee observed, 'there is a wide spectrum of need on the part of tribunal applicants, ranging from moral support and encouragement at one extreme to experienced legal advocacy on difficult issues of law at the other' (paragraph 33). Although it is usual for tribunals to be considerably more interventionist and investigatory than courts, the Advisory Committee did not consider that a tribunal could itself provide a satisfactory substitute for effective representation, especially where the other side was represented (ibid., paragraph 37), and concluded that the issue to be considered was whether the advantages of informality outweighed those of representation: 'if they do, the right course, we suggest, would be to ban legal representation altogether; what cannot be justified is to restrict its benefits to those wealthy enough to afford it for themselves' (paragraph 38). The Advisory Committee expressed the view that legal aid should be extended to all statutory tribunals then within the supervision of the Council on Tribunals in which legal representation was permitted (paragraph 41). In their *33rd Annual Report* the Advisory Committee stated that they adhered to this view (1982–3, HC 137, paragraph 288). They distinguished between two kinds of representation in tribunal hearings: 'that which is required because of the inability of the applicant to present a case adequately, even though the case itself may be a simple one; and that which is required because of the difficulty of the case. The first kind of representation requires the services of an articulate spokesman; the second may require the services of a lawyer or other expert' (ibid., paragraph 268).

Identifying where the need for representation exists

9.33. The Advisory Committee considered that the general merit test for legal aid—that the applicant has reasonable grounds for taking proceedings—and that the present power to refuse legal aid where to grant it would be unreasonable, should apply in the case of tribunals. That would filter out the cases which the average citizen should be able to conduct unaided, as well as cases where some (though not specific legal) representation was required (ibid., paragraph 291). The Committee commended the criteria for the grant of legal aid proposed by the Council on Tribunals in their evidence to the Royal Commission on Legal Services (*Final Report*, 1979, Cmnd. 7648, paragraph 15.28). The list drawn up by the Council, which was not exhaustive, of the principal instances where legal representation might be appropriate was as follows:

(*a*) where a significant point of law arises;
(*b*) where evidence is likely to be so complex or specialized that the average layman could reasonably wish for expert help in assembling and evaluating the evidence and in its testing or interpretation;
(*c*) where a test case arises;
(*d*) where deprivation of liberty or the ability of an individual to follow his occupation is at stake.

The Advisory Committee observed: 'The difficulties of the case and its importance to the applicant must be the central tests' (*33rd Annual Report*, paragraph 294).

Priorities for representation

9.34. In the face of the refusal of any government so far to make provision for legal aid in all tribunals—which is what the Rushcliffe Committee envisaged in their report of 1945 (Cmd. 6641), the original Legal Aid and Advice Act, 1949 foreshadowed, and the Advisory Committee would still prefer—the Advisory Committee, in their *27th Annual Report* (1976–7), indicated that Industrial Tribunals were among the most pressing candidates for some form of legal aid (paragraph 73), and in their *30th* (1979–80) and *31st* (1980–1) *Annual Reports* identified Mental Health Review Tribunals as the tribunals for which an extension of legal aid was urgent (respectively, paragraphs 97 and 89). In their *33rd Annual Report* (1982–3) the Committee reiterated that legal aid should be available now in all tribunals, but reluctantly considered criteria for setting priorities for its extension to tribunals (paragraphs 302–4). The Committee warned, however, that while it was possible to identify those tribunals where a high proportion of cases is likely to require legal aid, that exercise should not be taken to imply that there are not cases in other tribunals for which legal aid is necessary. As they pointed out:

There may be cases even in the smallest tribunals where legal aid is needed. Indeed, it may be particularly important to make legal aid available there as it is unlikely that there will be a generally available alternative source of help and advice; the cost of extending legal aid to tribunals with small workloads is likely to be modest (*33rd Annual Report*, paragraph 304).

The Advisory Committee's *35th Annual Report* usefully included, at paragraph 134, a table showing the success rates of various forms of representation before the Supplementary Benefit Appeal Tribunal (as it then was) in 1983. The success rate where the applicant was unrepresented was 21 per cent. The figures speak for themselves (Table 9.1).

TABLE 9.1 Success Rate of Forms of Representation

Type of representative	No. of appellants Represented	Successful	% of total represented	Success rate %
Friend/Relative	9,164	2,279	54.00	24.9
Trade union official	155	50	0.92	32.3
Solicitor	601	240	3.57	39.9
Social Worker	3,259	1,521	19.36	46.7
CPAG	81	34	0.48	42.0
Claimants Union	707	305	4.20	43.1
Others (i.e. CABx, Tribunal Representation Units, Other Advisory Agencies)	2,860	1,341	16.99	46.9

9.35. The Advisory Committee's considered advice was that legal aid, in the form of assistance by way of representation, should be 'extended now to bail applications to the Immigration Appellate Authorities; they involve personal liberty. Of the two small tribunals we have discussed, we give priority to the Social Security Commissioners because there is no publicly funded source of expert assistance readily available. ... Among the larger tribunals, we see the most urgent need for legal aid in Industrial Tribunals' (*33rd Annual Report* paragraph 309). The other small tribunal referred to by the Committee was the Immigration Appeal Tribunal which then had a workload of about 500 cases. In about half of these representation was provided by the Home Office financed United Kingdom Immigration Advisory Service (paragraph 306). In the case of bail applications, the Advisory Committee considered that there should be provision for the applicant to be represented by an independent solicitor (*35th Annual Report*, paragraphs 143–8). In the case of appeals to the Social Security Commissioners, the appeal is only on a point of law from a Social Security Appeal Tribunal with leave. The one exception to this—an appeal as of right in national insurance cases where the SSAT are not unanimous—will disappear in April 1987. The numbers involved are small; in 1984 some 524 cases were decided after an oral hearing by the Social Security Commissioners.

9.36. The Advisory Committee have added the Vaccine Damage Tribunals to their priority list for representation (ibid., paragraph 150). Under the Vaccine Damage Payments Act of 1979 a single payment of, since 1 August 1985, £40,000 is made where the Secretary of State is satisfied on a balance of probabilities that severe disablement resulted from the vaccination. The tribunal's decision is final (though subject to judicial review) and the evidence is almost entirely medical.

9.37. The case for representation before Industrial Tribunals is more complex. As the Advisory Committee pointed out:

... Industrial Tribunals have now developed into what is effectively a court of law with a large body of case law based on increasingly complex legislation. We are concerned that effective representation is not available to all those appearing before the Tribunal and that there can be a serious imbalance in representation as respondents are often represented either by a lawyer or by an experienced lay representative. (Ibid., paragraph 155.)

The Royal Commission on Legal Services reached a similar conclusion:

These tribunals handle a complex body of recent statutory law which requires advice of a technical nature and a high standard of representation. A large proportion both of applicants and respondents are already legally represented before such tribunals. A survey conducted during October 1977 showed that 49 per cent of respondents and 33 per cent of applicants were represented by lawyers. Many other applicants were represented by their trade union or by other organizations . . . (*Final Report*, 1979, Cmnd. 7648, paragraph 15.8.)

The scope of Industrial Tribunals presents a particular difficulty. As the Advisory Committee observed:

Industrial tribunals handle a wide range of cases from the relatively straightforward to those relying on very complex points of law, such as, for example, the concept of equal value or the transfer of undertakings. Within this range there are clearly areas in which people need general advice, and others in which expert legal advice and expert legal representation are essential. There are very substantial difficulties in establishing which cases should therefore be eligible for legal aid . . . (*35th Annual Report*, paragraph 158.)

The Advisory Committee proposed a filter—an extended merits test (consisting of the general legal aid merits test plus the criteria proposed by the Council on Tribunals; see paragraph 9.33 above). They observed, 'The proportion of cases granted legal aid should be small as a result of the filter; the number of cases to be considered is enormous' (ibid., paragraph 156). If applications for legal aid were to be made in all Industrial Tribunal cases the result would be that the annual total of applications for legal aid would be inflated by nearly 12 per cent (ibid., paragraph 157). But the very sifting of applications presents a substantial problem on which the Advisory Committee commented:

We have considered the implications of this (filtering) for the legal aid administration of the Law Society and consider that any extension of legal aid to Industrial Tribunals would require a substantial increase in the resources available to the Law Society for handling the additional volume of work. (Ibid., paragraph 158.)

Failure to provide this would result in an intolerable burden on the legal aid administration and/or less stringent sifting with consequent greater demands on the legal aid fund. The Advisory Committee suggested the setting up of several pilot studies to test possible approaches to the extension of legal aid to Industrial Tribunals and identify the most efficacious (ibid., paragraph 159). These included the straightforward extension of legal aid or of assistance by way of representation on the basis of special criteria for tribunals, the extension of legal aid on the basis of certification of need by the tribunal chairman, and the use of lawyers in a 'resource' capacity—available to provide training, information, and consultancy for generalist advisers.

9.38. The failure of successive governments to extend legal aid to tribunal representation has created an artificial dividing line between advice and representation. The report of the Review of the National Association of Citizens Advice Bureaux, under the chairmanship of Sir Douglas Lovelock, KCB, observed that 'Where cases are in any way complicated advice shades into action on behalf of the client and action into advocacy.... In some cases advocacy may take a more direct form, such as representing clients at tribunals. We do not think it feasible to draw a line between strict advice work and action/advocacy of this type' (1984, Cmnd. 9139, paragraph 5.11). In his speech during the debate on the Address on 21 March 1974, the Lord Chancellor stressed the importance of encouraging the development by the legal profession itself of knowledge and expertise in the field of welfare and social law. Yet an obvious step towards that encouragement has still not been taken. Sections 2 and 2A of the Legal Aid Act, 1974 carefully preserve the dividing line between assistance and representation; the legislation in Scotland and Northern Ireland is to the same effect. The artificiality of this distinction in practice was exemplified in *McKenzie* v. *McKenzie* [1970] 3 All ER 1034, a unanimous decision of the Court of Appeal founded on a dictum of Lord Tenterden in *Collier* v. *Bicks* (1831) 2 B & A 663: 'Any person, whether he be a professional or not, may attend as a friend of either party, may take notes, may quietly make suggestions and give advice.' This decision had enabled solicitors acting under the green form scheme to attend hearings and assist clients without appearing for them. However, the Law Society of Northern Ireland reports that in a considerable proportion of the instances where solicitors have attended in this way, 'they have been subjected to questioning by members of the tribunal or invited and encouraged to address the tribunal thereby finding themselves acting in a *de facto* representative capacity'. 'This', comments the report, 'indicates that a considerable number of members of industrial tribunals consider representation by solicitors to be of material assistance to them in dealing justly and expeditiously with the cases before them' (1984–5, HC 11, p. 30). It must be said, however, that the financial inducements are not such as to make this a common experience for solicitors.

Advisory agencies

9.39. A consequence of not implementing the statutory provision for representation before tribunals that has existed since 1949 is that the legal profession has to some extent been distanced from tribunal work. A second consequence has been the development of other ways of satisfying the need for representation before tribunals.

Outside the legal aid system, there are a number of sources of tribunal assistance—solicitors instructed privately, generalist advice agencies (most notably the Citizens Advice Bureaux), legal advice centres, law centres, trade unions and employers' associations, voluntary specialist groups such as the Child Poverty Action Group and the British Legion, and statutory bodies such as the Commission for Racial Equality. The effective scope of each such body is restricted: private practitioners because of the need for their clients to pay; generalist advice agencies by their geographical spread and by the limited resources available for training voluntary workers; law centres and legal advice centres by their concentration in the major conurbations; trade unions and employers' associations by their restriction of their activities to their own members; and specialist agencies by their concentration on a particular field of tribunal work. Nevertheless, all at present provide valuable help to potential and actual tribunal applicants. (Advisory Committee, *35th Annual Report*, paragraph 271.)

Apart from private practitioners, all of these agencies are cash-limited rather than demand-led except to the extent that they are able to make use of the green form scheme. 'The evidence that has been submitted to us', observed the Royal Commission on Legal Services, 'indicates that there are wide variations in both the scope and quality of the advice and representation provided by agencies' (*Final Report*, 1979, Cmnd. 7648, paragraph 15.18). They continued:

15.19. Agencies which provide lay advice and representation before tribunals ... have devoted much time and effort to the subject and have acquired considerable expertise. They provide a sound and useful service and we do not think it necessary or desirable to establish a new national organization to provide lay representation before all tribunals. It would be preferable to encourage existing agencies to develop or expand where necessary the specialist services that they now provide.

The Royal Commission on Legal Services

9.40. The Royal Commission on Legal Services, under the chairmanship of Sir Henry (now Lord) Benson, GBE, inquired into the law and practice relating to the provision of legal services in England, Wales, and Northern Ireland and made a number of recommendations relevant to the present discussion (*Final Report*, 1979, Cmnd. 7648). The Royal Commission saw a need for a Council of Legal Services which would be responsible for advising the Lord Chancellor on the strategy of providing such services, leaving the administration of civil legal aid to The Law Society, as at present. Committees with full-time liaison officers should be set up to co-ordinate legal services in the existing fourteen legal aid areas (Recommendations 6.2 and 6.4). The Royal Commission observed:

6.16 We are satisfied that, if it is to operate satisfactorily, it should be the task of the Council for Legal Services to have regard not merely to work done under legal aid or otherwise paid out of public funds, but to legal services of every description. We consider therefore that the Council should keep under review the provision of all forms of legal services.

The Royal Commission also concluded that a competent, accessible, independent national network of generalist advice agencies was needed to 'offer initial advice or information to citizens on any problem and sift out for them those problems which have a legal element and may call for a legal remedy' (paragraph 7.1).

We believe that the availability of such advice agencies is an essential ingredient in a successful policy for providing legal services.

7.2 In the simpler cases, whether or not they have a legal content, these agencies should be able to provide a solution themselves, by advice, correspondence, negotiation or help in form-filling. Where the advice or assistance of a solicitor is needed, the agencies should be able to assist in the selection of a solicitor who is willing and competent to handle the particular problem. ... Special arrangements will be needed in those areas where solicitors are not available to do the work.

The CABx should provide the basic first-tier service—'it would be perverse to ignore what already exists and ... no other organization can rival the CABx in organization and experience' (ibid., paragraph 7.5). 'We take the view that the CABx are the most appropriate means now available of providing the first-tier advisory service. For this service to be provided effectively, the CABx must receive adequate support from public funds ...' (ibid., paragraph 7.20). The CABx should be backed up by a variety of advisers and agencies to whom cases could be referred, but in regard to legal advice, 'It would be better to preserve the general advisory character of the CABx, and to look for legal advice to the professional legal services which are already available from solicitors in private practice and from the citizens' law centres ...' (ibid., paragraph 7.25). In appropriate cases retainers should be paid to solicitors for this service (ibid., pargraph 7.15).

9.41. Though the Royal Commission were clear that the CABx service should continue to be financed out of public funds, they considered that it was not part of their function to suggest what proportion of finance should be provided respectively by central and local government. They did conclude, however, that if part of the funds were to continue to be provided by local authorities, that should be on the basis of a statutory duty (ibid., paragraph 7.22). In many localities there was a need for law centres, or, as the Royal Commission preferred, 'citizens' law centres' (CLCs), the main purpose of which would be to provide legal advice, assistance, and representation to inhabitants in their localities with special emphasis on welfare law (Recommendation 8.1 and 8.4). These centres should be financed wholly out of central funds through a small, government-appointed, but independent, agency, with local advisory committees (Recommendations 8.6 and 8.8):

The independence of the service, together with its continuity and efficiency, will, we consider, best be guaranteed if there is one national agency responsible rather than an increasing number of separate local entities operating with differing procedures and administration, sources of finance and professional standards. (Ibid., paragraph 8.28.)

The Royal Commission also recommended that half an hour's legal advice and assistance from solicitors who undertake legal aid work should be available to everyone, irrespective of means, free of charge. This should be paid for out of the legal aid fund (Recommendation 13.1).

In regard to tribunal representation the Royal Commission reached clear conclusions:

15.11 The present position is, in several respects, unsatisfactory. Representation by a lawyer is available only to those able to pay for it, unless the lawyer provides his services free of charge; the availability and quality of lay representation varies; and through nervousness or unfamiliarity with the procedure applicants often find it difficult to present their cases in person. In addition, proceedings before tribunals have become increasingly complex. As pointed out in paragraph 15.10, an applicant who is present or who is represented is more likely to be successful than one who is absent and unrepresented. It follows that it is desirable that every applicant before any tribunal should either be able adequately to present his case in person or to obtain representation. To achieve this it will be necessary to overcome each of the weaknesses mentioned above. For this purpose, three separate but linked policies will be needed. These are the simplification of tribunal procedures, the development of lay advice and representation and the extension of legal aid to tribunals. (Ibid., paragraph 15.11.)

In the matter of simplification of tribunal procedures, the Royal Commission doubted whether much would be possible unless the relevant legislation on which the work of tribunals is based was first made less complex. They considered it essential that a review of the question should be undertaken at an early date, under the general oversight of the Lord Chancellor, by the Council on Tribunals in association with the government departments concerned and other interested parties.

9.42. The Royal Commission concluded that advice and representation by lay agencies for applicants before tribunals should be encouraged (Recommendation 15.2). Agencies that wished to engage in this work should have adequate resources for the purpose and public funds should be made available to assist in the training of staff of approved lay organizations (Recommendation 15.12). Though self-representation by the applicant and representation by a trained member of a lay agency should be encouraged and 'should be effective in the majority of tribunal cases', the Royal Commission were satisfied, in the light of the volume of authoritative evidence they received, that 'before all tribunals, there are some cases in which legal representation is needed. In such cases legal aid should be available unless legal representation is specifically prohibited by statute' (ibid., paragraph 15.25). (The only surviving instance of that is in cases before the Family Practitioner Appeal Tribunal.)

9.43. The Royal Commission on Legal Services in Scotland, under the chairmanship of Lord Hughes, CBE, reported in 1980

(Cmnd. 7846). Its recommendations corresponded broadly with those of the Royal Commission on Legal Services mentioned above, but some recommendations particular to it deserve attention. The Hughes Royal Commission thought (though not unanimously) that legal aid should be administered by a Legal Services Commission (Recommendation 8.27), which would have the power to support financially the establishment of solicitors' offices in under-provided areas of the country (Recommendation 7.10). The Hughes Royal Commission observed:

Under no circumstances have we contemplated the possibility that legal aid might at some time become a cash-limited service. The task of the Commission would be to administer as efficiently as possible what must remain an 'open-ended' scheme in financial terms. The grant-aiding of advice services, on the other hand, is in our view susceptible to cash limits. (*Report*, paragraph 20.12.)

Legal aid should be available for representation at a tribunal, but only if the client would otherwise be unable to follow the proceedings and if there was no lay representation locally which was recognized by the tribunal as suitable (Recommendation 8.2). Tribunals should have the power to grant legal aid where substantial points of law arose or were likely to arise (Recommendation 8.3). At the moment Scotland has no equivalent to the Lord Chancellor's Advisory Committee. The Hughes Royal Commission recommended that a Legal Services Advisory Committee, similar to the Lord Chancellor's, should be established to keep under continuous review the interests of the citizen in relation to the legal system. It should have no executive responsibilities (Recommendation 20.2).

The Government's response

9.44. Four years after the Benson Royal Commission published their report the Government issued its response (*The Government Response to the Report of the Royal Commission on Legal Services*, 1983, Cmnd. 9077). This stated that in deciding what action to take on the relevant recommendations for which it was responsible, the Government had been guided by the principles that:

legal services should in general be provided by the private sector and as economically and efficiently as possible;

there should be effective access to the courts for the resolution of disputes and the defence or enforcement of rights;

legal aid from public funds should be available in appropriate cases to individuals who have inadequate resources;

full consideration must always be given to the need to limit public expenditure. (p. 3.)

The Government fully endorsed the Royal Commission's recommendation that The Law Society should remain responsible for the administration of legal aid but saw no need for the proposed co-ordinating Council for Legal Services:

[The Government] does not believe that a sufficient case has been made for a central Council for Legal Services nor for any direct Ministerial responsibility for the availability of legal services in any particular area ... The experience of the Greater Manchester Legal Services Committee suggests that such committees may have a useful role to play in some areas in bringing together those concerned with the availability and delivery of legal services. In the Government's view the value of such committees must depend on local circumstances, and the initiative for developing them in any area must rest with those who are directly involved there in the provision of legal services. (p. 6.)

The role of the CABx was recognized:

The Government entirely agrees that the Citizens Advice Bureaux, offering a free impartial and effective general advice service, are essential to underpin other more specialised advice agencies, including those providing legal advice. Much CAB work has a legal aspect; various arrangements have been developed to make legal expertise available within individual bureaux.

The Government welcomes these developments, which essentially involve action at local level by the CAB service itself and by the other interests concerned. (p. 7.)

The Government's views on the Royal Commission's recommendations for citizens' law centres were still under consideration; an announcement would be made in due course. The nearest there has been to that is the speech of Lord Skelmersdale, for the Government, in the House of Lords on 8 May 1985, in the course of which he confided that:

Since the publication of the report of the Royal Commission on Legal Services consideration has continued within Government on a range of possible initiatives on the funding of responsibility for law centres ... I cannot honestly say that I think the prospects of a specific national funding scheme for centres are very high. (*Hansard*, HL, vol. 463, no. 87, c. 728.)

Lord Skelmersdale's closing words affirmed the Government's view that financial support for law centres should be a local responsibility:

We recognise their worth, and indeed at a national level we have given direct assistance to the Law Centres Federation to help with developmental work. At local level, we have helped many individual law centres to get established. We have given them a fair wind. But in the longer term it is for the law centres themselves to convince local authorities of the value of their work, and I have no doubt that they will do this with the greatest success. (Ibid., c. 731.)

9.45. The Government accepted in principle all the Royal Commission's recommendations relating to tribunals,

subject to further consideration being given to timing and the availability of resources. Lay participation in advice and representation in tribunal proceedings is welcomed by the Government: Citizens' Advice Bureaux (whose parent body NACAB [the National Association of Citizens Advice Bureaux] is publicly funded) already provide this service as does, for example, the Royal British Legion in respect of the Pensions Appeal Tribunals. (Ibid., p. 18.)

The Government also accepted that a need existed for more information about legal services, and added that the amount and nature of all publicity already available was kept under regular review (p. 24).

The Scottish Legal Aid Board

9.46. In Scotland the pattern of legal aid closely resembled, until recently, that in England and Wales and Northern Ireland. The Legal Aid (Scotland) Act, 1986, the greater part of which is to come into force on 1 April 1987, produces a radical departure from the system established in 1949. The administration of legal aid by the Law Society of Scotland is to be replaced by the Scottish Legal Aid Board. This is to be a body corporate and 'neither an emanation of the Crown nor to be treated as the servant or agent of the Crown' (Act, Schedule 1, paragraphs 1 and 2). The Board is to have the general function of securing that legal aid and advice and assistance are available in accordance with the Act; and of administering the Fund from which the operation is financed. Its chairman and other members are to be appointed by the Secretary of State for Scotland (section 1(3), (4), and (5)) who may issue guidance to which the Board shall have regard in exercising its functions (section 3(4)). However, the guidance is not to relate to the consideration or disposal of applications for legal aid or advice and assistance. The scheme established by the Act is, like its predecessor, directed towards a service provided by private practitioners. The Board reports annually to the Secretary of State (section 3(3)), who lays the report before each House of Parliament (section 5(7)). As mentioned above (paragraph 9.31) the Act contains the usual provision for salaried professional staff (Part V) which has not been implemented. The importance of the Act is that it creates administrative machinery that is readily capable of being adapted, should that be considered desirable, to the more radical proposals now to be adopted in England and Wales, discussed later.

The Efficiency Scrutiny of Legal Aid

9.47. An Efficiency Scrutiny of Legal Aid, conducted by a team of officials drawn from the Cabinet Office Efficiency Unit, the Treasury, and the Lord Chancellor's Department, reported in June 1986 (*Legal Aid*, vols. 1 and 2, Lord Chancellor's Department). The Government's terms of reference for the Scrutiny were: 'Given the necessary judicial independence of the courts and existing reviews of court procedure, to consider the determinants of expenditure of the legal aid scheme by looking at its operation and administration in practice, and to make recommendations'. This remit led the Scrutiny team to examine relevant activity outside the legal aid scheme. It traversed much of the ground already examined by other bodies (though it made scarcely any reference to them), notably the Lord Chancellor's Advisory Committee in their *24th*, *33rd*, and *34th Annual Reports*, and consulted a wide range of informed opinion. The Scrutiny report was sharply focused, crisply presented (except in the matter of pagination and the numbering of paragraphs, the inadequacy of which was aggravated by the absence of an index) and expressed in a direct, confident, and somewhat assertive style. Its own recommendations were sweeping; some of them concerned the matter of advice, assistance, and representation in tribunal cases. The principal conclusion was that existing arrangements in this area do not ensure equal access to advice or make the most effective use of available resources (Scrutiny Report, vol. 2, chapter IV, paragraph 21). The report suggests that the advice element in its proposed service for advice and tribunal representation would be about £9m. cheaper than would be the cost of an equivalent service under the green form scheme, and that there would be considerable scope for increasing provision for tribunal representation within existing resources (vol. 2, Annex 35, paragraph 10).

9.48. The report confirmed that tribunals deal with a large number of cases which concern basic individual rights, particularly in the fields of welfare benefits, employment, and immigration; in 1983 the number exceeded 140,000 (vol. 2, iv, paragraph 14). It also confirmed that representation at a tribunal hearing makes a significant difference to the outcome of the case (ibid., paragraph 15 and Annex 33). The report commented that 'there is clearly a case for examining the procedure of tribunals to consider whether it can be simplified so that applicants could effectively represent themselves, as originally envisaged' (ibid., paragraph 16).

9.49. The Scrutiny team examined non-statutory agencies providing advice. It noted that a national network of 900 CABx has some 2,000 paid staff and 13,000 volunteers, and that there are some 50 law centres and some 600 legal advice centres. The main categories in which advice was given by these agencies in 1984–5 were: social security (18 per cent), housing, property, and land (16 per cent), and employment (10 per cent). The report observed that the great majority of this advice could have been dealt with under the green form scheme and concluded: 'There is no doubt that most of the advice currently provided under the green form scheme needs to be available from somewhere in order to secure access to justice' (ibid., paragraphs 8, 9, and 13). The report considered that the existing arrangements are wasteful.

... there is no co-ordination in the provision of advice agencies. Some areas have none, whilst others have a plethora of different agencies. Since legal aid is not available for tribunal representation, that work falls almost entirely to these agencies. The absence of co-ordinated provision means that representation depends upon whether or not there is a local law centre; or whether a local advice centre or CAB provides the service. (Ibid., paragraph 18.)

We also found a considerable overlap in the services provided by CABx and other agencies on the one hand, and by private practitioners on the other. The present arrangements do not permit decisions to be taken as to the way in which the expertise of the two sectors can most effectively be used. (Ibid., paragraph 19.)

Furthermore, there are some areas of the law—particularly welfare benefit and housing matters—where expertise is concentrated in CABx and other advice agencies rather than among private practitioners. (Ibid., paragraph 21.)

9.50. To achieve the objective of ensuring that persons of modest means have access to justice the report suggested that arrangements for advice and tribunal representation should, *inter alia*:

(*a*) provide skilled initial generalist advice in a form which clients can understand;

(*b*) ensure access to a specialist with expertise in the problem area where necessary;

(*c*) provide for representation at tribunals where necessary

(ibid., paragraph 20). In the majority of cases 'a trained lay advocate will be perfectly competent to present the case and representation by a lawyer should rarely be necessary' (ibid., paragraph 25).

9.51. The Scrutiny team proposed radical changes in the administration of legal aid services. It recommended the establishment of a nationally-based Legal Services Board responsible for all aspects of legal aid and legal advice and reporting to the Lord Chancellor, with a chairman and a chief executive, and fifteen Area Offices (as there are under the present scheme administered by the Law Society) each headed by an Area Director answerable to the chief executive (Report, vol. 1, IV, paragraph 51 and vol. 2, V, paragraph 24). In regard to advice and representation in tribunal cases, the Area Director would have the responsibility of making the best arrangements, within nationally prescribed criteria as to access to advice, competence of advisers, emergency advice arrangements, and tribunal representation; and within a budget allocated to him by the legal aid administration (Report, vol. 2, IV, paragraph 36). To achieve this the options open to the Area Director would, in the view of the Scrutiny team, comprise: (i) establishing agencies with salaried qualified staff; (ii) strengthening existing agencies by remunerated additional staff; (iii) engaging the service of experts to support the advice given in agencies; and (iv) entering into contracts for the supply of a co-ordinated service in a local area. A combination of these might be appropriate (Report, vol. 2, IV, paragraph 32 and V, paragraphs 34, 36, and 37). The green form scheme would be abolished (Report, vol. 2, IV, paragraphs 29 and 38).

9.52. The revised arrangements would, claims the report: 'provide a more cost-effective service than the present system' (Report ibid., paragraph 41). The main elements of the package proposed by the Scrutiny team for advice and tribunal representation comprise:

(*a*) free advice for everyone;
(*b*) access to trained lay advisers and to solicitors in appropriate cases;
(*c*) significant savings in the advice element providing scope for increased provision for tribunal representation within existing resources. (Report, vol. 2, vi.)

A new framework for legal aid in England and Wales

9.53. After much of this chapter had been drafted the Government issued a White Paper outlining a new framework of legal aid in England and Wales (26 March 1987, Cm. 118). It also contains the Government's response to the Efficiency Scrutiny's recommendations. The keynote of the Government's approach is that 'The aim must be to ensure that the needs and interests of all concerned, including both the taxpayer and the applicant, are properly balanced' (paragraph 19). The Government has concluded that the administrative apparatus of the legal aid scheme of 1949 is no longer appropriate and should be replaced by a new structure for the management and operation of the scheme in England and Wales. A new Legal Aid Board, such as now exists in Scotland, is proposed (paragraph 15).

The Board will act under the guidance of the Lord Chancellor. The Lord Chancellor will appoint the Chairman and members, who will act in a non-executive capacity, and will concur in the appointment of some key staff in senior positions. The Board will comprise both lawyers and non-lawyers, all of whom will be chosen for their particular experience and skills. (Paragraph 16.)

(In Scotland only the appointment of the principal officer of the Board requires the approval of the Secretary of State.) The existing network of Area Offices under the Law Society's scheme is to be retained (paragraph 17) and 'Initially, the new Board will do no more than take over those functions currently performed by the Law Society'.

The Government will, however, take powers which will enable the new Board to assume other tasks at a later stage. This will enable a more coherent and co-ordinated approach to be adopted towards the scheme than has hitherto been possible. New functions will be transferred when the Board has been able to satisfy the Government that it can perform these tasks more efficiently than under present arrangements. .... This gradual approach to the transfer of functions will ensure that any disruption is kept to the minimum, and that the necessary safeguards are preserved. (Paragraph 18.)

9.54. The Government has not accepted the most controversial of the Scrutiny's proposals—the abolition of the green form scheme—though the White Paper summarizes, in paragraph 21, the Scrutiny's arguments in its favour. But the door for abolition has been left open. In particular,

The Government is attracted to the principle of using the skills of advice agencies, especially to deal with those areas of work in which their special experience is likely to be greater than that of many solicitors in private practice. (Paragraph 24.)

25. The Government therefore intends to take powers to enable the new Board to make alternative arrangements for the provision of advice and assistance for particular categories of work where this would be a more efficient way of providing the service.

It will be the responsibility of the new Board to consider, on an area basis, the most cost-effective way of providing advice and assistance, including specifically whether better arrangements might be made by using advice agencies; it seems, however, that solicitors in private practice are to be excluded (paragraph 27).

Once the Board has set up suitable arrangements for contracting with agencies and other organizations for the provision of advice in the specified areas of work—for instance, advice on welfare benefits—these will be excluded altogether from the Green Form scheme. The detailed arrangements could well involve tenders being sought for the provision of advice in geographical areas covered by the Board's Area Offices, and the form of coverage might well be different in different geographical areas. (Paragraph 26.)

The Board's detailed proposals would not, it seems, be implemented without the Government's agreement. The risk of possible disruption during the transition from the green form scheme would be avoided, says the White Paper, by the thoroughness of these detailed arrangements. In other categories of work the green form scheme will survive (paragraph 27). The Government has, in fact, put in hand a study of the green form scheme; a report is expected at the end of 1987.

9.55. The Government has reaffirmed its policy on tribunal representation (see paragraph 9.45 above):

30. The Government's policy on extensions of legal aid and assistance by way of representation to further tribunals was set out in its response to the Royal Commission on Legal Services. Extensions of assistance by way of representation and legal aid are made where it is shown to be necessary and resources allow.

The Government is attracted by one of the possible approaches suggested by the Efficiency Scrutiny:

It is not clear that publicly funded representation is necessary for all tribunal proceedings. Another approach might be to simplify tribunal procedure wherever possible in order to render legal representation unnecessary. The Lord Chancellor's Department has recently commissioned research into the effectiveness of representation at tribunals. Against this background, the Government does not intend that there should be any general extension of publicly funded tribunal representation. (Paragraph 30.)

This study will start work in April 1987 and is expected to report in two years' time.

9.56. As the White Paper points out, many of its proposals will require primary legislation (paragraphs 6, 18, and 25); they are, therefore, subject to the hazards of the legislative process. Those of its proposals that do not require primary legislation will be introduced as soon as possible (paragraph 6). The power to make subordinate legislation in this area is given to the Lord Chancellor (Legal Aid Act, 1974, section 20(1)), who may make such regulations as appear to him necessary or desirable for giving effect to Part I of the Act (which governs civil legal aid and advice). It seems, therefore, that the Lord Chancellor could transfer responsibility for the management and operation of the Act's provisions from The Law Society to another body by regulation; but it would scarcely be possible to make the financial arrangements for the proposed Legal Aid Board without primary legislation. The Scottish Legal Aid Board has been established by statute. It seems probable, therefore, that the White Paper's proposals will be also, especially as the White Paper presents no more than an outline of the proposals. Much will depend on the detailed arrangements to be made within the new framework. Some general comments may, however, be made now.

9.57. The Government has followed the advice of the Royal Commission and the Advisory Committee in proposing the statutory involvement of the advisory agencies in the provision of advice and assistance, though not in the way contemplated by those bodies.

The White Paper proposes a market approach, within a budget, for the provision of the requisite services where that will produce a better service at lower cost (paragraph 24). The reference in paragraph 26 to contracting with agencies and other organizations, and to tenders being sought, provides a good deal of latitude. It would, presumably, be possible for groups or units to be formed specifically for the purpose of tendering. A variety of methods of providing the requisite services is acceptable, and may even be desirable, especially if it is better able to deal with the difficult problem of advice for the disabled and those in rural areas. But there are two essentials which must be secured. The first is that proper standards are maintained, the second that confusion is avoided. This calls for adequate supervision and good co-ordination. The White Paper says little about the first and less about the second, though the Royal Commission and the Advisory Committee drew attention to both. In view of the Government's evident concern with cost, the White Paper is strangely unspecific about whether payment is to be required for advice and assistance in areas where the green form scheme has been phased out. The implication is that where the green form scheme is abolished advice and assistance will be free of charge, but the matter is not clear.

9.58. The Government's proposals for the provision of advice and assistance lean heavily on the various advice agencies and assume their continued existence, but the White Paper has nothing to say about the financing of these agencies and does not address itself to the important points made about that by the Royal Commission. The Government has made it clear that it considers both the advice agencies and the law centres to be a local responsibility, save to the extent that the National Association of Citizens Advice Bureaux (a charity and a company limited by guarantee to which individual CABx affiliate themselves, as distinct from the CABx themselves) will continue to receive a grant-in-aid from central funds (at present through the Department of Trade and Industry). The financial position of many of these agencies is precarious. Thus, the current financial support for some ten law centres provided under the Urban Aid Programme of the Department of the Environment is due to run out in 1987 (Advisory Committee, *36th Annual Report* (1985–86), Appendix E). There is certainly a danger to be guarded against that a budgeted, rather than a demand-led, service could achieve economies at the expense of a good service.

9.59. The Government's intention that the green form scheme should be abolished for those areas in which advice agencies are involved will have the effect of distancing the legal profession from the areas concerned and will deprive the applicant of modest means of one natural point of entry to the advice system. The contractual arrangements with the agencies must make it possible for them to obtain necessary professional advice. The abolition of the green form scheme could, in fact, pose a threat to the survival of law centres, some of which depend on it quite heavily for their continued existence. It would be unfortunate if the further development of flexible arrangements and co-operation that at present exist in some geographical areas between agencies and solicitors were to be inhibited. The distancing of the legal aid profession from tribunal work could also deprive the tribunals of the influence of the general law with which the profession is familiar.

9.60. In the face of an abundance of carefully considered advice from numerous commissions, committees, and councils, including, most recently, the Efficiency Scrutiny on Legal Aid, about the need for tribunal representation, the White Paper repeats the somewhat imprecise formula, first produced in the response to the Royal Commission in 1983 (see paragraph 9.45 above), that 'extensions of advice by way of representation and legal aid are made when it is shown to be necessary and resources allow' (paragraph 30). The point made in the same paragraph—'It is not clear that publicly funded representation is necessary for all tribunal proceedings'—is curious in view of what the Government's advisory bodies have actually said. The objective of self-representation in tribunals has not been realized in forty years. As the Royal Commission pointed out: 'Although at present lawyers are retained in only a minority of tribunal cases, the total volume of such work is large, being comparable with the case-load of the civil courts' (*Final Report*, paragraph 4.5). However, the White Paper does not, it seems, completely shut the door—'the Government intends no general extension of publicly funded representation' (paragraph 30)—and it is to be hoped that the Lord Chancellor's study of tribunal representation (paragraph 9.55 above) will enable a more positive response to the need to be made. Before the report of that study is available a decade will have passed since the Royal Commission's report and six years since the Advisory Committee's 'blueprint' for advice and representation in tribunals in its *33rd Annual Report*.

9.61. The Government's failure to respond positively to the clear case for representation made by the Advisory Committee in the tribunals it has identified (paragraphs 9.34–9.37 above) leaves, in our view, a serious gap in the provision of legal aid in this country. In four of the five instances the demand on resources would be small. The case of Industrial Tribunals is more difficult. But these are courts in all but name and it is illogical to deny representation to applicants before these tribunals when legal aid is available for litigation.

Legal Services Committees

9.62. In responding to the suggestion of the Royal Commission that a Council for Legal Services and regional committees should be established to advise on legal services, the Government said that it believed that no sufficient case had been made for direct ministerial responsibility for the availability of legal services in any particular area. It accepted, rather grudgingly, that the experience of the Greater Manchester Legal Services Committee suggested that regional committees might have a useful role to play in some areas in bringing together those concerned with the availability and delivery of legal services. The key to the success of this regional committee: 'has been the profitable partnership between a voluntary committee composed of committed representatives of the local legal and advice services and a full-time Secretary employed by The Law Society, who is in effect a regional liaison officer' (Advisory Committee, *32nd Annual Report* (1981–2), paragraph 174). The remunerated appointment was agreed to by the then Lord Chancellor in 1977 and has been sanctioned by his successor, 'and this has proved to be a decisive factor in the history of the Committee' (Advisory Committee, *36th Annual Report* (1985–6), paragraph 134). The Committee now covers the whole of the North West Legal Aid Area (No. 7). The Committee's functions are usefully detailed in the Advisory Committee's *36th Annual Report* (paragraph 136). They are:

(*a*) to identify existing legal services in areas and assess their effectiveness;

(*b*) to identify geographical and other gaps;

(*c*) to co-ordinate the work of various local agencies providing legal services, to stimulate improvement within the service, and to promote legal services where there are gaps;

(*d*) to keep the public informed about the availability of legal services;

(*e*) to act in a representative capacity for those involved in a cross-section of legal services, and, in effect, provide a forum that draws together those involved locally in legal services and thus is credibly able to speak on their behalf.

The importance of this activity is self-evident and its value has been confirmed in the Annual Reports of the Advisory Committee (especially the 33rd and the 36th). The need for it now is the more important in view of the White Paper proposals. Although the Government envisages wider responsibilities for the new Legal Aid Board than those presently discharged by The Law Society, those responsibilities should not include the functions of the regional legal services committees because of the need for an independent stance which the Board will not have. The Law Society itself saw the need for an independent organization so long ago as the early 1970s when it advocated an independent Advisory Liaison Service (The Law Society, *24th Report* (1973–4), Appendix 18, paragraph 5). The Government's view about extending the remunerated core staffing necessary for such committees was conveyed in its response to the Royal Commission: 'the initiative for developing such committees in any case must rest with those directly involved in the provision of legal services in the locality' (1983, Cmnd. 9077, p. 6). This view was affirmed by the Lord Chancellor in a debate at Westminster on 19 March 1985 (*Hansard*, vol. 461, c. 429–30). In our view this attitude reflects a failure to appreciate the reality that only with support from central funds can an adequate, independent network of regional committees be developed.

Conclusions on legal aid and advice

9.63. A need exists for primary advice to the citizen about sources of assistance in tribunal cases. The observations of the Advisory Committee, in their *36th Annual Report* (1985–6), on the problems of rural areas (paragraph 123) provide a clear summary of the practical steps that should also be taken to satisfy the general need:

there is no single or simple solution to the provision of legal services in rural areas. Much needs to be done to improve the initial access points for information and advice, building on the many experiments over the last few years and making full use of new technology where appropriate. But it is also crucial that the initial advice point should have speedy and reliable recourse to appropriate specialists, whether lawyers, specialists in housing and welfare rights, or conciliation services. The best way to do this is to have a co-ordinated approach, building on existing resources and making full use of the private profession where appropriate. The experience in urban areas has been that better provision of legal services generates more demand and that the private profession far from losing work to the advice sectors tends to gain in terms of increased referrals. It must develop expertise to meet these new sources of work. Such an approach cannot be sustained on enthusiasm alone: it requires planning, administration, and equipment. Above all it needs funding.

9.64. In the matter of advice and assistance, we emphasize that whatever the outcome of the Government's proposals for the modification of the green form scheme, two points are important: (*a*) any transitional arrangements must ensure that the interests of applicants do not suffer, and (*b*) access to competent legal advice, when that is necessary, must be assured.

9.65. In the matter of tribunal representation, we recognize that the problems involved in the provision of a service bear some resemblance to those encountered by transport undertakings which have to deal with wide variations in demand. As the Benson Royal Commission emphasized, before all tribunals there are some cases in which legal representation is needed (*Final Report*, paragraph 15.25). This is either because of the nature of the case or of the limitations of the applicant. The essential problem is that of identifying where there should be representation. Successive governments have done very little to tackle the problem for reasons which are easy to understand. There are annually six times as many tribunal cases as contested civil cases disposed of at trial before the High Court and the county courts combined (Council on Tribunals, *Annual Report*, 1985–6, paragraph 2.19). The case-load of lawyers involved in tribunal matters is comparable with that in the civil courts (Royal Commission, *Final Report*, paragraph 4.5). The demand on resources if legal aid were to be extended generally to tribunals would no doubt be considerable. But the need for such representation is as strong as it is in the case of litigation. We do not believe that a proper solution to the problem is to deny aid for representation before all save three tribunals. The right approach has been indicated in the reports of the advisory bodies. The Advisory Committee in particular have addressed themselves to the problem of providing an appropriate filter to identify the tribunal cases where representation is necessary. The Government should follow the Advisory Committee's advice on this.

9.66. No impartial observer can doubt the value of the work done over the years by the Lord Chancellor's Advisory Committee. Their annual reports are a mine of information and sound comment on all aspects of the subject. The White Paper sows doubt about the future of the Advisory Committee by suggesting that their role and function will inevitably change when the Legal Aid Board has been established and adding that the Government has taken no view on the future of the Committee (paragraph 59). The Advisory Committee is a statutory body constituted, in accordance with section 21 of the Legal Aid Act, 1974, by the Lord Chancellor. It is, in our view, necessary that the existing character of the Advisory Committee should not be significantly altered and that their independence should be preserved.

9.67. If in the preceding paragraphs we have dwelt on this topic at some length it is because we have been impressed by the gravity of the situation disclosed by the reports of the various advisory bodies to which we have referred. The proposed new framework for legal aid offers the prospect of improving that situation; we have therefore taken the opportunity of emphasizing what seemed to us the critical points.

Appeals

9.68. The position in regard to appeals from tribunals has been somewhat modified by the introduction of the application for judicial review under the revised RSC Order 53 (on which we commented in chapter 6 above) and by the judicial decisions on fact finding by tribunals on which we commented in chapter 7 (paragraphs 7.6–7.11 above).

9.69. The Council on Tribunals have made many recommendations for the rationalization of the very varied forms of statutory appeal from tribunals and have pressed, in particular, for a right of appeal on a point of law to the courts in many instances. The Immigration Appeal Tribunal is an example where there is still no such right of appeal despite repeated recommendations of the Council on Tribunals that there should be. We support the general principle that there should in all cases be a right of appeal to the courts on a point of law.

9.70. The late Professor W. A. Robson was critical of appeals from tribunals going ultimately to the House of Lords and advocated an administrative appeal tribunal that would hear appeals on law from all tribunals. The Franks Committee did not favour this. If the system of tribunals were to be created anew there would be much to be said for the proposal, but, in our view, appeals from tribunals are reasonably integrated into the general judicial system and the provision for appeal from tribunals is broadly adequate. The House of Lords has produced many important decisions concerning the work of tribunals and we would not wish to disturb arrangements that appear to work reasonably well. Nor have we received any significant criticism of the present system.

9.71. The Administrative Appeals Tribunal (AAT) of Australia (see further paragraph 9.74 below) is not, generally speaking, a second-tier appeal body of the kind envisaged by Professor Robson. Recently, however, there have been instances in which the AAT has been given this role. As the AAT has jurisdiction to reach its own conclusions on issues of fact and discretion, as well as law, such second-tier appeals are more comprehensive than any found in this country. It was strongly represented to us by a visiting member of the AAT that second-tier appeals of this kind would be beneficial in the field of social security in this country also. The counter-argument is that limited resources are better employed in improving the quality of first-tier appeals than in providing for comprehensive second-tier appeals. This was the approach adopted in the reorganization of the structure of social security tribunals expressed in the Health and Social Security Adjudications Act, 1983 (see paragraph 9.15 above).

Fewer tribunals

9.72. Tribunals have proliferated in the United Kingdom. Professor W. A. Robson was critical of this trend and advocated amalgamation of existing tribunals. The Franks Committee considered the subject in depth but concluded that there was not, in fact, much scope for complete integration of existing tribunals; it advocated consideration of an extension of the jurisdiction of existing tribunals rather than the creation of new ones whenever appeals from administrative decisions were provided by legislation. The Council on Tribunals have expressed themselves clearly on this question: 'We are increasingly impressed by the need to avoid undue proliferation of tribunals by, wherever possible, organising them into fewer and stronger units and to ensure that each group has a proper structure and, where necessary, adequate arrangements for appeal' (*Annual Report*, 1969–70, paragraph 44). The Council have repeatedly acted on this view both by objecting when the establishment of a new tribunal was, in their view, unnecessary, and by recommending the amalgamation of existing tribunals. A recent success for the Council in this respect has been the reorganization of appeals provided by four separate Acts (Child Care, 1980; Residential Homes, 1980; Nursing Homes, 1980, and Children's Homes, 1982) into a single Registered Homes Tribunal (*Annual Report*, 1981–2, p. 16). In our view the Council on Tribunals have this matter well in hand; the cause for concern is that too little attention appears to be paid to their recommendations.

General tribunal

9.73. In his evidence to both the Donoughmore and the Franks Committees, Professor W. A. Robson advocated a general administrative tribunal that would (i) hear appeals from first instance tribunals, and (ii) provide a residuary first instance tribunal for appeals against administrative decisions for which no special tribunal existed. Both Committees rejected this proposal, though the Franks Committee expressed much sympathy with Professor Robson's desire to provide machinery for hearing appeals against administrative decisions generally and pointed out that their conclusion had been reached in relation to their limited terms of reference, which covered only administrative decisions reached after a special statutory procedure involving an inquiry or hearing (1957, Cmnd. 218, paragraph 121). The Whyatt Report (*The Citizen and the Administration*, JUSTICE 1961), advocated a general tribunal such as exists in Sweden, to deal with at least some of the residue of discretionary decisions for which there is at present no appeal to a tribunal. The considerations for and against this approach were rehearsed in our Discussion Paper (1981, paragraphs 81–2).

9.74. In Australia the Federal Parliament, while leaving judicial review substantially intact, has bypassed its limitations. This has been achieved by the creation of a new institution known as the Administrative Appeals Tribunal ('the AAT'). This body has had conferred upon it express power to review on their merits specified statutory decisions. In particular section 43 of the AAT Act, 1975 (as amended) provides that for the purpose of reviewing a decision the Tribunal may exercise all the powers and discretions that are conferred by any relevant enactment on the person who made the decision. In particular the AAT can affirm or vary the decision under review or, in setting it aside, may make a new decision in substitution for the original decision or may remit the matter for reconsideration in accordance with its own directions or recommendations. Consistently with the sweeping nature of this provision it has been laid down by the Federal Court (per Bowen CJ and Deane J. in *Drake* v. *Minister for Immigration and Ethnic Affairs* (1979) 2 ALD 60, 68): 'The question for the determination of the Tribunal is not whether the decision which the decision-maker made was the correct or preferable one on the material before him. The question for the determination of the Tribunal is whether that decision was the correct or preferable one on the material before the Tribunal.'

9.75. As the above passage implies, the AAT is not confined to the evidence which was before the original decision-maker and it is not bound by his findings of fact. It has even been argued that the original decision-maker's findings of fact and reasons for deciding are irrelevant to the AAT. This extreme position has been rejected and it has been held that they are part of the relevant material which is to be put before the Tribunal though they do not bind it (per Daryl Davies J. in *Re Control Investment* (No. 2) (1981) 3 ALD 88). Nor is the AAT bound by ministerial or departmental policy unless obliged by statute to base its decision on that policy. This means that the AAT is in nearly all cases where policy has any part to play free to express its own views. Constitutionally all this is possible because the AAT is in theory part of the administration and does not exercise the judicial power of the state. It was established 'to exercise a function in the sphere of government' (per Smithers J. in *Sullivan* v. *Dept. of Transport* (1978) 1 ALD 363, 368).

9.76. In a written submission to us the President of the AAT, Mr Justice Daryl Davies, put it thus: 'The Tribunal in fact functions as an extension of the judicial arm of Government though it derives its authority from the Executive. It provides a means by which the judiciary and other experienced lawyers become involved in the review of administrative decision-making.' He was critical of the account which we gave of the AAT in our Discussion Paper (p. 24) in so far as we suggested that its jurisdiction is somewhat limited. In fact there has been a steady accretion to the list of statutes under which decisions can be reviewed by the AAT: 'The Tribunal provides review on the merits and thus is able to investigate and determine the facts. It applies the law to the correct factual situation, not to the facts as presented to the decision-maker or as found by him.' Commonly there is no discretion to be exercised at all. It is simply a question of applying correct law to correct facts. Where there is a discretion to be exercised the AAT will exercise it but not necessarily in the same way as the first decision-maker: 'The function which the Tribunal performs has very little to do with Ministerial responsibility. The function of the Tribunal is to see that the rights which are conferred upon members of the community by Parliament are fulfilled'. Although jurisdiction has been conferred on the AAT under a large number of statutes the main case load falls within certain well-defined fields. An interesting account of some fifteen statutory areas of jurisdiction of the AAT was given by the Registrar of the AAT in Appendix 4 of the 6th Annual Report (1981–2) of the Administrative Review Council.

9.77. We have considered whether there should be a single appeal tribunal similar to the AAT in place of the multitude of tribunals which exist at present. In our Discussion Paper the provisional conclusion which we reached on this proposal was as follows:

Despite its apparent attractions, there are serious difficulties with the proposal for a general tribunal in this country. The sheer volume of statutory provisions conferring a discretion on Ministers, and a population of some 55 million, indicate that the potential jurisdiction of the general tribunal would be vast and the task of selection baffling. A more fundamental constitutional objection is that it would substitute for Ministerial answerability in Parliament an unaccountable policy-making tribunal.

On further reflection we do not think that the last sentence of the passage quoted is an adequate basis for rejecting an Administrative Appeals Tribunal or that it gives a fair picture of the achievements of that institution in Australia. No conflict of policy need arise. (It is really only with the immigration cases that there has been serious difficulty at times.) The most serious objection remains the problem of scale. For this reason we think it would not be sensible to dispense with the network of specialized tribunals and to replace them with a single administrative appeal tribunal. We do not consider that the adoption of such a system here would be either practicable, having regard to the much larger volume of business undertaken by tribunals in this country compared with that of the AAT, or productive when the gain is balanced against the disruption that such a change would cause initially. In our view effort should be directed towards the improvement of existing institutions in this field rather than towards their wholesale replacement. Improvement of the United Kingdom system is more likely to be achieved by the amalgamation, where appropriate, of existing tribunals as discussed in paragraph 9.72, and the extension of their jurisdiction.

9.78. But there remains the area of administrative decision-making from which there is no appeal on the merits. We think the first task is to ascertain the extent of this problem. We recommend that this inquiry should be one of the first tasks to be undertaken by the Administrative Review Commission, the establishment of which we recommended in chapter 4. We envisage that when the extent of this problem is ascertained, it can then be decided whether to provide an appeal on the merits in this area by further specialized tribunals or whether one general appeal tribunal would be better. The requirements of the European Convention on Human Rights, to which we now turn, would be relevant to such a review.

Relevant international obligations

9.79. We have made the point above that tribunals, unlike courts, are the forum where the merits of administrative decisions can be re-examined. We think it may be helpful to draw attention in this context to certain obligations which the United Kingdom has undertaken through its adherence to the European Convention on Human Rights, requiring citizens to be given the opportunity to have the merits of certain decisions re-examined by an independent body. Two Articles in the Convention have been interpreted by the Human Rights Commission and the Human Rights Court in a way that has significance for this country.

The European Human Rights Convention: Article 6(1)

9.80. The first relevant Article in the Convention is Article 6(1), the first sentence of which provides: 'In the determination of his civil rights and obligations or of any criminal charge against him, everyone is entitled to a fair and public hearing within a reasonable time by an independent and impartial tribunal established by law . . .'. The phrase 'determination of his civil rights and obligations' is now being liberally construed. For example in *Le Compte* v. *Belgium* (1981) 4 EHRR 1 it was held to cover a decision which suspended a doctor from practice for three months. Where the Article applies there must be access to a 'tribunal' which is 'established by law', which is 'independent' and 'impartial' and provides a 'fair' and 'public' hearing. The European Court of Human Rights has held that the 'right to a court' and the right to a judicial determination of the dispute which is implicit in Article 6(1) cover questions of fact just as much as questions of law (see the *Le Compte* case at p. 19). It follows from this and from the limited scope of review which is available on an application for judicial review that the High Court, hearing an application under Order 53 (and the same would be true of the Court of Session in Scotland when exercising its supervisory jurisdiction—*Brown* v. *Hamilton District Council* 1983 SLT 397) cannot itself be the 'tribunal' which satisfies the requirements of Article 6(1). The Convention would only be satisfied if either the scope of judicial review were to be widened or if at some tier below the High Court there was an adjudication by a body which satisfied all the requirements specified above for an Article 6(1) 'tribunal'. This conclusion is again clearly spelled out in the court's decision in *Case of Albert and Le Compte* (10 February 1983, paragraph 29 of the judgment of the majority). A further striking aspect of that judgment is the statement (in paragraph 30) that the Article 6(1) requirement of a 'fair' trial in relation to the determination of civil rights and obligations imports the specific rights expressly conferred in relation to criminal charges by Article 6(2) and (3)(a), (b), and (d), namely the presumption of innocence, the right to have prompt notice of the accusation and to have adequate time and facilities for the preparation of the defence, and the right to call witnesses and to cross-examine opposing witnesses. The full implications of the Human Rights Court's interpretation of Article 6(1) are still being worked out. The words 'the determination of his civil rights and obligations' are clearly capable of being extended to an ever-widening range of subject-matter. It seems that any professional or other body which controls the right to practise a profession or carry on a livelihood may be within the potential scope of this provision. Questions will arise as to what is meant by the concept of a tribunal 'established by law' and as to whether a tribunal is 'independent' if it is wholly or mainly composed of the professional peers of the defendant. The *Le Compte* case makes it plain that it is not possible to conjure up a 'tribunal' on (as it were) a mosaic basis, by tacking the publicity of the High Court and its full examination of legal questions on to the factual investigation and exercise of discretion by some inferior body. All the requirements must be satisfied in relation to one tribunal.

Article 5(4)

9.81. The second relevant article of the Convention is Article 5(4) which provides: 'Everyone who is deprived of his liberty by arrest or detention shall be entitled to take proceedings by which the lawfulness of his detention shall be decided speedily by a court and his release ordered if the detention is not lawful.' In *X. v. United Kingdom* (1981) 4 EHRR 188 the European Court of Human Rights held that the procedures open to a mental patient to challenge his continuing detention did not satisfy the requirements of the Convention. It held, in particular, that the limited scope of review by the High Court on a habeas corpus application did not provide an adequate opportunity for a challenge as to the facts or the reasoning underlying the order for detention (see at pp. 208–10 of the report). In the mental health field, account was taken of this decision by the enactment of Section 28(4) and the First Schedule of the Mental Health (Amendment) Act, 1982 (now consolidated in Mental Health Act, 1983) giving power to Mental Health Review Tribunals to direct the discharge, on proof of certain facts, of patients on whom a restriction order has been placed by the court. Formerly their role in this connection was limited to the giving of advice. It seems possible, however, that the court's interpretation of Article 5(4) could be of importance in other types of case where the lawfulness of a detention order is challenged.

9.82. An example may perhaps be provided by deportation cases of the class where the Home Secretary certifies pursuant to sections 13(5), 14(3), and 15(4) of the Immigration Act, 1971 that exclusion or deportation is 'conducive to the public good'. The statute excludes any right of appeal. In practice the alien is allowed a hearing before three advisers who may make a recommendation to the Home Secretary. There is no obligation on the advisers to particularize the charges against the alien, or to give reasons or to disclose their report. The alien has no right to legal representation though he may be helped by a friend (see Wade, *Administrative Law*, 5th edn., p. 207). These arrangements fall a long way short of a 'decision' by a

'court' as to the lawfulness of the detention (if Article 5(4) applies).
When the alien alleges that there was no material before the Home
Secretary on the basis of which he could have formed the view that
deportation was conducive to the public good, no procedure exists
for a proper judicial determination of this issue.

The Council on Tribunals

9.83. The Council on Tribunals submit annual reports to the Lord
Chancellor and to the Lord Advocate who must lay them before
Parliament with such comments as they think fit to attach (Tribunals
and Inquiries Act, 1971, section 4 and Transfer of Functions
(Secretary of State and Lord Advocate) Order, 1972, SI 1972/
2002). In these reports the Council have over the years offered a
great deal of sensible advice, made important recommendations,
and demonstrated their vigilance to ensure that tribunals are conducted in accordance with the spirit of Franks. The Council's
objective in this regard is well summarized in one of their recent
reports:

2.9 In short the procedure should make the tribunal easily accessible to the
public; it should be cheap, swift and free from technicality. The whole
proceedings should be, and be seen to be, independent and impartial, and
fair to the powerful and the professional, but also to the vulnerable (1985–6,
HC 42).

9.84. We have referred above (paragraph 4.13) to the Council's
Special Report on their functions (1980, Cmnd. 7805) and to the
Government's disappointing response that the case had not been
made out for any substantial widening of the council's powers or
functions on the lines proposed in the Special Report. The Government did accept that it would be desirable to restate in clearer and
more general terms the Council's right to be consulted about
procedural rules for tribunals and inquiries, and also accepted that it
might often be helpful and appropriate for departments to consult
the Council about draft primary legislation affecting matters within
their field. Despite this it appears that the Council have continued to
experience some difficulty in ensuring that they are consulted, or
consulted in reasonable time to enable them to make an adequate
response, about proposed rules for tribunals and inquiries, and
when relevant primary legislation is being considered. The Council
are, correctly, always concerned to secure in legislation the affected

citizen's right to a hearing and to an appeal, as well as the equal treatment of parties to tribunal proceedings.

9.85. Despite their justified disappointment at the Government's rebuff to their sensible and imaginative Special Report, the Council on Tribunals have quietly extended the scope of their work and, in the absence of wider statutory powers, have endeavoured to secure improvements by persuasion. It is obvious from reading their annual reports that the Council lack the resources that would enable them to carry out in full the functions contemplated by Franks. That is a loss for the tribunal system and those who use it, and we regret it. The annual cost of the Council is modest, as may be seen from that for the year ended March 1986 (Table 9.2). The further discussions on the question of resources and research which the Council state are now taking place (*Annual Report*, 1985–6, paragraph 3.80), are welcome. We admire the way in which the Council on Tribunals have striven to overcome their difficulties, and see them as a model for the Commission with wider responsibilities, and stronger resources, that we have discussed earlier.

TABLE 9.2 Cost of the Council on Tribunals

	Council on Tribunals	Scottish Committee
Accommodation, utilities, etc.	199,022	(not available)
Salaries:		
Staff	173,051	20,587
Chairmen and members	48,390	7,938
Administration (including travel)	42,089	5,703
TOTAL EXPENDITURE	£462,552	£34,228

(*Annual Report*, 1985–6, paragraph 6.10.)

CHAPTER 9. RECOMMENDATIONS

1. Appointments of members of tribunals should be for not less than three years.
2. All tribunals should be placed under the supervision of the Council on Tribunals (paragraph 9.16).
3. The Council on Tribunals should be given adequate resources to

perform the full research role that it ought to be carrying out (paragraphs 9.16 and 9.85).

4. Efforts should be made to ensure that whenever possible the premises of the respondent government department are not used for tribunal hearings (paragraph 9.18).

5. The Government should authorize and enable the Council to carry out a review of the procedures of all tribunals, which should include an examination and revision of the varying rules of individual tribunals (paragraphs 9.19 and 9.21).

6. As a general rule, tribunal hearings should be held in public (paragraph 9.20).

7. Current training schemes for tribunal members should be expanded in order to secure proper standards of investigation and adjudication (paragraph 9.22).

8. The importance of prompt hearings in Mental Health Review Tribunal cases should be impressed upon those responsible for making the practical arrangements (paragraph 9.24).

9. In any modification of the existing green form scheme for legal advice and assistance, it is essential that standards be maintained and confusion avoided during the transition to a new system. Economies should not be achieved at the expense of a good service (paragraphs 9.57–9 and 9.64).

10. Provision for tribunal representation (not confined to legal representation) should be made in accordance with the recommendations of the Lord Chancellor's Advisory Committee and other bodies. To deny all representation before tribunals is not a proper solution to the problem (paragraphs 9.60–1 and 9.65).

11. There is a need for regional legal services committees, which should be independent of the proposed Legal Aid Board. Their core staffing should be supported from central funds (paragraph 9.62).

12. The practical steps to provide access to assistance in tribunal cases summarized by the Lord Chancellor's Advisory Committee in their *36th Annual Report* should be taken (paragraph 9.63).

13. The existing character of the Lord Chancellor's Advisory Committee should not be altered significantly and their independence should be preserved (paragraph 9.66).

14. There should be a right of appeal on a point of law to the courts in tribunal cases (paragraph 9.69).

15. The Administrative Review Commission we have proposed (chapter 4) should undertake an inquiry into the extent of the problem of administrative decision-making from which there is no appeal on the merits (paragraph 9.78).

10

Inquiries

SUMMARY OF ARGUMENT. Though often referred to in the same breath as tribunals, inquiries have quite a different origin, purpose, and status and their development has been quite different. In the last forty years inquiries have been appropriated to the purposes of land-use control to such an extent that the planning inquiry has become the typical inquiry. We have, therefore, found it convenient to divide this chapter into a consideration of planning inquiries, involving some discussion of their background, on the one hand, and, for want of a better term, *ad hoc* inquiries on the other.

Although the planning inquiry became the dominant type forty years ago, its decline in the last twenty years has proceeded rapidly. Today, over 85 per cent of what was formerly allocated to the planning inquiry is dealt with either by means of written representations or by informal hearings. Deregulation has also reduced the scope for inquiries. Simultaneously with its decline the planning inquiry has undergone a continuous process of refinement, especially since the early 1970s. This has culminated in the coincidence of a report from the Environment Select Committee of the House of Commons and the reports of various departmental initiatives for the improvement of planning inquiries, usefully brought together in the Government's response to the Committee's report in a White Paper published in December 1986 (Cm. 43).

Though the volume of planning inquiries has very considerably diminished, they have continued to command much public attention. It is, in fact, the smallest category of planning inquiries, those which are concerned with major projects, that generates the greatest public controversy. The White Paper contains draft revisions of inquiries procedure rules and a Code of Practice on Preparing for Major Planning Inquiries (the fruit of seven years of departmental labour), which provide a high degree of elaboration for this numerically least significant type of inquiry. This is not a criticism. The 'spin-off' for the general body of planning, and other, inquiries, and for administrative processes in general, of this concentrated consideration is valuable.

We have fewer recommendations to make for the improvement of planning inquiries by reason of the work of the Environment Select Committee and of the concentrated departmental programme of review and action detailed in the Government's response to the Committee's report. Yet there remain some necessary improvements to which the Government continues heedless.

By contrast, the procedural development of *ad hoc* inquiries has been limited. Many are not regulated by rules at all. Such inquiries have not captured public attention to anything like the extent that have planning inquiries, and for this reason, as well as for the multivarious nature of the category, it is not easy to collect information about them. The category comprehends inquiries into accidents, administrative irregularities, child abuse, and rule-making. Such inquiries have the common feature that, unlike the majority of planning appeals, they are generally retrospective and tend to be more inquisitorial. They may, as Lord Salmon put it, 'take a fresh turn at any moment'. Because of this the requirements of natural justice are not always easily satisfied at such inquiries and there have been strong expressions of concern about this. We endorse the recommendations of the Marre Committee for a general code of practice for formal *ad hoc* inquiries and we support many of the recommendations of the Blom-Cooper panel that inquired into the death of Jasmine Beckford.

In this country, in contrast to the United States, the inquiry is little used in the process of rule-making. With the privatization of major utilities and services and the development of supervisory bodies, its usefulness for this purpose is worthy of consideration. The superficial resemblance of inquiries to judicial proceedings tends to encourage expectations of a judicial result that cannot be satisfied. To dispel dissatisfaction with the outcome the limitations of inquiries should be made clear at the outset of the proceedings.

Origins and purposes of inquiries

10.1. Inquiries require separate consideration for a number of reasons. Although often linked with tribunals, their historical origins and purpose are quite different. Tribunals had their origin in the need to adjudicate disputes, especially those between citizen and state arising from the welfare functions of Government, more efficiently and cheaply than was possible in the courts. They are, or should be, essentially judicial and most of them, properly regarded, are courts of a special character adjudicating against a background of legal precedent.

10.2. Classically, inquiries were limited to investigation, making no final decision but providing the material upon which a decision could be made by a government minister. Inquiries had their origin in this context, in the need to provide an alternative to Private Bill procedure under which objectors to proposals for the acquisition of powers by Government or public authorities had to appear before parliamentary committees. As the activities of central and local government increased, Parliament became a cumbersome, expensive, and inappropriate forum in which to deal with objections. More and more decision-making was delegated by Parliament to ministers of the Crown, and a public local inquiry became the substitute for a hearing before a parliamentary committee.

10.3. Although the public inquiry has some place in other common-law systems, for example in the Commonwealth and the United States, it has developed over the years in the United Kingdom in a unique way. Comparison with continental systems shows how advanced and sophisticated an institution the public inquiry in this country has become. (A useful comparison between the nature and purpose of the French and English public inquiries is made in *Public Inquiry and Enquête Publique*, Institute of European Environmental Policy, 1982.)

The right to be heard

10.4. One reason for the development of the public inquiry here has been the belief that a citizen has the right to be heard before an administrative decision is taken which may affect him. In France and other countries with administrative courts, as the Environment Select Committee of the House of Commons noted (1985–6, HC 181–I, paragraph 167), the emphasis is on providing compensation for infringement of rights rather than permitting proposed administrative action to be challenged. In this country, just as Parliament accorded the citizen affected by Private Bills the right to be heard, the courts found the same rule in the common law. In *Cooper* v. *Wandsworth Board of Works* (1863) 14 CB (NS) 180, a case now recognized as a landmark though neglected for many years, Byles J. expressed the vital principle as follows:

... a long course of decisions beginning with *Dr. Bentley's case*, and ending with some very recent cases, established that, although there are no positive words in a statute, requiring that the party shall be heard, yet the justice of the common law will supply the omission of the legislature.

That was a case of a demolition order for a house, an order made pursuant to a purely administrative discretion, and there are, of course, many modern decisions establishing that administrative decisions affecting the rights, interests, or legitimate expectations of individuals must be exercised according to natural justice, or as it is now said, 'fairly'.

Limits on scrutiny of administrative action

10.5. Although the courts established the individual's right to be heard, they also accepted that the administrator's decision could not be readily challenged. For instance in *Local Government Board* v. *Arlidge* [1915] AC 120 the House of Lords held that local inquiries were purely administrative and that consequently there was no need to show the report of an inquiry to the appellant, to offer reasons for the decision, or to disclose any extrinsic evidence taken into account by the decision-maker. More recently the largely unfettered discretion of the administrator (which was a feature of administration in the first half of this century) was greatly circumscribed by the simple requirement that reports of inquiries be published and that decisions of ministers be supported by reasons. Both were recommendations of the Franks Committee's Report on Administrative Tribunals and Enquiries 1957 (Cmnd. 218) and were given legal effect in the Tribunals and Inquiries Act, 1958. (Earlier attempts to achieve this by the Haldane Committee on the Machinery of Government in 1918 and by the Donoughmore Committee on Ministers' Powers in 1932 had failed. The Ministries of Transport and Education adopted two of the recommendations—advance notice of proposals and publication of reports—in the 1930s, but the Ministry of Health and its successors resisted the innovations until 1958.)

The Franks Committee

10.6. The Franks Committee in their report (paragraph 269) had this to say about the purpose of inquiries:

The intention of the legislature in providing for an enquiry or hearing in certain circumstances appears to have been twofold: to ensure that the interests of the citizens closely affected should be protected by the grant to them of a statutory right to be heard in support of their objections, and to ensure that thereby the Minister should be better informed about the facts of the case.

The duty of an administrator to inform himself properly before taking the decision has received judicial recognition. In *Secretary of State for Education* v. *Tameside BC* [1977] AC 1014, 1065, Lord Diplock said 'the question for the court is: did the Secretary of State ask himself the right question and take reasonable steps to acquaint himself with the relevant information to enable him to answer it correctly?'

Public Participation

10.7. A further function of the public inquiry has come to be recognized in recent years, that is, its role in facilitating public participation in the making of administrative decisions. Some impetus to participation in the making of town and country development plans was provided by the report of the Skeffington Committee, *People and Planning* (*Report of the Committee on Public Participation in Planning*), HMSO, 1969. Whatever the strict legal position may be, the accepted practice is to allow all interested parties to have their say at public inquiries. In planning inquiries, only the planning authority and the appellant have, at the moment, a legal right to be heard (Town and Country Planning Act, 1971, section 36(4)), though the Government proposes to extend this to third parties who notify the Secretary of State of their wish to appear at an inquiry and who provide a written statement of their submission (*Planning: Appeals, Call-in and Major Public Inquiries— The Government's Response to the Fifth Report from the Environment Committee, Session 1985–86*, Cm. 43 (henceforth referred to as '*The Government's Response*, Cm. 43'), paragraphs 27 and 28). In compulsory purchase orders, the class of statutory objector covers all those persons served with notice of the order. Each statutory inquiry has its own category of persons with the legal right to be heard. However, the discretion of the inspector presiding at the inquiry is so widely and generally exercised in all cases that third parties can almost invariably get their views put forward and publicized. So questions of standing rarely arise. The basis of present practice is contained in a report made by the Council on Tribunals in 1962 (Cmnd. 1787, paragraph 29).

Types of inquiry

10.8. Many statutes today provide for public local inquiries. Sometimes the power is merely discretionary, for example, under such legislation as the Education Act, 1979, the National Health Service Act, 1977, the Fire Services Act, 1947, the Social Security Act, 1980, the Mental Health Act, 1983, the Merchant Shipping Acts, 1970 and 1979, and the Child Care Act, 1980. These enabling powers are usually widely drawn. The statute commonly uses language such as 'The Minister may cause such inquiries to be held as he may deem necessary or desirable for the purposes of this Act'. Sometimes an inquiry is mandatory. Thus both parties to a town planning appeal (the authority and the developer) can require that an inquiry be held. Similarly an objector to a compulsory purchase order can require that his objection (unless related to compensation) be heard at a public inquiry. Where inquiries are discretionary there are usually no statutory rules of procedure, though there may be departmental guidance. Where an inquiry is mandatory there are almost invariably procedural rules designed to ensure that persons interested know in advance the case for the administration and are in a position to secure a fair hearing. Separate, though similar, sets of rules apply to the three statutory varieties of planning appeal: the Town and Country Planning (Inquiries Procedure) Rules 1974 (SI 1974/419), which apply where the decision is to be taken by the Secretary of State in cases other than enforcement appeals, and which are shortly to be revised; the Town and Country Planning (Determination by Appointed Persons) (Inquiries Procedure) Rules 1974 (SI 1974/420); and the Town and Country Planning (Enforcement) (Inquiries Procedure) Rules 1981 (SI 1981/1743). Very similar rules apply to inquiries into compulsory purchase orders, new trunk roads, and other projects under the Highway Act 1980, and inquiries under the Electricity Act, 1971.

10.9. There are nevertheless large areas of administration (often involving decisions of great importance and affecting many interests) in which it has not been the practice for a public inquiry to be held as a prelude to administrative action. Examples are hospital closures, the introduction of comprehensive schools, the award of television franchises, and the siting of nuclear missile bases. Similarly, the exercise of interventionist economic powers of the Government (such as the creation of special development areas) commonly takes place without any prior public inquiry.

10.10. Public inquiries can be classified in various ways. Some are concerned with prospective action; some are clearly retrospective, having the character of a post mortem. Sometimes an inquiry is both retrospective and prospective, as in the case of enforcement appeals where the purpose of the inquiry is both to acertain whether there has been a breach of planning control and to consider whether permission for the development in question should be given. Some inquiries (for example, planning) have an appellate nature. Others permit a citizen to object to proposed administrative action (such as the designation of the line of a new trunk road). Some inquiries (such as those into aircraft accidents) are investigatory. In practice, inquiries relating to the use of land so far outnumber all the others that the greater part of this chapter must be devoted to them. In the land-use category we include not only straightforward planning inquiries but also major inquiries as well. Inquiries into exceptional projects, such as nuclear power stations, raise further issues calling for consideration. The chapter concludes with some discussion of the wide-ranging group of *ad hoc* inquiries.

Land-use inquiries

10.11. The apparatus for the regulation of land use in the United Kingdom, of which planning inquiries form a part, affects interests of great concern to the parties involved whether as developers, objectors, or third parties. It has been described as 'a system of politically based decision making which operates within a series of constraints laid down by law' (*Urban Planning Law*, Malcolm Grant, 1982, p. 6). It deals with a very large number of cases annually. In 1984, in England alone, there were over 400,000 planning applications. Nearly 90 per cent of these were approved. In 4 per cent there were appeals against the refusal of planning permission: 35 per cent of these 16,000 appeals were successful. The framework of the system is largely provided by primary and subordinate legislation, but it is filled out, and some of its essentials are supplied, by administrative practice, by policy circulars, and by ministerial press statements. The essence of the system is the exercise of discretion informed by policy, rather than the application of law. The system employs the machinery of both central and local government, drawing on political and technical resources, and presents the most open form of our public administration. There is here a greater degree of supervision than is found in other areas of administration.

10.12. Apart from the internal surveillance of the Department of the Environment and, in particular, of the Planning Inspectorate, inquiries are subject to the supervision both of the Council on Tribunals, which is particularly concerned with procedural matters, and of the Parliamentary Commissioner for Administration, who is concerned with the preliminaries, the conduct, and the sequel of inquiries. The courts, by means of statutory appeals and applications for judicial review, supervise the legality of inquiries. Finally, since the Secretary of State is answerable for planning inquiries in Parliament, both Houses retain a direct interest in them. The annual reports of the Council on Tribunals leave no doubt that the Council is vigilant to ensure that the spirit of the Franks Report informs changes in development control practice, notably in the matter of draft inquiry rules.

10.13. The general planning system is less than forty years old. 'Primarily', observes Sir William Wade, 'it is a comprehensive and drastic licensing system under which any kind of new development of land requires permission, and the power to refuse permission, so that the legislative scheme contains a large element of expropriation without compensation...' (*Administrative Law*, 5th edn., 1982, p. 163). This does not infringe the European Convention on Human Rights, the provisions of which, according to the First Additional Protocol, do not 'in any way impair the right of the state to enforce such laws as it deems necessary to control the use of property in accordance with the general interest...' (see further paragraphs 11.44 and 11.45 below).

The right of appeal

10.14. Specific permission is required by law for all development, unless it is already authorized in some way (as to which see paragraph 10.31 below). Permission is obtained by means of an application made to the District Council, which is required at present (but see paragraph 10.32) to have regard to (*a*) the provisions of the structure plan prepared by the County Council and approved by the Secretary of State, (*b*) any local plan in force in the area, and (*c*) any other material considerations. Permission may also be granted as an outcome of enforcement proceedings (see paragraph 10.34).

10.15. The advantages of obtaining planning permission and, conversely, the economic consequences of refusal, are such that the law has for long recognized that if permission is refused by the democratically elected local planning authority, the applicant should be able to appeal against the refusal to the Secretary of State. The principle of an applicant's right of appeal against a local authority's refusal to grant permission was established in 1932 by section 10(5) of the Town and Country Planning Act of that year. That basic right has been extended considerably in later legislation and now rests on sections 36 and 37 of the Town and Country Planning Act, 1971. The Secretary of State is empowered to deal with the application as though it had been made to him in the first instance. He has a corresponding jurisdiction, under section 88 of the 1971 Act, in regard to appeals against enforcement notices requiring alleged breaches of planning control to be remedied.

10.16. The right of appeal confers upon the appellant the right to be heard by a person appointed by the Secretary of State. By long-established practice, now fortified by inquiry procedure rules, this right takes a forensic form with the parties simultaneously present and able to cross-examine one another's witnesses. This right was first provided in the Housing, Town Planning, etc. Act, 1909, but was little used during the ensuing thirty-eight years. When this right was reaffirmed in the Town and Country Planning Act of 1947 it could scarcely have been envisaged that in twenty years appeals would have risen to 16,000 or so per annum. At the end of November 1973 some 16,354 appeals were outstanding and the average period from receipt of an appeal to decision could be as much as sixty-five weeks. The intake of appeals in that year was the highest ever recorded, 18,300; the second highest was in 1985 when the intake was 17,053. It is evident that for many years the machinery for dealing with appeals has been overburdened. One reason for this is the conflict between central and local government policies. Central government has from the outset of the present planning regime emphasized the presumption in favour of development (Ministry of Town and Country Planning Circular 69/49, paragraph 5). At local government level, however, there is frequently pressure to restrict development. The Environment Select Committee of the House of Commons recently considered the success rate for appeals over the last decade and concluded: 'the figures . . . persuade us that there is a substantial mismatch between central and local planning objectives'. The rising success rate for planning appeals (by the first quarter of 1986 it had risen, in England, to 41 per cent) had encouraged more appeals (1985–6 HC 181–I, paragraph 83). The Government discounts any such simple causal link but agrees that clear expressions of national policy are needed to reduce uncertainty and the consequent scope for appeals (*The Government's Response*, Cm. 43, Part I, paragraphs 7 and 11).

10.17. The delays involved in appeals were, and still are, unacceptable. As early as 1958 the Ministry of Housing and Local Governemnt had already taken the view that the appeal procedures were likely to be brought into discredit by delays (Circular 9/58). One early major change was a move away from the public hearing of the inquiry as the method for dealing with appeals in favour of a written representation procedure. According to the Ministry 'the chief advantage is the saving of time and expense to both local planning authorities and to appellants' (Circular 32/65, paragraph 2). Since the late 1960s sustained attempts have been made to introduce greater efficiency and speed into the appeal machinery, and since the *Review of the Development Control System* by George Dobry QC in 1975 (HMSO; ISBN 0 11 750896 9), there have been numerous circulars and reports designed to streamline the system. Recently the pace has quickened under the impetus evident in the two White Papers, *Lifting the Burden* (July 1985, Cmnd. 9571) and *Building Businesses... not Barriers* (May 1986, Cmnd. 9794). 'As a result of detailed reviews, intensive efforts have been made in the last three years to identify changes in legislation, guidance and administrative practice with this end (to achieve speed of decision without sacrifice of quality) in view. This programme of work is not yet completed and a considerable number of changes are only now in process of implementation' (*The Government's Response*, Cm. 43, p. 2, paragraph 2). These efforts have included a number of commissioned studies, the reports of all of which have now been published, such as *The Implementation Of Planning Policies And The Role Of Development Plans*, September 1985, *The Appellant's Perceptions of the Planning Appeal System*, August 1985 (Working Paper No. 93), both the work of teams from the Oxford Polytechnic Department of Town Planning; *The Relationship between Development Plans, Development Control and Appeals*, February 1986, from the Department of Land Management, the University of Reading; and *The Process of Local Plan Adoption*, April 1985, from the Coventry (Lanchester) Polytechnic Department of Urban and Regional Planning. In a press statement (No. 413 of 14 August 1985) on the study of appellants' perceptions, Mr Neil Macfarlane, MP, the Parliamentary Under-Secretary, observed: 'The study team, by listening carefully to the opinions of those who actually use the appeal system, have cut through generalities to give us hard facts as a basis for action.' The Department itself undertook two reviews: (i) an efficiency scrutiny by a team led by Richard Wakeford, *Speeding Planning Appeals—A review of the handling of transferred written representation planning appeals* (dated October 1985 but not published until May 1986, ISBN 0 11 751858 1) and (ii) a management review reported on by Michael Ash, *Speeding Planning Appeals—The handling of inquiries planning appeals* (March 1987, ISBN 0 11 751901 4). Both of these contain a Departmental Action Plan showing the decisions taken in response to the proposals and the action needed to produce results.

10.18. A quite independent initiative was that of the Environment Select Committee of the House of Commons which early in 1986 began to take evidence on a number of separate but inter-related planning issues: the planning appeals system, call-in, deemed consent, third-party appeal and major public inquiries. The publication of the Committee's Fifth Report for the Session 1985–6, *Planning Appeals, Call-in and Major Public Inquiries* in July 1986 (1985–6 HC 181–I) provided the Government with an opportunity to state its position on a number of important issues concerning the planning system in its White Paper, *The Government's Response*, Cm. 43. The second volume of the Environment Committee's report (1985–6 HC 181–II) contains the evidence received by the Committee from many informed contributors. It is a valuable source of information on the subject. A draft circular of the Department of the Environment ('DoE') on the award of costs of appeals and other planning proceedings and of compulsory purchase inquiries was published in August 1986 and a consultation paper, *The Future of Development Plans* in September 1986. A joint departmental circular (DoE 18/86, Welsh Office ('WO') 54/86), published in December 1986, deals with more than its title, 'Planning Appeals decided by Written Representations', suggests (with sections devoted to 'The Conduct of All Planning Appeals in the Early Stages', 'Inquiry Appeals', and addresses for correspondence with local planning authorities). A later circular is to be published setting out changes to accelerate the processing of appeals where a public inquiry or an informal hearing is held. Revision of the procedure rules for various inquiries is intended.

10.19. As planning applications have to be decided against the background of policy as it appears in structure and local plans, there needs to be an opportunity for the public to make representations about those policies before they are adopted. In the case of structure plans, objections are ventilated not at an inquiry in the usual sense but at an Examination in Public (EIP). Local plans, however, do involve a local inquiry, although the plan-making authority has itself to decide what action to take on objections in the light of a report by a departmentally appointed inspector (see paragraph 10.25). This chapter next considers the appeal procedures including written representations, informal hearings, the system of Examination in Public, the local plan procedures, and enforcement inquiries.

Written representations

10.20. This alternative procedure to the traditional inquiry is a purely administrative mechanism that enables some appeals to be determined on the basis of written submissions in place of oral evidence and argument. Time-limits and the power to award costs have now been introduced by the Housing and Planning Act, 1986, amending the Town and Country Planning Act, 1971 (Schedule 8, paragraph 9 and Schedule 11, paragraph 9(1)). Appellants are encouraged by the Department to use the procedure, on grounds of economy and speed. Local planning authorities favour it because it makes fewer demands on their resources. This method of disposing of appeals is estimated to achieve a saving of nearly 50 per cent in the time taken to reach a decision (DoE Circular 18/86, WO 54/86, paragraph 12), though time will be lost if the parties do not observe the Department's strict timetabling—and the Department has no real means of ensuring that they do. The proportion of appeals dealt with by written representation has increased substantially during the last two decades. In 1963 the procedure was used in 36 per cent of all planning appeals; by 1972 the proportion had increased to 65 per cent and by 1985 it was about 85 per cent. The procedure is available for both Secretary of State appeals and those transferred to inspectors, but is not suitable for appeals where the facts are in issue.

Informal hearings

10.21. 'We are not impressed by the likely value of this procedure', observed the Council on Tribunals when the Department of the Environment, in a consultation paper in October 1980, first proposed to institute informal hearings on a trial basis in place of formal inquiries in some cases (Council on Tribunals, *Annual Report* 1979/80, paragraph 6.28). But, six years later, the Oxford Polytechnic survey reported that: 'users declared unequivocal support for the informal hearing ... The only reservations came from individuals who wanted the appeals system simplified and speeded up; they were wary of any new tier of procedure' (Working Paper No. 93, 1986, paragraph 8.7.1). Informal hearings, unlike written representations (which are a purely administrative procedure), are based on the same statutory right to be heard by a person appointed by the Secretary of State (the term 'inspector' is not used in planning legislation) that is the basis of the local planning inquiry (now section 36(4) of the Town and Country Planning Act, 1971).

They are not governed by statutory rules; instead they operate under a simple code of practice on which the Council of Tribunals has been consulted. The Chief Planning Inspector first referred to their use in his report for 1982 (paragraph 23). During that year some seventy hearings were held in simple appeals. The Department's approach was cautious; it conducted a critical examination of the first sixty hearings and concluded that 'careful selection remains vital'. But this type of informal hearing was nevertheless adopted as a regular procedure to be offered to parties in place of inquiries in cases which the Department considered to be appropriate. The *Chief Planning Inspector's Report for 1984* notes that:

> The informal hearing is now established as an effective way of dealing with the simpler appeals which nonetheless need to be dealt with orally. Nearly 300 were held during the year. Parties appreciate the relaxed atmosphere, the direct approach to the key issues and, as often happens, the opportunity to continue the discussion on the site. (Paragraph 37.)

The cost to the Department of informal hearings is about half that of public inquiries though rather more than that of written representations cases. No insurmountable difficulties have been found with the procedure. The median time to decision during the fifteen month period ended March 1986 was twenty-five weeks (*Chief Planning Inspector's Report . . . to March 1986*, paragraph 18).

10.22. Informal hearings are inappropriate where: (i) many members of the public are likely to wish to attend, or (ii) complicated matters of policy or substantial legal issues are involved, or (iii) there is a need to test opposing evidence by cross-examination. The initiative for proposing an informal hearing lies with the Secretary of State who, however, will only offer such a hearing where he considers it appropriate and if one or both of the parties have already expressed a desire for an inquiry. An informal hearing can only be held with the agreement of both parties who must also agree to abbreviated minimum periods for notice of the date of the hearing as compared with those for an inquiry (35 not 42 days) and for service of the planning authority's statement (21 not 28 days). The appellant must furnish a statement of the case he will present at the hearing not less than 21 days before the hearing. The Code of Practice stresses the importance of adhering to the prescribed time-table. At the hearing the arrangements are designed to eliminate or reduce the formalities of the typical local inquiry. A small committee room is preferred with a table round which the inspector and the parties sit. The inspector can at any time close the proceedings for a formal local inquiry to be arranged if the parties do not adhere to the timetable or fail to provide necessary information, or if the need for a more formal procedure becomes apparent. At the hearing the inspector, in the words of the Code, 'leads the discussion'; he begins by reviewing the case, outlining what he sees as the main issues, and indicating the matters on which he requires more information. The appellant, who may be represented, starts the discussion. Written material is not read out. The inspector asks questions himself or allows them on points calling for clarification or amplification. There is no right to cross-examine. The appellant may make final comments before the dicussion is closed. The inspector may adjourn the hearing to the site if it is more convenient to do so and no one is disadvantaged, if all parties at the hearing can attend at the site, and if there are no objections. No costs are awarded.

Examinations in Public

10.23. The replacement of the inquiry as part of the process of adopting structure, that is strategic, plans by examinations in public (EIP) was achieved by the Town and Country Planning (Amendment) Act, 1974 (section 3(1)), though the principal Act of 1971 had retained the public inquiry for this purpose. The *Report of the Committee of Inquiry into the Greater London Development Plan* (HMSO, 1973) supported the substitution on the grounds that without such a change it would be 'very difficult to avoid an entrenched defensive presentation of a structure plan over a long period against many objectors' (paragraph 2.16). As a means of reducing the length of proceedings the EIP has undoubtedly been successful. The inquiry into the Greater London Development Plan (1970–2) involved some 237 working days and 28,000 objections (of which 20,000 concerned transport). No EIP has taken longer than six weeks and structure plans have now been approved for most of England, Wales, and the whole of Scotland so that for the future EIPs will only be concerned with the review or alteration of structure plans—unless the Secretary of State exercises his discretionary power (under section 10(8) of the 1971 Act as amended by the Local Government, Planning and Land Act, 1980 (section 89 and Schedule 14, paragraph 5)) to dispense with them in particular cases.

10.24. The EIP is not an inquiry though it is subject to the supervision of the Council on Tribunals (Town and Country Planning Act, 1971, section 9(6) as amended). A price has been paid for its administrative advantages. The Secretary of State decides which, if any, of the aspects of a structure plan should be considered at an EIP. The character of the proceedings is a probing discussion focused on predetermined issues. Only those objectors to the structure plan who are invited by the Secretary of State are entitled to appear and put their point of view, but he is obliged to consider all objections made in accordance with the regulations (1971 Act as amended, section 9(3)(c)). The power to make regulations prescribing the procedure to be followed at EIPs (1971 Act, section 9(4)) has not been exercised. Instead there is a code of practice, the latest edition dating from 1984. The Secretary of State need give no reasons for rejecting the recommendations of the EIP panel and his decision may be based on matters not raised in the panel's report or at the EIP itself, though in the departmental guidance on the EIP there is an undertaking that normally such matters, if likely to influence the Secretary of State's decision, will be published and comments on them will be considered. The initia-tive at an EIP lies with the presiding panel rather than with the participants—who are not allowed to cross-examine one another.

Local plans

10.25. By contrast, the traditional inquiry has been retained for one aspect of the new style of development plans, namely the consideration of any objections that are not withdrawn to the local plans, which provide the details of forward planning (1971 Act, section 13(1)). The inquiry is conducted by an inspector appointed by the Secretary of State, but his report is addressed to the local planning authority which is not bound by his recommendations, but which must give reasons for its decision (Town and Country Planning, (Structure and Local Plans) Regulations, 1982 (SI 1982/555), regulation 29(1)). A recent survey of 76 authorities has shown that some 684 out of 767 recommendations made by inspectors (89 per cent) were accepted in full (*The Process of Local Plan Adoption*, G. Crispin, P. Fidler, and V. Nadin, Coventry (Lanchester) Polytechnic Department of Urban and Regional Planning, April 1985). The Secretary of State may call in the local plan at any time after its deposit for public inspection (1971 Act, section 12(2)). If there are objectors and the local planning authority have not held an inquiry, the Secretary of State must arrange one. No rules of procedure have been prescribed; the forensic pattern is invariably adopted.

10.26. The numbers of local plan inquiries started in the years 1980 to 1985 are as follows:

1980	24
1981	54
1982	82
1983	94
1984	93

In the fifteen months from January 1985 to March 1986 there were ninety-three local plan inquiries. Anxiety about delays in arranging inquiries at the end of 1984 led the Department to recruit a panel of twenty-six fee-paid inspectors to deal with local plans. Procedures have also been devised and adapted to meet new requirements; thus, at the request of local planning authorities, a team of three inspectors considered simultaneously six local plans where there were overlapping policies, issues, and objections (*Chief Planning Inspector's Annual Report for 1984*, paragraph 7). Another interesting innovation has allowed local plans and associated section 36 (refusal of planning permission) appeals to be considered, by agreement, at concurrent hearings. Here, the inspector's role as adviser to the local planning authority is combined with that of departmental reporter or determiner. In the course of a fourteen-day hearing at Barnstaple, two called-in planning applications, two listed building applications, five section 36 appeals, and 230 objections to the local plan were considered (*Chief Planning Inspector's Annual Report for 1983*, paragraph 10). Another team of three inspectors took the concurrent hearings of the Tyne and Wear Green Belt subject plan and associated local plans in Newcastle upon Tyne (3) and South Tyneside (2). The team approach was used also at Wakefield where there were three separate and not overlapping plans, but policies common to them all were considered at a special inquiry session (*Chief Planning Inspector's Report ... to March 1986*, paragraph 33). In this case there was an unsuccessful High Court challenge to the procedure.

New style development plans

10.27. A radical change in the nature of development plans in England and Wales has recently been initiated. This came about somewhat abruptly. In September 1984 a joint departmental circular (DoE 22/84, WO 43/84) gave a comprehensive and detailed description of the two-tier system based on structure and local plans in force since 1974; but a year later the change had begun with the enactment of the Local Government Act, 1985 and the publication of another circular, DoE 30/85. Some of the ideas associated with this change had been canvassed at least as early as the 8th Report from the Expenditure Committee of the House of Commons on planning procedures (1976–7, HC 395). The Committee expressed themselves 'concerned at the extent to which the hierarchy of plans is apparently not fulfilling its role in relation to development control'. They noted the use in Scotland of non-statutory policy statements prepared by the structure planning authority and the adoption there of local plans in advance of the approval of structure plans (paragraphs 83–5). The Committee called for structure plans in England and Wales that were flexible, frequently reviewed, and revised when necessary. This desirable state of affairs has not been achieved. The Expenditure Committee recommended a review of the system of plans then in use that would consider the extent to which in practice the plans were a realistic basis for development control and also possible alternatives to the existing system (paragraph 86). The consultation paper issued by the Department of the Environment and the Welsh Office in September 1986 conceded that the problems concerning structure plans (mainly slowness, length, complexity, and an awkward relationship with local plans) were as bad then as nine years earlier (paragraph 25). As many as two-thirds of the policies in some of the structure plans submitted for approval had required modification or deletion by the Secretary of State. The average time taken to approve a structure plan or a proposed alteration of it has, since 1981, been not less than twenty-eight months; from public participation to approval, the average time has been forty months (paragraph 18 and Table 1).

Unitary development plans

10.28. The object of the reform is to make the local plan the principal means of conveying authorized planning policies within a particular area; this is one of the ideas floated by the Expenditure Committee in 1977. From 1947 to 1974 local planning authorities, responsible for both the preparation of plans and for development control, were County Councils and County Borough Councils. The

Local Government Act, 1972, distributed responsibility for planning between two tiers of the newly reorganized local government and modified plan-producing responsibilities accordingly. The new County Councils became responsible for the preparation of structure plans, and for certifying the conformity of local plans to them, and for dealing with planning applications in certain 'county' matters. The new District Councils were responsible for local plans and for the greater part of development control. In Greater London somewhat different arrangements had already been introduced by the London Government Act, 1963, and the Town and Country (Local Planning Authorities in Greater London) Regulations, 1965. The abolition of two-tier planning authorities in the metropolitan areas called for some reorganization of the system for producing development plans. The Local Government Act, 1985, and the Housing and Planning Act, 1986, provide for a new type of development plan in those areas, though neither regulations for the procedures for the preparation of such plans nor any commencement orders for the statutes have yet been made. Once such an order is made the local planning authority will be required to prepare a unitary development plan, which is intended to provide a clear and concise statement of policies and proposals for development and conservation in the geographical areas concerned. Existing structure plans, local plans, and any surviving old style development plans in the area will be superseded by the single plan combining the principal features of the two-tier plans and providing a reasoned justification for both the general and the detailed policies it contains. A key element of the unitary development plan will be the strategic guidance given by the Secretary of State to assist in its preparation. This guidance will be composed after consultation with the relevant authorities and, in provisional form, will be offered for discussion and comment by interested parties (DoE Circular 30/85, Annex 5). The Secretary of State's approval is not required for a unitary development plan, but he may call in a draft plan, in whole or in part, for his approval. He may also direct the planning authority to modify the plan. If the Secretary of State has not intervened in one of these ways, and if any objections to the plan from the public have been considered, either with or without a public inquiry, the local authority may adopt it by resolution of their Council. The authority are to be required to give 'adequate publicity' in their area to the proposed contents of the unitary development plan, but the extent and time of any consultation on the proposed contents is at their discretion. The draft plan is to be deposited with the Secretary of State; objections and representations may then be made within a period of six weeks from the time of deposit. The local planning authority are required to arrange a public local inquiry or other hearing for the purpose of considering objections (unless all objectors indicate in writing that they do not wish to appear). For the alteration or replacement of a unitary development plan, however, authorities may use a shortened procedure which telescopes the publicity/consultation and the deposit/objection stages.

District development plans

10.29. The consultation paper of September 1986 proposes the adaptation of the unitary development plan to the non-metropolitan areas of England and Wales. A separate consultation paper for Scotland contains much more limited proposals which do not involve the abolition of structure plans. County planning authorities, instead of producing structure plans, would in future prepare county policy statements—the equivalent of the Secretary of State's guidance for unitary development plans—by setting out in broad terms strategic policies on matters specified by the Secretary of State (paragraphs 46–8). The status of these county statements would be no more than that of guidance. A procedure similar to that for the adoption of structure plans is proposed but it would be the county planning authority, not the Secretary of State, that would decide whether to hold an examination in public and to which the EIP panel would report. The Secretary of State would retain power to call in the proposed statement, to require its modification, and to direct its adoption as modified by him (paragraph 78).

10.30. Under the present system, as the consultation paper points out, development control has relied to a considerable extent on informal sources of policy, such as non-statutory plans, supplementary planning guidance, and the 'established practice' of officials (paragraph 32). The House of Lords has condemned the practice and has held that proposals in a local plan must disclose fully the planning authority's intentions and that matters of policy must not be excluded from the structure plan and included instead in non-statutory guidelines: *Westminster City Council* v. *Great Portland Estates Plc* [1985] AC 661. Under the proposed regime the District development plan would be expected to contain all the land-use policies for the locality, save possibly for mineral plans (paragraph 60), and thus would become the dominant mandatory instrument for land-use planning in the particular area. A new definition of 'rural conservation area' is also proposed to replace 'the existing array' of non-statutory definitions, and in these areas planning applications would be considered against the criteria set out in the county policy statement (paragraph 52 and Annex D 3).

10.31. The procedure proposed for the origination, consideration, and adoption of the District development plan would, with small changes, be similar to that which exists for local plans. One stated objective of the proposals, however, is the involvement of the public at the formative stage of the District plan (paragraph 82), though this is somewhat weakened by the intention that: 'It would be for local authorities to decide whether and how they involved the public at this stage' (paragraph 83). A consultation paper would be prepared by the authority and informal arrangements made for the public to comment on it and, presumably, to offer alternative proposals. The authority would then prepare a draft District plan and deposit it with the Secretary of State. Observations and recommendations could be made during a period of six weeks from the date of deposit, as in the case of unitary development plans. If any of these remained unresolved, a public local inquiry would be held. The inspector would, as now, report to the local authority, but it is suggested that he might be given power to consider all aspects of the plan and not only those objected to (paragraph 90). His report would be made public at the time it was submitted to the authority.

10.32. *The Chief Planning Inspector's Report . . . to March 1986* points out (paragraph 54) that, according to recent research conducted by the Department of Land Management and Development at the University of Reading (*The Relationship between Development Plans, Development Control, and Appeals*, 1986), development plans rarely contain policies relating to the minor developments that make up the bulk of planning appeals, and so most successful planning appeals do not conflict with approved or adopted local policies: '. . . no less than a third of the appeal decision letters [examined in the course of the study] contained no reference to policy of any kind, statutory or non-statutory, national or local, written or unwritten. They were determined purely on the facts of the case, the arguments put forward and the inspector's judgment' (p. 53 and Table 6.1). Even where there is conflict it is for the authority to demonstrate that the adopted policies remain relevant to current needs and conditions (Circular DoE14/85, WO 38/85). 'Indeed', observes the Reading University report, 'in 41% of the appeals in which a policy was mentioned, it was not regarded as a determining factor by the inspector' (ibid.). The Expenditure Committee noted that:

We were also told that in some parts of the country the greater part of the land released for residential development was made available only as the result of an appeal, and it may be assumed that in most cases the land had not been allocated for this use in the development plan. (1976–7, HC 395–I, paragraph 77; HC 395–II, p. 142.)

The Reading University report emphasizes the loose nature of the relationship between development plans and development control:

It has allowed planning to be policy-led where it matters, especially over the strategic issues of the allocation of land for development and the conservation of resources whether in the countryside or in the cherished built environment. Yet at the same time it has permitted flexibility in the interpretation and application of policy where that is warranted, and indeed enables control to be exercised even in the absence of policy.

The relationship works precisely because of the way in which it permits the balance between policy and control, between the market economy and the public interest, between restraining and encouraging development, to be made in the circumstances of the locality and the individual proposal, yet with the safeguard through the appeals system of exercising the national interest. (p. 87.)

However, the same report notes that without the policy guidance provided by the development plan, or contained in non-statutory forms, development control becomes arbitrary, inefficient, and unaccountable:

In the absence of policy, acting as a filter, the appeal case load would surely increase and would involve rehearsing each time in lengthy detail all the arguments that might be relevant or material in the circumstances of the particular appeal and which are now in the development plan. (p. 88.)

10.33. The declared intention of the Department's proposals is that 'the plans should provide a comprehensive but simple and intelligible statement of policies to guide prospective developers and others concerned with development and conservation' (DoE consultation paper, paragraph 59). This is unexceptionable, but the successful combination of comprehensiveness and simplicity is not always easily accomplished. There is a danger that the price paid for it will be excessive rigidity. If it is to be realized the plans should, as the Expenditure Committee advocated, be flexible, frequently reviewed, and revised when necessary, and the process of producing them should accordingly be simple and swift, open and accessible to the public. The local inquiry has an important part to play in this process. We support the proposal that the inspector conducting the District development plan inquiry should be able to comment on the plan as a whole, rather than only on those aspects of it to which objection has been raised. The same should apply in the case of unitary development plan inquiries. We wish to emphasize, however, that the occurrence of public participation at the formative stage of plan-making should not, if the system is to be just, be seen as a reason for depriving applicants for planning permission and participants at site specific inquiries of the ability to question the policy of the District development plan; and section 29(1) of the 1971 Act should be operated accordingly.

Avoidance of the necessity for inquiries

10.34. Into this category fall (i) extensions of automatic planning permission, such as the enlargement of the General Development Order and the rationaliztion of the Use Classes Order; (ii) blanket permission areas such as Enterprise Zones and Simplified Planning Zones (SPZs); (iii) the use of special development orders; and (iv) a more indulgent operation of development control.

Deregulation philosophy

10.35. The trend towards the more automatic grant of planning consent is largely the consequence of a change in the attitude of Government towards planning. The White Paper, *Lifting the Burden*, the joint departmental circular DoE, 14/85 WO 38/85, and the Housing and Planning Act, 1986, represent the most significant shift of strategy in this area since the White Paper, *Town and Country Planning* (1967, Cmnd. 3333) and the legislation of 1968. The Government considers that the pre-existing system imposed an unnecessary degree of regulation on firms and individuals and so thwarted enterprise. The presumption in favour of development is underlined, as is the burden on planning authorities to show that development refused permission would cause demonstrable harm to interests of acknowledged importance. Development plans are devalued; they are not to be regarded as overriding other material considerations. Circular 14/85 ends with a reminder of the sanction of costs for unnecessary appeals. The Government's strategy also includes greater indulgence in the application of planning control such as moderation in the imposition of conditions and negotiation over infringements to avoid enforcement proceedings— which in 1985 accounted for about 20 per cent of the time of inspectors (*Chief Planning Inspector's Report . . . for March 1986*, paragraph 5). In its most recent White Paper, the Government emphasized that 'the appeal process should not be used unless it is absolutely necessary: it is an instrument of last resort'. (*The Government's Response*, Cm. 43, paragraph 14.)

Improving the appeal machinery

10.36. This change of direction in planning policy may serve to reduce the occasion for inquiries, but the White Paper also lays emphasis on the need to improve the appeal machinery. Simplification, speed, and efficiency are the Government's watchwords. Among the first fruits of this preoccupation are the departmental reports of an efficiency scrutiny of the handling of appeals by the written representation method and of a management review of the handling of planning appeal inquiries mentioned above (paragraph 11.17). The action plans of these two reports, each with the title 'Speeding Planning Appeals', consist of a summary followed by detailed tables indicating the extent to which the Government accepts the recommendations of the reports and the action required to implement them. In the case of written representations the objective is to reduce, without loss of quality, the median handling time, over a period of three years, from twenty to eleven weeks. This is to be achieved by the adoption of several clearly outlined procedural and organizational changes.

10.37. In the case of planning appeal inquiries the main weaknesses identified by the Ash Report are: (i) the time needed to fix inquiry dates, and (ii) the failure of parties to exchange material sufficiently in advance of the inquiry, which frequently leads to last-minute cancellation and postponement of inquiries. The Government's objective is to reduce the median handling time for such appeals, which constitute 15 per cent of the annual total, from thirty to seventeen weeks. This is to be done by:

(*a*) streamlining the procedural stages,
(*b*) revising the inquiries procedure rules, and
(*c*) securing the energetic co-operation of the parties in improving the operation of the inquiry system and, in particular, encouraging improved communication between authorities and appellants in the pre-inquiry stage to identify issues, attempt to agree facts, and, if possible, negotiate agreement without proceeding to appeal.

The revision of the procedure rules for inquiries into the limited category of call-in applications and appeals reserved for the Secretary of State's decision is programmed for mid-1987 (*Chief Planning Inspector's Report . . . to March 1986*, pp. 38 and 39). A target timetable for each appeal will be rigorously applied. Additional resources of staff and finance are to be committed. More salaried, contract, and part-time inspectors are being recruited and administrative staff are to be increased. The additional financial commitment will be principally for investment in information technology. We welcome these measures, but we sound a note of caution. The quest for improved efficiency in the despatch of business should not be at the expense of the quality of the final decision.

Enforcement appeal inquiries

10.38. Enforcement appeal inquiries combine the functions of determining (i) whether there has been a breach of development control, and (ii) if so, and notwithstanding the fact, whether planning permission for the particular development should be granted. The Secretary of State has power to vary an enforcement notice. The statutory basis for enforcement appeals is section 88 of the Town and Country Planning Act, 1971, and there are separate regulations for the inquiry procedure which, however, is little different from that of other planning inquiries. In section 88 appeals, no less than in other types, the Government strongly favours the resolution of differences, where possible, by negotiation rather than proceedings. A planning authority's responsibility in law is only to issue an enforcement notice if they consider it expedient to do so (Town and Country Planning Act, 1971, section 87). The joint departmental circular DoE 22/80, WO 40/80 advises local planning authorities to take enforcement action (and only they can) only where planning reasons clearly warrant it and the authority consider that there is no suitable alternative to proceedings—'an enforcement notice should only be used as a last resort' (paragraph 15). This advice is reaffirmed in the joint circular DoE 20/85, WO 49/85, paragraph 6. Moreover, the authorities are required, in their response to an appeal against the notice, to state whether, and if so on what terms, they would be prepared to grant planning permission (Town and Country (Enforcement Notices and Appeals) Regulations 1981 (SI 1981/1742), regulation 6). They may also withdraw an enforcement notice (without prejudice to their power to issue another) at any time before it takes effect (Town and Country Planning Act, 1971, section 87(1) as amended). The report of a study commissioned by the Scottish Development Department, *The Enforcement of Planning Control in Scotland* (J. Rowan-Robinson, E. Young, and I. McLarty), 1984, found that enforcement notices were issued in respect of only 17 per cent of alleged breaches of planning control (584/101, p. 24). The *Chief Planning Inspector's Report ... to March 1986* notes (paragraph 26) that the guidance of DoE Circular 22/80, WO 40/80, is being followed. The comment of the DoE Audit Inspectorate is more revealing:

Virtually all authorities adopt a passive enforcement role, partly on grounds of cost and having regard also to the advice of the DoE not to enforce, unless an unauthorized development is really objectionable. Generally therefore they tend to respond to complaints from members of the public, although a number use their building inspectors to monitor the implementation of conditions to specific consents. It is common practice for the bulk of this work to be dealt with by a small separate team of junior officers without formal planning qualifications. (*Local Planning: The Development Control Function*, 1983, HMSO (ISBN 0 11 751979 0), p. 16.)

Despite this 20 per cent of the time of English salaried staff (that is, full-time) inspectors (and only they take enforement appeals) is spent on work arising from enforcement appeals (*Chief Planning Inspector's Report ... to March 1986*, paragraph 26).

10.39. Once an enforcement notice has been issued an appeal against it must be lodged with the Secretary of State before it takes effect (which cannot be in less than twenty-eight days after its issue). The joint departmental circular DoE 20/85, WO 49/85, stresses that: 'It is vital that all intending applicants are made aware of this absolute time-limit, which the Secretary of State has no discretion to vary, for making a valid appeal' (paragraph 3). The written representation procedure is available for enforcement appeals (DoE Circular 38/81, WO 57/81). Section 88 inquiries differ from other planning inquiries in two particular respects: (i) the evidence is usually taken on oath, and (ii) it is for the appellant to establish his grounds of appeal. An application for planning permission is, however, deemed to have been made whenever an appeal is brought against an enforcement notice (Town and Country Planning Act, 1971, section 88(7)) and there the presumption in favour of development applies.

10.40. In 1985 some 4,847 enforcement appeals were lodged in England (22 per cent of all planning appeals brought) compared with 17,053 appeals against the refusal of planning permission. This was an increase of 19 per cent over the previous year. Of these appeals, 2,029 were withdrawn, turned away, dismissed, or allowed on the grounds of the respondent authority's failure to comply with the regulations governing the proceedings. In the same year 2,433 appeals went for determination, of which 95 per cent were taken by inspectors, with the following results:

enforcement notices upheld,   727 (29 per cent)
enforcement notice quashed,   961 (42 per cent)
enforcement notice varied,   745 (29 per cent)

(*Chief Planning Inspector's Report . . . to March 1986*, paragraph 25 and Appendix A. Tables A 2.1 and A 2.2). In approximately one-third of these cases the alleged breach was not contested and the issue was simply whether the planning permission should be granted. In the remaining two-thirds the local planning authority's allegations were disputed (ibid., paragraph 28). The issues in such appeals are often complex and call for both an up-to-date grasp of court-case law, which has become somewhat technical, and a familiarity with planning policy. No figures are published of the number of enforcement appeals dealt with respectively by inquiry and by written representations, but because disputes of fact commonly occur in enforcement proceedings there tend to be more hearings in section 88 than in section 36 (planning permission) appeals.

A standing Enforcement Tribunal?

10.41. A suggestion that enforcement inquiries should be replaced by a three-man standing Enforcement Tribunal, nominated at regional level and with a legally qualified chairman, has been made by Professor Jeffrey Jowell and Mr Denzil Millichap ('The

Enforcement of Planning Law: A Report and Some Proposals' [1986] JPL 482). Their argument is that legal skills are particularly important in the area of enforcement, which is 'fraught with technical problems', and that the visible independence of such a tribunal, as against that of the departmental staff inspector, would be enhanced. In their view adjudication of development is more appropriate to a tribunal than to a functionary. They suggest also the abolition of the power to grant planning permission as an outcome of enforcement proceedings. The proposal for three-man planning tribunals was considered by the Government in 1967 in the White Paper, *Town and Country Planning* (Cmnd. 3333, paragraph 35). It was rejected on the grounds that it would be difficult to achieve consistency, and to find the necessary staff. We see the force of the objections of principle to the present arrangements for inquiries into enforcement issues. It is also true that few inspectors have any legal training; the report commissioned by the Scottish Development Department, *The Enforcement of Planning in Scotland*, 1984, found that in Scotland legal issues figured in one-third of enforcement appeals (p. 103), and it seems reasonable to suppose that the proportion is not much different in England and Wales. We have noted, however, that the dissatisfaction with the enforcement process focuses on the laxity of local planning authorities in initiating proceedings rather than on the inquiry as a means of dealing with appeals. The existing institution is well established, integrated into the whole system and generally understood. The issue seems to us to be finely balanced. We recommend that the proposal be examined by the Department when convenient to see if the practical difficulties of satisfying the objections raised by Professor Jowell and Mr Millichap could be overcome without excessive disruption.

The altered position of the inspector

10.42. Much of the improvement in the handling of planning proceedings has thus been due to the self-examination by the Department of the Environment, the Scottish Development Department, and the Welsh Office. However, the improvements in speed of decision and the use of written representations would have been difficult to achieve if the role of the inspector had not undergone a significant change from that of reporting and recommending to that of decision-taking. In 1972, 60.7 per cent of appeals were transferred for decision to planning inspectors, and those retained for decision by the minister were the more important ones. By 1982 the proportion of transferred cases had risen to 93.6 per cent. With this transfer to inspectors for decision of this preponderance of appeals, the inspector has become a visible decision-maker. The position today is very different from that which obtained in 1968 when the inspector's report was advisory and was considered by the decision branch of the then Ministry of Housing and Local Government, which was responsible for the actual decision taken. The isolation of the inspector inevitably tends to reduce the consistency of determinations. This has more significance now that the weightier appeals are determined by inspectors. No adverse consequences of this have yet become apparent but it will not be surprising if inspectors find themselves in a more controversial position than formerly. The quickly written decision letter has replaced the carefully composed report of the inquiry. Simultaneously, the decision letter has acquired greater authority, and availability, as a precedent. Copies of decision letters are available from the inspectorate, the Secretary of State issues press releases on important cases, reports of significant planning decisions are carried in several publications, and in 1986 a new quarterly periodical devoted to their publication was launched. The most obvious effect of transferring the bulk of decisions in planning appeals to inspectors, as the Council on Tribunals has pointed out, has been to convert the inquiry into a tribunal hearing (*Annual Report*, 1979/80, HC 246, paragraph 6.41). There are examples of tribunals with a single judge, but more frequently a tribunal has two or more members. We appreciate that an inspector's decision letter is scrutinized by the support group at the Planning Inspectorate. We also understand that the great majority of appeals involve relatively small issues, however important to the appellant, for example extensions to a dwellinghouse or other applications classed by the Department as minor dwellings. Nevertheless, we think the time has come to re-examine a concept introduced and accepted, almost without argument, as an obvious means of dealing with delays which were becoming intolerable. We think that it is significant that nearly 20 per cent of those in the Oxford Polytechnic Study (Working Paper No. 93) whose cases had been dealt with at inquiry had a negative opinion of the inspector (paragraph 8.4.1) though the majority thought the inspector was fair, thorough, and helpful. This report was commissioned by the Department to find out the views of 'occasional' appellants, the one-time or infrequent appellant or agent, who accounted for about 70 per cent of the current list of appellants.

10.43. The areas we would like to see examined are these:

1. Out of 300 inspectors 80 have local government or public service backgrounds. We think that the independence of the inspectorate would be more apparent and more substantive if it were more broadly recruited.

2. In the more complex cases involving an inquiry, we suggest that two inspectors should hear the case, one being a full-time inspector and the other appointed from a panel of persons with relevant knowledge and experience outside the public service. We believe there are many people in the private sector who would be willing to make a contribution, limited in time, in the way we suggest. This would also meet the objection voiced in the previous paragraph as to the public service background of the inspectorate. If the two inspectors were unable to agree the case would be referred for decision to the Secretary of State.

3. There should, in our opinion, be regular and continuous training for the inspectorate. In the Oxford Polytechnic study (Working Paper No. 93), 55 per cent of appellants were dissatisfied with the explanation given for the decision (paragraph 7.6.1) and we think that this percentage is too high (in 95 per cent of cases the complaints came from those who had lost their appeals). As planning becomes more pragmatic it is vital that special efforts are made to ensure that there is consistency of decision. Longer induction and regular in-service training should help to secure this. We are, of course, aware that newly appointed inspectors are closely guided and supervised for their first two years, but the training we suggest is more than this, and would require resources that are not available to the Planning Inspectorate at present. It is also noteworthy that 55 per cent of those consulted in the Oxford Polytechnic study thought that the inspector's decision was founded on unsound policy.

Written representation cases

10.44. We are perplexed by the fact that only about 38 per cent of written representation appeals are successful as against about 52 per cent for those that go to inquiry. *The Government's Response*, Cm. 43, points out that there is a relatively low appeal success rate (28 per cent in 1985) for 'minor residential development' appeals;

90 per cent of such appeals are handled by the written representation procedure (paragraph 10). It may be that because the written representation procedure offers a cheaper and quicker option appellants are readier to fight weak cases. But the Oxford Polytechnic study (Working Paper No. 93, paragraph 7.2) does not support such a simplistic view. We think it may be that people without professional agents find it difficult to set out their case in writing, though the study found that some certainly prefer to do so than to present it orally (paragraph 7.2.2). The Department prefers unaccompanied site visits because they are administratively easier to arrange and arranges such visits wherever a site can be seen from the public highway. The result of this policy is that many appellants never meet the person who will be the judge of their case (about 40 per cent of site visits are unaccompanied). For his part the inspector must decide on what he reads and sees on the site visit. Even where an accompanied site visit takes place (because an appellant requests it or entry on private land is unavoidable) the inspector is not allowed to discuss the case presented, although the parties may point out features on the site. The Oxford Polytechnic study shows clearly that appellants like to be present during site visits (paragraph 7.5.2) and want to meet the inspector at some stage (paragraph 7.7.1). 'It was really the hour with the Inspector that showed that justice was being done' remarked one appellant interviewed. There were also suggestions that some controlled discussion should be allowed, as it is not at present, on the site (paragraph 7.5.2).

10.45. The Environment Committee recommended that the appellant, the local authority, and any directly affected third party should be invited to accompany the inspector on a site visit made as part of a written representation appeal (1985–6 HC 181–I, paragraph 97). However, as the Chief Planning Inspector pointed out when giving evidence to the Environment Committee, 'Once you start discussions you would have to allow interested persons there and an open air hearing would be difficult to organise' (1985–6 HC 181–II, Q 862). Other reasons for the departmental reluctance to allow discussion on site included the greater difficulty of arranging accompanied visits (already mentioned, involving an extra two weeks' delay), the greater burden on the planning authority of having to send a case officer rather than a junior representative to the site, the need for procedural rules to set limits to the extent to which oral submissions could be made, and the practical difficulty of note-taking on site (*The Government's Response*, Cm. 43, paragraphs 40 and 41).

10.46. The Oxford Polytechnic study found that over 70 per cent of those who conducted their appeals by written representation were content with the procedure; 93 per cent of those who were not content had lost their appeal. Most of the unrepresented appellants consulted had read the DoE booklet, *Planning Appeals, A Guide* and so had been exposed to the department's advocacy of the written representation procedure (paragraphs 1.13, 2.7, and 2.8). The booklet states clearly enough that a written representations appeal is decided on the basis of written evidence and that no discussion of the merits may take place on a site visit (paragraph 2.5). Nevertheless, in view of the hard evidence of consumer preference for some contact with the inspector, we feel that unaccompanied site visits should be the exception.

10.47. The DoE booklet can leave the reader in no doubt that the Department prefers the written representations procedure to inquiries. The point that the procedure is much more common is repeated in almost identical words three times (paragraphs 1.13, 2.5, and 2.7). Also stressed are its cheapness (paragraphs 2.4 and 2.7) and its swiftness (paragraphs 1.13 and 2.7). 'We would urge you', exhorts the booklet, 'to consider the written method very seriously and opt for an inquiry only if you are sure it is essential' (paragraph 2.8). Thus far the Department's anxiety to steer appellants into the written representations channel does not carry it beyond acceptable bounds. It seems to us, however, that at one point the Department has allowed itself to be carried away: 'The outcome of your appeal will depend only on the planning merits, and not on the choice of procedure' (paragraph 2.7). This dangerous generalization crumbles in the face of the 30 per cent higher success rate for inquiry appeals as compared with those dealt with by written representations. In view of the obvious risk that appellants may be misled by it to their detriment, we recommend the deletion of this sentence from the booklet.

10.48. We think it proper and timely to adopt procedures designed to ensure speed of decision in planning appeals, but we are concerned about the danger of going too far in that direction and so jeopardizing the fairness or quality of the system. We also consider that attention should be paid to how more can be done for the appellant who lacks professional assistance. Both considerations loom prominently in the area of written representations.

Informal hearings

10.49. A French view of the English public inquiry is that 'the atmosphere and proceedings could appear daunting to lay members of the public' (*Public Inquiry and Enquête Publique*, 1982). A less awe-inspiring venue than a Council chamber and greater informality of the proceedings, with the inspector acting as chairman of a round-table discussion, make informal hearings very suitable for cases of moderate complexity especially where appellants are not employing an agent. Of the appellants with whom the inspectorate are dealing, 70 per cent are involved in their first ever appeal and the adversarial and judicial atmosphere of the public inquiry may well intimidate the inexperienced. The Oxford Polytechnic study found that informal hearings gave parties an opportunity of achieving a compromise and were satisfying to the parties because they could participate in the discussion. All appellants who responded to a questionnaire 'thought that their case has been adequately presented and thoroughly examined at the hearing' (Working Paper No. 93, paragraphs 8.7.2 and 8.7.4). The study team thought that there was much to be said for increased use of informal hearings relative to the alternatives of local inquiry and written representation (paragraph 8.7.4). The Ash Report of the review of the handling of inquiry planning appeals recommends greater use of the cheaper (and popular) informal hearing procedure. But the Department of the Environment 'when pressed ... admitted that they have deliberately not sought to encourage people to transfer from written representations to informal hearings' (Fifth Report from the Environment Committee, 1985–6 HC 181–I, paragraph 99). The *Chief Planning Inspector's Report ... to March 1986* observes that the informal hearing

is a popular and efficient alternative to a formal local inquiry and an informal hearing will be offered in lieu of an inquiry wherever possible ... The criteria have been reviewed to enable the procedure to be offered in an extended range of cases. It is, however, not proposed to offer informal hearings as an alternative to the written representation procedure because it is not so cost effective in terms of inspector resources. (Paragraph 18.)

More explicitly *The Government's Response* to the Environment Committee notes: 'Inspectors can decide three written representation cases for every two cases decided by informal hearing' (Cm. 43, paragraph 43). The Environment Committee itself considered that informal hearings offered benefits lacking in both the more formal public inquiry and the somewhat remote written representation procedure. The Committee were 'convinced that the benefit of informal hearings are such that they should be available to those who require them' and recommended that an appellant should be able to opt for an informal hearing appeal (1985–6 HC 181–I, paragraph 100).

10.50. Informal hearings are thus emerging as a second alternative to the inquiry albeit in an at present limited number of cases. The question arises whether the Government is right to deny appellants a choice between written representations and informal hearings. We understand the attraction for the Government of the former method and recognize that there are some cases for which the latter is unsuitable, such as those where extensive development is proposed or third-party interests will be substantially affected or the appeal is against an enforcement notice. We realize also that the burden on the inspector is greater in these cases, and that that may be be a limiting factor, though it should become less so if our recommendations as to recruitment and training of the inspectorate can be implemented. We recommend that there should be a presumption in favour of the appellant's choice of procedure and that reasons for denying it should always be given. Furthermore, the informal hearing procedure and its advantages should be fully described in the DoE booklet, *Planning Appeals—A Guide*.

The public local inquiry—the verdict

10.51. Despite the criticisms that can be made of the public local inquiry in the field of land use, the refinements and improvements over the past three decades seem to have made it an effective instrument of administration which is also, by and large, regarded by participants as fair and satisfactory, even if its formality is inhibiting for non-professionals. The 'coal-face' experience gained by the Inspectorate over many years has been distilled as a statement of good practice which, for the first time, has been reproduced in the *Chief Planning Inspector's Report . . . to March 1986*. It contains much practical advice for the effective and expeditious conduct of inquiries, and it should be made available to the main parties at all inquiries.

10.52. Appellants may challenge the conduct and the conclusions of planning inquiries in the High Court by means either of the statutory appeals procedures, on a point of law, or,with leave, of judicial review. The only means of challenge available to third parties is, again with leave, judicial review. Challenges to the inspector's performance by the statutory procedures are rare and by judicial review even rarer. The court adopts a benevolent construction of inspectors' decisions and assumes, for example, that departmental policy statements which have not been specifically referred to have been taken into account unless the contrary is clearly established: *Hatfield Construction Ltd* v. *Secretary of State for the Environment* [1983] JPL 605. An inspector's decision must be supported by adequate evidence, though the weight to be attached to that evidence is a matter for him: *Banks Horticultural Products Ltd* v. *Secretary of State for the Environment* [1980] JPL 33. There must be adequate, proper, clear, and intelligible reasons for the inspector's decision, which must deal with the substance of the submissions made to him: *Re Poyser and Mill's Arbitration* [1964] 2 QB 467, 478, per Megaw J. Departures from a ministerial policy statement must be supported by a clear explanation of the reasons in order that the recipient of the decision may know why the decision is being made as an exception to the policy and the grounds upon which the decision is taken: *Gransden and Co. Ltd and Falkbridge Ltd* v. *Secretary of State for the Environment and Gillingham B.C.* [1986] JPL 519, per Woolf J. In 1981 there was a jump of 100 per cent over the previous year in legal challenges to inspectors' decisions in section 36 appeals, which caused some perplexity and consternation in the Inspectorate (*Chief Planning Inspector's Annual Report 1981*, paragraph 13). In the three years to the end of March 1986 the rate of High Court challenges to inspector's decisions in England was about 0.6 per cent of decision letters issued. The *Chief Planning Inspector's Report ... to March 1986* notes that in four years to the end of December 1984 only 91 decisions were quashed in the High Court out of a total of 46,215— in percentage terms some 0.2 per cent, or 1 in 500 letters (paragraph 60). However, in considering these statistics the cost of High Court proceedings should not be overlooked. The success rate for High Court challenge to inspectors' decisions in enforcement appeals is somewhat higher, 0.86 per cent for the three years to the end of December 1985.

10.53. Delay in reaching a decision has remained a common, and we think, justified, criticism, but the inquiry is only part of a long process which starts with the consideration of applications by the local planning authorities, too many of which are not blameless in the matter of speed of decision-taking at first instance, or in their handling of appeals. Another critical factor is, obviously, the ratio of work-load to resources. The Chief Planning Inspector's letter to the Secretaries of State presenting her report to March 1986 shows that the implementation of proposals for improvement may take longer than was initially expected. It refers to 'lost ground', accounted for by teething problems in organizational changes, and to the 'seemingly inexorable increase in appeals received' (*Report*, p. 3). This growth in appeals appears to have resulted from an increase in the proportion of planning applications refused by local authorities and to a significant increase in the proportion of appeals against refusal (paragraph 13). The consequence has been a continuing rise in the number of cases in hand, that is, the arrears. The time taken in England to determine appeals transferred to inspectors deteriorated from twenty-eight weeks in 1984 to thirty-two weeks in 1985 and thirty-three in the first quarter of 1986. On the other hand the median time taken to complete written representation appeals improved from twenty-five to twenty weeks, and by the first quarter of 1986 had fallen to eighteen weeks. The picture in Wales is similar.

10.54. To be commended is the Government's sense of purpose evident in the various publications mentioned earlier and especially in *The Government's Response* (Cm. 43) to the Environment Committee, which covers virtually the whole range of planning inquiries. If we have had less to recommend in this area than elsewhere it is largely because many of the necessary changes have now been put in hand. We particularly welcome the Government's assertion of its firm commitment to securing clarity and precision in two vital respects: (i) the expression of national policy on planning issues, and (ii) the framing of reasons for refusal of planning permission or the imposition of conditions (Cm. 43, paragraphs 11 and 15). The main criticism of public inquiries relates to major inquiries or those for exceptional projects. These also are the subject of special consideration in the White Paper, Cm. 43. Before discussing them we should also comment on suggestions made by the respondents to our Discussion Paper.

Suggestions made to the Committee

(a) Ordinary planning appeals should be decided by the county planning authority rather than by the inspector

10.55. What underlies this suggestion is the constitutional objection that, under the present system, the decision of the elected members who comprise the local planning authority may be overturned by an inspector—who may be a civil servant. Hence, we have been urged to recommend that the inspector should submit a report, not as previously to the Secretary of State (and as he still does in about 5 per cent of cases), but to the county planning authority which has responsibility for the structure plan. We prefer the present system. The inspector is an impartial adjudicator and the Secretary of State is sufficiently distanced from local political pressures.

(b) Comment by the parties on the inspector's findings of fact

10.56. In Scotland the parties to a planning appeal are given the opportunity to comment within fourteen days on the provisional findings of fact of the reporter (the equivalent of the inspector) before the decision is issued. The Franks Committee recommended the adoption of a similar procedure in England and Wales (*Report*, paragraph 345) and it is followed by some departments, such as the Department of Education, in connection with compulsory purchase orders. The argument against it is the delay and the additional scope for controversy involved. We think that the Scottish procedure should be tried out experimentally in England and Wales, but with strict time-limits, with a view to assessing whether it should be adopted generally.

(c) Costs

10.57. The general rule of civil litigation in the United Kingdom that costs follow the event does not obtain in the case of planning inquiries. We considered whether it should, for there is in such proceedings no less of a contest between differing interests than in court proceedings. In the end we reached the conclusion that to introduce the costs-follow-the-event rule at planning inquiries would alter the whole character of the system. Both the Environment Committee (1985–6 HC 181–I, paragrah 50) and *The Government's Response*, Cm. 43 (paragraph 46) reached the same conclusion. The award of costs at statutory inquiries was comprehensively considered by the Council on Tribunals in 1964 after receiving evidence on the subject.[1] The Government accepted that costs should be awarded to successful objectors to compulsory purchase and analogous orders; but not to unsuccessful ones.[2] The distinction is often illogical but the problem of discriminating fairly between deserving and undeserving unsuccessful objectors, which influenced the Government's decision, is a real one. In planning appeals the present rule is that costs are not awarded to successful appellants though they may be awarded *against* a party in cases of unreasonable behaviour.

10.58. The Environment Committee made detailed proposals for the award of costs (1985–6 HC 181–I, paragraphs 53–60) and also recommended that the Secretary of State should publish a new comprehensive circular giving detailed guidance as to the types of case where he would anticipate that costs would be awarded. The Secretary of State promptly complied by issuing, in August 1986, a draft circular, 'The Award of Costs of Appeals and Other Planning Proceedings and of Compulsory Purchase Order Inquiries'. The majority of its proposals are in line with those of the Committee. But the Secretary of State has rejected the Environment Committee's idea of a scale of costs/penalties to be laid down (subject to periodic indexation) for breaches of various procedural requirements (1985–6 HC 181–I, paragraph 58). In our view he was right to do so.

10.59. The Secretary of State's policy to award costs against a planning authority that refuses planning permission unreasonably, and against an appellant who pursues an appeal that has no prospect of success, also seems right to us. The draft circular usefully provides illustrations of cases where it is appropriate to award costs and guidance on the making of applications for them. The Secretary of State's policy is that applications for costs should be made at the inquiry and that he will refuse, save in exceptional cases, to entertain applications made after the close of proceedings. Since 1985 inspectors have adopted the practice of advising parties that if they wish to apply for costs they should do so at the inquiry, and this seems to

[1] Report of the Council on Tribunals on the award of costs at statutory inquiries. Cmnd. 2471.

[2] MHLG Circular 73/65. Costs against the respondent will usually be ordered after an inquiry into orders or proposals submitted for confirmation or approval of the following kinds: (i) compulsory acquisition of land; (ii) Clearance Orders; (iii) Unfitness Orders; (iv) proposals to designate land as subject to compulsory purchase; (v) orders revoking or modifying a planning permission; (vi) orders requiring the discontinuance of use or the alteration of removal of buildings or works.

have accounted for an increase in applications from 1 in 8 to 1 in 5 (*Chief Planning Inspector's Report* ... *to March 1986*, paragraph 76). However, some updating will now be needed of the references to costs in the most recent edition (1984) of the DoE booklet, *Planning Appeals—A Guide*, to take account of both the new policy and the power to award costs in written representation cases under the Housing and Planning Act, 1986.

10.60. We also endorse the JUSTICE proposal to the Environment Committee that a provision similar to that contained in section 53 of the Administration of Justice Act, 1985, be adopted to enable the reimbursement of the parties' costs out of public funds where, through no fault of any of the parties, costs are thrown away in relation to inquiries, as where a decision is quashed in the High Court or where the inspector is taken ill, or dies, after the hearing but before report (1985–6 HC 181–II, p. 411).

(*d*) Statutory appeals

10.61. It has been suggested to us that the existence of a statutory right of appeal exercisable within six weeks of the determination of a planning appeal alongside the possibility of an application for judicial review, which may be made within three months, is a confusing duplication of remedies. We for our part, however, would be reluctant to see the abolition of statutory appeals as of right, which are of very long standing.

(*e*) Appeals against the grant of planning permission

10.62. In this country there is no appeal, as there is in several Australian states, against the grant of planning permission. Persons who claim to have suffered an injustice by the grant of planning permission can complain to the Local Ombudsman if they are in a position to allege maladministration. It is possible for the grant of planning permission to be revoked, but in practice this is a remote possibility because compensation is involved. An objector to the grant of planning permission can also apply for judicial review of the decision by demonstrating that there was illegality, impropriety, or unreasonableness. He would first have to satisfy the *locus standi* requirement (which we have discussed in chapter 8 above) and obtain leave to make the application. He would also have to finance the application and incur the risk of having to pay costs. The power of the Secretary of State to call in an application for decision by him provides some safeguard for the interests of objectors to development, though his 'general approach is ... not to interfere with the jurisdiction of the local planning authority unless it is necessary to do so and to require reference to him only where matters of more than local importance are raised by the application' (*The Government's Response*, Cm. 43, paragraph 50).

10.63. The Environment Committee of the House of Commons in their report, *Green Belt and Land for Housing* (1983–4 HC 275–I) recommended a right of appeal for third parties against planning permission granted in the Green Belt. A number of witnesses urged the Committee, when it was considering the planning system, to recommend a similar right of appeal against the grant of planning permission anywhere. But the Committee, on reflection, came to the conclusion that in their Green Belt report they had used the term 'right of appeal' too loosely. What they proposed in their Planning report (1985–6 HC 181–I, paragraph 130) was that there should be a separate right of third parties to require the Secretary of State to call in an application where a local authority does not propose to refuse it in cases where the proposed development would harm an interest of acknowledged importance, or where it relates to a site in which the authority own an interest, or where the applicant has offered, if planning permission is granted, to provide 'some financial or other non-planning advantage going beyond criteria established in the DoE circular on Planning Gain' (22/83) (1985–6 HC 181–I, paragraph 130). The Government considered it to be as inappropriate to give third parties a right to require call-in as it would be to give them a right to appeal (*The Government's Response*, Cm. 43, paragraph 52). We agree. The disadvantages of introducing rights of appeal or of call-in for third parties against the grant of planning permission seem to us to outweigh any possible advantages and the practical difficulties of doing so are formidable.

Major Inquiries

10.64. The great majority of public inquiries into planning matters are completed very quickly. Of the 3,000 inquiries in 1984, 76 per cent were over in one day; 95 per cent lasted for less than five days. Only 1 per cent took as long a sixteen days or more. It is in relation to this 1 per cent, or rather to a few well-publicized cases within this group, that there has been concern over the years. Several bodies with practical knowledge of inquiries into major projects have made suggestions for improvement, including the Council for the Protection of Rural England (Submission to the House of Lords Select Committee on Procedure, September 1976), the Town and Country Planning Association (Policy Statement, 'Energy Policy and Public Inquiries', February 1978) and the Sieghart Working Party (*The Big Public Inquiry*, June 1979). A Secretary of State himself tentatively proposed a procedure for handling major inquiries in a speech at Manchester ('Peter Shore on Major Planning Inquiries', DoE Press Notice 488, 13 September 1978), remarkable for its strong rejection of the Planning Inquiry Commission introduced by statute only ten years earlier but never used. Most of the proposals aimed to provide better opportunities for public discussion of need and the consideration of alternative sites, as well as the detailed siting and design of the project. A feature of all the proposals has been the elaboration of pre-inquiry procedures.

10.65. The recognition that the ordinary inquiry procedure was insufficiently refined or comprehensive to provide all that was necessary for the proper consideration of major issues led the Department of the Environment in 1980 to embark upon the preparation of a Code of Practice for such inquiries. In June 1984 a draft of this was released as a consultation document. A revised draft appears as Annex 2 to Appendix II of *The Government's Response*, Cm. 43 with the title 'Proposals for Revision', and comments were again invited on this. Paragraph 11 of Appendix II points out that there are limitations to what can appropriately be done by means of statutory procedure rules. It proposes the issue of the Code as a non-statutory form of guidance on the pre-inquiry stages of all major inquiries where the Secretary of State has ordered a pre-inquiry meeting and in other cases to the extent considered appropriate by the Planning Inspectorate and the main parties. It would be available to all parties proposing to appear at such inquiries. The purpose of the Code is succinctly described in the Environment Committee's 5th Report: 'The Code recognises the value frequently emphasised in evidence of thrashing out, so far as possible, ideas and facts in advance in an informal way and of clearly establishing what it is that actually needs to be subjected to the adversarial public inquiry process' (1985–6 HC 181–I, paragraph 183).

10.66. Major inquiries are defined in the 1986 version of the draft Code, rather more fully than in the 1984 version, as inquiries into development proposals 'of major public interest because of [their] national or regional implications, or the extent or complexity of the environmental, safety, technical or scientific issues involved and where for these reasons there are a number of third parties involved as well as the applicant and the local planning authority'. They often involve development by a public authority or agency and their hearings usually extend to at least eighty days.

10.67. The Department's Code is less ambitious than some of the proposals made by independent organizations. In essence it constitutes an elaboration of the ordinary public local inquiry procedure based on a number of experiments during the five years preceding 1981 and the formalization of procedures such as pre-inquiry preparations that have been found useful. The Code is now more closely linked than in earlier drafts to the inquiries procedure rules which it is proposed to revise. For the present the intention is to apply its full provisions only to those major cases to which rule 5 of the proposed revision of the Town and Country Planning (Inquiries Procedure) Rules (the draft of which is in Annex 1 of Appendix II of Cm. 43) applies. These are cases of such significance that the Department will provide the inspector with the support of a secretariat (Cm. 43, paragraph 30). However, *The Government's Response* suggests that elements of the Code might usefully be applied to other cases where appropriate and seems to contemplate that this would be only with the agreement of the main parties (Cm. 43, paragraph 30 and Appendix II, paragraph 11). The initiative for proposing such 'partial use' of the Code to the main parties at an inquiry would lie with the Planning Inspectorate.

10.68. The 1986 draft takes as its legal basis the provisions of the proposed revised inquiries procedure rules so far as applicable. It makes detailed provision for:

(*a*) the public announcement of the application of the Code and an invitation to participate;
(*b*) the registration of intending participants;
(*c*) the preliminary notification of inquiry arrangements;
(*d*) the request for outline statements of case;
(*e*) arrangements for the pre-inquiry and programme meetings;
(*f*) any informal meetings needed;
(*g*) written statements of the parties' and major participants' cases;
(*h*) statements of evidence; and

(*i*) the introduction of new evidence, any consequent adjourn-
ments, and costs.

A feature of the 1984 draft that is omitted from that of 1986 was a
provision that the inspector would bring to the attention of the Chief
Planning Inspector any requests that he considered had merit for
information, studies, and research that were beyond the resources of
the participants proposing them and that were unlikely to be
supplied by other participants. The Chief Inspector would consider
whether it was feasible to obtain the material and whether it would
be justifiable to do so at public expense. This measure was intended
to meet the needs of those of limited means who wished to participate in the inquiry, and also to serve as an offset to the additional
burdens imposed by the Code of Practice. We regret its omission
from the 1986 draft and hope that it will reappear in the final
version. The substance of the matter can possibly be covered by
paragraph 20(b) of the Code now proposed ('identification of any
material required by the Inspector . . . and consideration of how this
is to be provided'). But a specific reference to the needs of participants whose resources are limited would, we believe, serve a useful
purpose.

10.69. The Department's draft Code of Practice for the Preliminary Stages of Major Inquiries seems to us to offer sensible proposals. We welcome the fact that its provisions are, to a considerable
extent, already applied and we recommend that it be introduced as a
standard for big inquiries as soon as possible. We understand the
arguments for not giving the Code legislative force at the present
time, but suggest that the question of doing so might usefully be
reconsidered after adequate experience of its operation and effectiveness has been gained. Vigilance will be needed to ensure that the
procedures for major inquiries do not invade the lesser planning
inquiries and so make a simple but effective system more complicated than is necessary.

Counsel to the inquiry

10.70. The burden of major inquiries, which are still essentially
adversarial, on the interested individual or group is heavy and, as
legal aid is not available, it may prove prohibitive. Various solutions
to the problem of supporting useful interventions have been canvassed, some of which are discussed below. A possible part-solution
is for the appointment of counsel to the inquiry to be made standard

practice for major planning inquiries as it is for inquiries under the Tribunals of Inquiry (Evidence) Act, 1921, and for most accident inquiries. Counsel to the inquiry would then provide a channel through which interested parties could present their points. The Environment Committee referred to the usefulness of counsel to the inquiry but in a somewhat subsidiary way (1985–6 HC 181–I, paragraph 186). According to *The Government's Response* the Government has not ruled out the possibility of making further appointments of this kind in appropriate cases, but considers that the effect of such appointments may be to lengthen the proceedings (Cm. 43, paragraph 61). We do not doubt that, but it is hardly the point. If the quality of the proceedings is improved, as we have no doubt it is, by the appointment of counsel to the inquiry, that is a decisive consideration. Such appointments should be the rule rather than the exception.

Financial support for third parties at major public inquiries

10.71. The larger an inquiry the more apparent is the disparity of resources—the 'inequality of arms'—between the developers (often the Government) on the one hand and unofficial objectors on the other. The Environment Committee recommended that the Government should devise a scheme for financial assistance for third parties (1985–6 HC 181–I, paragraphs 193 and 194). The Government has rejected this for the following reasons:

   (*a*) the additional burden imposed on third parties (objectors) by the requirements of the Code will be outweighed by the reduction in length of inquiries that will result from the more efficient handling of business it promotes;

   (*b*) the lack of financial support for objectors encourages groups making similar submissions to combine (thus also reducing the length of inquiries and the burden on objectors);

   (*c*) most objectors participate in public inquiries to defend their own interests. It is quite proper for them to do so but that is no reason to finance them out of public funds;

   (*d*) there is no obvious way of identifying those objectors who appear out of purely altruistic motives in the public interest;

   (*e*) if the Government were to support some objectors and not others it would lay itself open to accusations of bias and manipulation;

   (*f*) support for third parties from public funds would do nothing

to improve the efficiency of public inquiries and would tend
to make them longer; and

(g) the local planning authority and other publicly financed
bodies already defend the public interest at inquiries.

(Cm. 43, paragraphs 63, 64 and 65.)

10.72. Whilst some of the reasons savour of complacency, it has
to be recognized that the difficulties of supporting third parties at
inquiries from public funds are formidable. Though the idea of doing
so has been current for at least a quarter of a century no one has yet
devised a wholly workable scheme. We do not pretend to have done
so and simply record that we are persuaded of three points of
principle: (i) it is important that the evidence at inquiries be rigorously tested; (ii) it is equally important that unofficial participants
should be able to present evidence; and (iii) it is wrong that the
public should enjoy the benefit of this participation entirely at the
expense of private persons. We consider that the Government too
lightly dismisses the obligation of society to third parties at inquiries.
The real problem is how to achieve the desired objective without
unacceptable public expense or discrimination. This involves three
questions: (a) who selects? (b) what criteria for selection should be
adopted? (c) how much aid should be provided?

10.73. As to the first point, it seems desirable that a decision on
funding of third parties should be made by someone who can
appreciate the significance of the particular objector's proposed
intervention. This argues for giving to the inquiry itself the responsibility of disbursing publicly provided funds to third parties at major
inquiries, and this is what the Sieghart Working Party proposed (*The
Big Public Inquiry*, 1979). If counsel to the inquiry is appointed,
then we think that the inspector, advised by counsel to the inquiry, is
best able to decide who should be funded within limits laid down in
advance by the Government for the inquiry. Anyone denied assistance should have a right of appeal to the Secretary of State responsible for the inquiry.

10.74. As to the second point, the legal aid test of reasonable
grounds and reasonable prospects is not quite the right approach.
The Town and Country Planning Association proposes the test of
'relevance', which seems nearer to what is required, so long as the
discretion is exercised, in borderline cases, in the objector's favour.
The third point, the extent of inquiry aid for a particular inquiry,

would largely be a matter of negotiation and judgment on the part of the disbursing agency. As a test of commitment and seriousness of purpose the pound for pound approach to disbursement of public funds, suitably modified, seems to us the right answer.

Disruption at inquiries

10.75. Public dissatisfaction with the limitations of major inquiries has received much attention in the press, notably in the case of highway inquiries. Four attempts in the last ten years to hold an inquiry into highway proposals for Archway Road, North London, were disrupted by rowdy behaviour and the decision to hold an inquiry was in the end abandoned. The Council on Tribunals has recommended (*Annual Report*, 1983/84, HC 42, paragraph 4.5) that the criminal law be extended to cover misconduct such as disruption of the inquiry and harassment of the inspector. A feature that has contributed to this disruptive behavior seems to have been the sense that a ritualistic inquiry was being used to 'legitimate' decisions already taken and to some extent measures have now been taken to satisfy this disquiet. The inquiry may also have been seen as a focal point for protest. We share the concern of the Council on Tribunals. Those who disrupt inquiries prevent the legitimate expression of views by interested parties. Harassment of the inspector is intolerable. While we consider that the existing common-law remedies are in general sufficient, we welcome the proposal to give the inspector explicit powers under the inquiries procedure rules to exclude from inquiries those who indulge in disorderly behaviour (*The Government's Response*, Cm. 43, Appendix II, Annex 1, paragraph 14).

The question of need

10.76. One of the principal issues at major inquiries is the question of need and national policy. In highway inquiries, for example, the necessity for the new road and its route are likely to be live issues but they are also matters of settled policy. The question 'Is the policy right?' is understandably asked by those whose interests are affected. The Franks Committee considered this matter and reached the following conclusion:

We recognise that broad policy is something for which a Minister is answerable to Parliament alone and we have no wish to suggest that these statements of policy should be automatically open to debate in the restricted forum of an enquiry. The Minister should be free, when issuing a statement of policy, to direct in writing that the whole or certain parts of it are not open to discussion at the enquiry, though it would obviously be unfair if the statement, and in particular the part excluded from discussion, were so framed that the objectors were unable to put their case. This power would avoid useless discussion of policy in the wrong forum, but the manner of its exercise would itself be open to criticism in the right forum—Parliament. (Cmnd. 218, paragraph 288.)

But, as Sir William Wade has pointed out, 'The line between general policy and its local application may not be easy to draw, and it is often the underlying policy which objectors wish to attack' (*Administrative Law*, 5th edn., 1982, p. 850). A recent illustration of this occurred in *Bushell* v. *Secretary of State for the Environment* [1981] AC 75 where objectors wished to dispute the need for a motorway. In conformity with the strict Franks view (paragraph 288) the Secretary of State announced before the inquiry that the policy of building motorways would not be open to discussion though the proposed lines would. The inspector allowed evidence to be given by objectors on the issues of need but denied them the opportunity of cross-examining departmental witnesses on the method of computing general traffic flow predictions—which were, in fact, superseded soon afterwards. The House of Lords held that the technique of traffic prediction was a matter of general policy and so not within the proper scope of the inquiry into a particular route as prescribed by the Secretary of State.

10.77. In practice, and notwithstanding *Bushell*, discussion of need is commonly allowed today at highway inquiries. The Council on Tribunals has for some years been pressing that the discussion of both need and government policy should formally be permitted at highway and other inquiries, subject to the discretionary exclusion of discussion or cross-examination on the grounds that these were repetitive, irrelevant, or obstructive, and that this should be incorporated in the inquiries procedure rules. A concession in this direction announced in the White Paper, is that the inspector at an inquiry at which a departmental witness gives evidence will not be required to disallow a question addressed to that witness which is directed to the merits of government policy if the witness is prepared to answer it (*The Government's Response*, Cm. 43, Appendix II, paragraph 18(iii)).

10.78. The Standing Advisory Committee on Highways under the chairmanship of Sir George Leitch has provided a means of ventilating anxiety and objection to policies and proposals lying outside the scope of highway inquiries and namely seems to have done much to reduce the desire to turn such inquiries into a debate on national policies. But it should, in our view, always remain open to a person whose interests will be affected by a highway proposal to challenge the technical considerations that underlie an adopted policy. This, in fact, now seems to be accepted in practice.

10.79. For many years the Department was most reluctant to concede the opportunity to discuss need at major inquiries. It does appear that there has now been a substantial abandonment of that position. Indeed the Government has expressed the view, albeit in somewhat vague terms, that discussion of policy at a public inquiry is not only permissible but desirable:

Over the last 20 years, both local residents and pressure groups claiming to represent the general public have increasingly demanded the right to express a view on the policy assumptions underlying a major development proposal, particularly in the public sector, as well as on the local effects of the proposal. . . . in certain other countries, objectors have resorted to direct action against projects. We must do everything possible to prevent this from becoming the normal form of protest against a major and controversial project. The Government considers therefore that adequate provision must be made for this kind of public debate to take place, in one forum or another. (*The Government's Response*, Cm. 43, paragraph 55.)

Conclusion—major inquiries

10.80. If inquiries can be improved by the appointment of counsel to the inquiry; if there is some degree of public funding for third parties; if there is reasonable scope to discuss 'need', then we think that the new procedures in the Code of Practice of the Department of the Environment should go a long way to ensuring that inquiries into major projects are a good instrument for allowing the public to have their say and for informing the government minister who will take or recommend a decision.

The exceptional project

10.81. Until recently none of the official publications on inquiries contemplated a category of exceptional inquiries. Yet it can scarcely be denied that such a category exists. In most years there will be in progress one major inquiry concerning a project which for one reason or another must be treated as exceptional. The Government is now considering whether any additional measures are needed to accelerate decisions in appeals which take up to twelve months or more to decide (*The Government's Response*, Cm. 43, paragraph 23). Thus a category of exceptional inquiries is officially recognized. But the test is not only size and complexity of issue. There are other factors which lift a particular inquiry into a different class of major inquiry. Most major inquiries are about matters of major local or regional importance. Occasionally, however, a local or regional issue will assume such importance that the inquiry will have to be treated as exceptional. The Archway Inquiry (see paragraph 10.75 above) was on the face of it an inquiry into a local road. Yet it became the vehicle of protest for all those who felt that the inquiry process was a charade and that a full and fair investigation of any highway proposal was not possible under existing rules. Mr Peter Palumbo's scheme to demolish listed buildings near the Mansion House in the City of London and to replace them with an office tower and plaza became a battlefield for the champions of modern architecture on the one hand and conservationists on the other, even though the real issue was whether the proposal complied with local planning policies. The inquiry into the Okehampton Bypass can be considered to be in the exceptional project class. In itself it was a local issue as to whether a route for a bypass south of the town, as promoted by the Department of Transport, was to be approved. However, as land of special status was involved (the Dartmoor National Park), the Order required confirmation under special parliamentary procedure, which in turn meant a hearing before a joint committee of both Houses. The Joint Committee eventually settled in favour of the northern route round Okehampton avoiding the National Park. The Government, nevertheless, persuaded both Houses to vote for its own preferred route to the south, which had been supported by the inspector at the local inquiry. The Vale of Belvoir Coalfield inquiry was on the face of it a local or regional issue as to the effect of the three proposed pitheads on the environment of the area. However, the National Coal Board was soon challenged on the national need for coal, in particular the Belvoir coal, so that a local issue quickly became a national one.

10.82. It is very often the question of national need which transforms a major inquiry into one of the exceptional class. The inquiry in 1977 into nuclear reprocessing at Windscale and the recent inquiry into the Sizewell 'B' Pressurized Water Reactor Power Station clearly raised matters of national policy. Indeed at Sizewell only a relatively small part of the lengthy proceedings were concerned with the effects upon the local environment of the scheme. The debate was about national nuclear policy.

10.83. There is no doubt that some nationalized industries are irked by the great length and expense of inquiries into projects of national importance. Mrs Thatcher's second administration too was prepared to take action in controversial cases without the sort of inquiry which many people regard as desirable. The first example was Mr Heseltine's decision to promote a special development order to secure an acceptable office development scheme on the Arunbridge site south of the Thames at Vauxhall Bridge. By this procedure, the Secretary of State could cut out the local authority who seemed to him unwilling to see the site developed. No inquiry was held into the proposal, the architectural competition which followed it or the winning scheme. Ironically, the site remains vacant as the winning developer went out of business.

10.84. More recently the Enterprise Zone legislation (Local Government and Planning Act, 1980) has opened the door to development without the need to make an application for express consent—consent is granted, subject to certain limitations, in the Act itself. There is accordingly no possibility of any antecedent public inquiry. A very controversial case was the approval of about 10 million square feet of new offices at Canary Wharf in the designated Enterprise Zone of London Docklands. The Secretary of State for the Environment refused to hold a public inquiry into the proposal because no planning application was needed within the Enterprise Zone. The Canary Wharf scheme is also interesting because the essential link from the City to the Isle of Dogs could only be built if London Regional Transport were to succeed in the promotion of a Private Bill. But discussion of the rail link route and its feasibility are not a substitute for discussion of the merits of the office scheme itself. Stansted Airport is another case of the promotion of a Private Bill, this time by British Rail in 1986, for the provision of a rail link to the airport expansion scheme announced in June 1985.

10.85. At Sizewell, at the Vale of Belvoir, and at Stansted the appointed inspectors examined the question of 'need' and the inquiries were far ranging and, as a result, enormously protracted and expensive. Two major projects where discussion of need or the issue of principle could not be raised were (*a*) the Dounreay plutonium reprocessing plant in Scotland and (*b*) the Channel Fixed Link. As Mr Anthony Barker has observed (in his paper (April 1986) to the Political Studies Association of the United Kingdom) these two schemes can be regarded as exceptional because they represent international commitments by Britain. The inquiry at Dounreay sought, therefore, to exclude policy issues, and the hearings before two select committees in the case of the Channel Fixed Link will do likewise.

10.86. As we pointed out at the beginning of this chapter, the public inquiry, as a piece of constitutional and administrative machinery, has been more developed in Britain than elsewhere in the world. Where there have been serious criticisms they have been largely in relation to those inquiries that may properly be considered exceptional. An inquiry has great merit both in informing the decision-maker (usually the Government) and meeting the public's desire to participate. It would be disastrous if the benefits of this unique process were to be lost because of irritation and resentment, however well justified, at the expense, complexity, and length of inquiries into exceptional projects. There is no simple answer to the problems which these exceptional inquiries pose. We think that the Code of Practice will help, as will the appointment of counsel to the inquiry and some system of funding reputable objectors, perhaps on a pound for pound basis on the lines discussed earlier. Good management of these inquiries can make a great difference, as can a willingness on the part of departments and bodies sponsoring development to be ready to explain national policy and 'need' considerations and to put their cards on the table so that there can be some informed discussion on public policy. The point, first articulated in *The Big Public Inquiry*, 1978, and enthusiastically endorsed by the Government more recently, is that the more real issues can be identified and clarified, and the more information can be extracted from the parties and exchanged between them before the public hearing begins, the shorter and cheaper the inquiry is likely to be.

10.87. At least as important on the question of delay is the need for Government to speed up the decision-making process after the inspector has prepared his report and recommendations. To judge from *The Government's Response* (Cm. 43), the measures necesary to achieve this seem now to have been identified and put in hand.

AD HOC INQUIRIES

Preliminary

10.88. For the purpose of this chapter, *ad hoc* inquiries include all inquiries not concerned with land use. The term is, of course, inexact since some land-use inquiries have an *ad hoc* character, but it serves as a convenient substitute for a more precise, but lengthier, description. Too frequently in the recent past some of these *ad hoc* inquiries have, in the words of one of our respondents, become a festival for the media, thus inhibiting sensible and purposeful discussion. The recent report on the *Jasmine Beckford* case, *A Child in Trust* (LB Brent, 1985) provides useful detail on this regrettable tendency and its consequences.

Proposals and past events

10.89. Most *ad hoc* inquiries are retrospective, examining why something occurred or did not occur.

The court [of inquiry] should accept the inquisitorial route (assisted of course by counsel for all parties) of discovering the cause rather than merely the task of deciding between two or three contestants at arms length. (Report of the Cairns Committee on Civil Aircraft Accident Investigation and Licensing Control, CAP 169, 1961, paragraph 104.)

It is inherent in the inquisitorial procedure that there is no *lis* . . . The inquiry may take a fresh turn at any moment. (Report of the Salmon Royal Commission on Tribunals of Inquiry, Cmnd. 3121, 1966, paragraph 30.)

These two quotations highlight a broad but fundamental distinction between the consideration of, on the one hand, proposals for the future (the position in most land-use inquiries), where the issues for the inquiry are clearly defined in advance and, on the other, the investigation of past events. Nevertheless, even where questions of land use do not arise, there can be inquiries into future proposals, as for example, those into dock reorganization schemes under the Harbours Act, 1964, and into dock licensing under the Docks and Harbours Act, 1966; into water abstraction licensing appeals under the Water Resources Act, 1963, and into the revision of water charges under the Water Act, 1945. The confirmation or rejection of by-laws provides another example of an *ad hoc* inquiry which is prospective rather than retrospective in character.

10.90. Inquiries of the second group are usually instituted on account of some accident, deficiency, material irregularity, or other cause for complaint. In this category are complaints about marketing schemes under the Agricultural Marketing Act, 1958, where the inquiry is conducted by a standing Committee of Investigation, as, for example, in the case of the inquiry that followed *Padfield* v. *Ministry of Agriculture* [1968] AC 997. In England and Wales inquiries into violent deaths and fatalities in dubious circumstances take the form of coroners' inquisitions, but in Scotland fatalities are investigated by means of public inquiries (industrial deaths: Fatal Accidents Inquiry (Scotland) Act, 1895; sudden or suspicious deaths: Fatal Acidents and Sudden Deaths Inquiry (Scotland) Act, 1906).

Statutory inquiries

10.91. There are numerous statutory provisions for inquiries into accidents. The Civil Aviation (Investigation of Accidents) Regulations, 1983 (SI 1983/551) contain provisions for the setting up of inquiries into aviation accidents. Inquiries into railway accidents are held under the Railways Regulation Act, 1871. Deaths at sea and 'shipping casualties' are investigated by inquiry under the Merchant Shipping Acts. Notifiable mining accidents (which include deaths, personal injuries, and foreseeable hazards underground) may, at the minister's discretion, be the subject of a public inquiry. The Ronan Point inquiry into flats damaged by a gas explosion was held under section 318 of the Public Health Act, 1936, and section 290 of the Local Government Act, 1933 (now section 250 of the 1972 Act). Other statutes enable ministers to order inquiries into competence and proper functioning, as in the case of a ship's master's competence under the Merchant Shipping Act, 1979, or the functions of a social services committee, adoption agency, or voluntary organization under section 76 of the Child Care Act, 1980. Powers to order inquiries expressed in wide terms (such as 'The Minister may cause such inquiries to be held as he may deem necessary or desirable for the purposes of this Act') are conferred in such statutes as the Education Act, 1944 (section 93), the National Health Service Act, 1977 (section 84), the Fire Service Act, 1947 (section 33), the National Assistance Act, 1959 (section 54) and the Mental Health Act, 1983 (section 125). A notable inquiry, conducted under section 70 of the previous National Health Service Act, 1946, was that into the fire at Shelton Mental Hospital, Shrewsbury, in 1968 in which twenty-four patients died. The Health and Safety at Work Act, 1974, section 14, confers on the Health and Safety Commission the power to appoint an inquiry into 'any accident, occurrence, situation or other matter whatsoever which the Commission thinks it necessary or expedient to investigate for any of the general purposes of' Part 1 of the Act. The power to hold inquiries is also conferred by many Local Acts.

Non-statutory inquiries

10.92. Non-statutory inquiries may also be ordered. Examples are the inquiry into the oil rig 'Sea-Gem' in 1967, the Summerland Fire Inquiry on the Isle of Man in 1973, the DHSS inquiry conducted by Sir John Foster, QC into the cult of Scientology, and the inquiry by Judge Brian Gibbens, QC into the administration of punishment at the Home Office approved school of Court Lees. This is a rare example of a purely fact-finding inquiry; the report contained no recommendations (1967, Cmnd. 3367). The most celebrated non-statutory inquiry was that of Sir Andrew Clark, QC into the disposal of land at Crichel Down (1954, Cmnd. 9176). Local authorities may also initiate non-statutory inquiries, as for example, the Inner London Education Authority inquiry into the William Tyndale Junior and Infants School, though usually such inquiries are private. An important category, to which we return later, comprises inquiries into child abuse.

Procedure at accident/occurrence inquiries

10.93. For very few of the accident/occurrence statutory inquiries are there statutory rules of procedure. The Lord Chancellor has power to make such rules, after consulting the Council on Tribunals (Tribunals and Inquiries Act, 1971, section 11), but he has made little use of it for mandatory, and none at all for discretionary, inquiries. The general principles that should be observed at inquiries are obviously uniform, and we have no evidence to suggest that they are not followed. The requirements of natural justice at inquiries are enforceable by means of judicial review.

10.94. Such responsibilities as the Council on Tribunals have in regard to statutory inquiries are expressed in section 1(1)(c) of the Tribunals and Inquiries Act, 1971:

to consider and report on such matters as may be referred as aforesaid, or as the Council may determine to be of special importance, with respect to administrative procedures, involving, or which may involve, the holding by or on behalf of a Minister of a statutory inquiry, or any such procedure.

The annual reports of the Council on Tribunals contain few references to accident inquiries.

The Davies Committee and the Salmon Royal Commission

10.95. The Davies Committee on Hospital Complaints Procedure (DHSS, HMSO 1973) proposed a code of practice for formal inquiries in the context of its area of concern. The Salmon Royal Commission on the Tribunals of Inquiry (Evidence) Act, 1921, in their report (1966, Cmnd. 3121) made some fifty recommendations, including six 'cardinal principles' on such matters as terms of reference, preliminary meetings, legal representation, *locus standi* (involvement in inquiry), the making of allegations, and the examination and cross-examination of witnesses. The majority of these and, in particular, the 'cardinal principles', were accepted by the Government, including the recommendation that there should be no statutory rules of procedure because, the White Paper ([1]1973, Cmnd. 5313) suggested, of the need for flexibility and to avoid unnecessary delay by alleged breaches of statutory rules (paragraph 12). The Government intended that the White Paper itself should serve as a guide to future tribunals except where the recommendations of the Royal Commission required legislation (paragraph 4). In fact the legislation needed to implement some of the Royal Commission's recommendations has never been introduced.

Some criticisms

10.96. The criticisms made to us have been that no procedure has yet been devised that satisfies either the public or those involved as witnesses, that too often the terms of reference of the inquiry are either too wide or too narrow, and that in some cases the reports of inquiries have been unrealistic or superficial—the true facts never being ascertained. The advantages of legal representation are that it tends to achieve a more formal structure and provides a safeguard for witnesses. The disadvantage is an enormous duplication of effort when, as often happens, at least six lawyers have to cross-examine. But the absence of legal representation places a heavy burden on the

[1] *Tribunals of Inquiry set up under the Tribunals of Inquiry (Evidence) Act, 1921— Government views on the recommendations of the Royal Commission on Tribunals of Inquiry.*

chairman, enables witnesses more easily to conceal important information and can lead to a degeneration of the inquiry into a morass of discussion from which it is difficult to construct a useful or accurate report. Private inquiries with representation are certainly no shorter than those without. The absence of representation at private inquiries likewise imposes a heavy burden on the chairman, puts at risk the observance of natural justice, and increases fears of 'secret' courts.

The Marre Committee

10.97. *Ad Hoc Inquiries in Local Government* (SOLACE 1978, ISBN 0 905566 02 5), the report of the Marre Committee, sponsored jointly by the Society of Local Authority Chief Executives and the Royal Institute of Public Administration, drew on both the Davies and the Salmon Royal Commission reports in proposing both a code of practice and statutory procedural rules for formal inquiries. But this was in the context of the Committee's view that local inquiries were to be preferred to ministerial inquiries, which should be reserved for cases with a national element, and a proposal that, by a change in the law, local authorities should have statutory power to initiate public inquiries with the compulsory powers of existing ministerial inquiries under section 250 of the Local Government Act, 1972. The proposed rules of procedure would cover such matters as: rights of hearing, rights of representation, reimbursement of costs, right to call witnesses of complainant and person(s) complained against, a discretionary power to hear 'public interest' bodies, evidence (the power to subpoena and to admit hearsay), rights of persons adversely criticized, and reports. The code of practice would cover such matters as: chairman, membership of inquiry panel (chairman plus two preferred, need for members with professional experience of main issues under investigation, lay 'consumer' representation on panel), staffing, solicitor to the inquiry (optional—contrary to the Davies Committee's view that a solicitor was essential), secretary to the inquiry (essential), assessors, terms of reference, and whether the inquiry should be public or private. It will be evident that the considerations underlying these proposals are significantly different from those that apply to land-use inquiries. In this area questions of reputation and liability are dominant and these account for the more forensic character of the recommendations. We are not persuaded that it is desirable for local authorities to enjoy a statutory power to initiate *ad hoc* inquiries with compulsory powers comparable to those of ministerial inquiries, but we do endorse the Marre Committee's recommendations of a code of practice for formal *ad hoc* inquiries. In any guidance offered on the conduct of such inquiries there should be a reference to the Salmon Royal Commission's six cardinal principles and to the substance of Lord Scarman's opening statement at the preliminary hearing of the Red Lion Square Inquiry 1974 (reprinted in Appendix 13).

Civil aviation inquiries

10.98. Accidents involving civil aircraft are a regular occasion for public inquiries nowadays though between 1922 and 1947 only three were held, of which one concerned the loss of the R101 airship (Cmd. 3825). The regulations governing such inquiries are now contained in the Civil Aviation (Investigation of Accidents) Regulations, 1983 (SI 1983/551), but are quite similar to the regulations of the same name introduced in 1951 (SI 1951/1653), principally to comply with international requirements. They contain the necessary adaptations to make them apt for Scotland and Northern Ireland. The regulations provide for two quite different types of inquiry. The first is an investigation held at the discretion of the Chief Inspector of Accidents, who is appointed by the Secretary of State for Transport. If held, an investigation is carried out by the Chief Inspector or an inspector appointed by him. The Chief Inspector gives public notice of the investigation in such manner as he may think fit and invites those who wish to make representations to do so within a time-limit. The investigation is held in private. The inspector may allow persons to appear before him, to call evidence, and to examine witnesses. Regulation 4 recites:

The fundamental purpose of investigating accidents under these Regulations shall be to determine the circumstances and causes of the accident with a view to the preservation of life and the avoidance of accidents in the future; it is not the purpose to apportion blame or liability. (SI 1983/551.)

10.99. The second type of inquiry into civil aircraft accidents is the public inquiry. The Secretary of State is responsible for directing that such an inquiry be held by a Commissioner (known as 'The Court') who is a judge or a barrister of not less than ten years standing and who is assisted by not fewer than two Assessors possessing technical skill or knowledge. These appointments are made by the Lord Chancellor (regulation 17(1) and (2)). When the

Secretary of State has directed that a public inquiry be held, he remits the case to the Attorney General under whose direction the Treasury Solicitor prepares and presents the case (ibid. 17(3)). The Attorney General is required to serve a notice of the inquiry on the owner, operator, carrier, and commander of any aircraft involved in the accident and on any other person who in his opinion ought to be so served (ibid. 17(4)). Before 1983 the service of such a notice was at the Attorney General's discretion and the notice itself contained a statement of the questions which the Attorney General intended to raise on the hearing of the inquiry. The 1983 Regulations did away with that. The Attorney General and any person served with a notice are deemed to be parties to the proceedings (ibid. 17(5)); other persons may by leave of the Court become parties to the proceedings (ibid. 17(6)). Such parties have the right to address the inquiry, to lead evidence, and to cross-examine witnesses (ibid. 18(2)). Affidavits and statutory declarations may be used as evidence by leave of the Court (ibid. 17(9)). The Court has the powers of a Magistrates' Court and in addition has the power: (i) to enter and inspect any place, building, or aircraft; (ii) to require the attendance of witnesses to answer questions and furnish information, and the production of books and papers; and (iii) to administer the oath or require a solemn affirmation (ibid. 17(8)). The Court's proceedings follow the forensic pattern. The inquiry is held in public save to the extent that the Court directs that it be held in private 'in the interests of justice or in the public interest' (ibid. 17(11)). The inspector who carried out an investigation into the accident which was the subject of the inquiry and a member of the Council on Tribunals are entitled to attend proceedings held in private (ibid. 17(12)). There is no provision for any appeal. The Secretary of State can, however, order a rehearing of the whole or part of the public inquiry and is required to do so if new and important evidence not available at the inquiry is subsequently discovered, or if he has reason to suspect a miscarriage of justice.

10.100. The Court is required in its report to the Secretary of State to give a full account of the circumstances of the accident and to express an opinion 'touching the cause or causes of the accident or on the particular matter referred to the Court and adding any observations and recommendations which the Court thinks fit to make with a view to the preservation of life and the avoidance of similar accidents in future' (ibid. 18(5)). In the 1951 Regulations the same sentence continued: 'including recommendations for the cancellation, suspension or endorsement of any licence, certificate or other document'. It will be apparent that this obligation involved two, somewhat conflicting, requirements.

10.101. The conflict just referred to was fully considered by the Cairns Committee on Civil Aircraft Accident Investigations and Licence Control, 1961 (CAP 169), which had this to say about the essential purpose of accident inquiries:

> In our view it should be more widely appreciated that the main purpose of an accident investigation is to determine the cause, or causes, of an accident so that appropriate action, based on the findings, may be taken to avoid further accidents. Although this is implicit in the regulations . . . we do not consider that this should be left as a mere implication. (Paragraph 62.)

> If somebody is grossly at fault he should be punished, but the object of accident investigation is remedial and not retributive. It is therefore usually more valuable to state the thing that was wrong than to identify the person who was responsible. (Paragraph 82.)

10.102. The Government's response to these recommendations, contained in the White Paper *Aviation Safety* (1962, Cmnd. 1695), accepted them. It stated: 'the purpose of accident investigations is to determine the cause of the accident, and not to ascribe blame' (paragraph 103). This was reflected in the 1969 and 1983 Regulations by the exclusion of the additional words of the 1951 Regulations referred to above.

10.103. The views expressed by the Cairns Committee and by the Government of the day in its White Paper do not entirely remove the problem common to many accident inquiries, and indeed also to coroners' inquisitions, that the investigation of the cause of an accident may expose the culpability of some person or persons. We see this as the principal area of difficulty. The very process of cross-examination poses such a threat. Proceedings to test culpability invariably have the safeguards of requiring notice of precise allegations and the tendering of only the best evidence. In its nature, an inquiry cannot always provide these. Its purpose being to expose the truth, it is obliged to probe and that may have to be done at the cost of some unfairness.

The *Mahon* case

10.104. The reality of the consequences of an investigative inquiry was considered by the Privy Council in *Mahon* v. *Air New Zealand*

Limited [1984] AC 808. The circumstances of the case were unusual. They arose from a disaster in which 257 persons lost their lives when the aircraft in which they were flying crashed into Mount Erebus in Antarctica. The New Zealand Chief Inspector of Air Accidents held an immediate inquiry and found that the probable cause of the accident was pilot error. A judge of the New Zealand Supreme Court was appointed to conduct a Royal Commission to investigate the cause and circumstances of the disaster. He exonerated the pilot and other members of the crew from blame, identified the actions of executive officers and of the ground staff as the principal causes of the disaster, and found that there had been a predetermined plan to cover up those actions; the Commissioner described this as 'an orchestrated litany of lies'. He ordered the airline to pay $150,000 towards the costs of the Royal Commission. The airline moved for judicial review of that order. The Court of Appeal of New Zealand held that the Commissioner, in making the order, had acted in breach of the rules of natural justice. The Privy Council affirmed the Court of Appeal's decision.

10.105. The Privy Council emphasized that, while the technical rules of evidence applicable to civil or criminal litigation formed no part of the rules of natural justice, such justice nevertheless required that the Commissioner should ensure that any person represented at an inquiry who might be adversely affected by a finding should be warned of the possible criticisms against him and given an opportunity to answer any that were made.

10.106. Bearing in mind Lord Salmon's observation that an inquiry 'may take a fresh turn at any moment', the requirements of natural justice may not always easily be satisfied. But it is the continuing duty of the person holding the inquiry to ensure that persons affected have the chance to answer both new matters as they arise and adverse criticisms as they crystallize in his own mind.

Child abuse inquiries

10.107. A resolution adopted at the Annual General Meeting of the British Association of Social Workers ('BASW') in 1981 recorded the Meeting's 'rejection of committees of inquiry into child abuse' and requested the Secretary of State urgently to review the validity of such inquiries 'the recommendations of which often fail to attract sufficient resources to improve the management of child abuse cases'. The resolution also called for a committee of the

Association 'to examine alternative procedures and to devise an acceptable one to deal with situations which require detailed study'. The Association accordingly set up a project group the report of which (*Child Abuse Inquiries*) was adopted by the Council of the Association in June 1982. The report concluded that some form of inquiry was necessary and desirable following the death of a child caused by abuse:

It would be irresponsible to suggest otherwise ... the objective must be to maximise the value and reduce the harm of inquiries rather than to rely exclusively upon alternative ways of learning lessons, advancing knowledge and examining accountability.

10.108. It is evident that the 1981 BASW resolution was prompted by a widespread sense of dissatisfaction among those professionally involved in child care about the fairness and efficacy of inquiries. The report accepted that the professionals must expect an external investigation to be undertaken when tragedies or mishaps occur and it clearly outlines the advantages of inquiries. 'But', it continues,

many of these inquiries have also proved to be remarkably blunt instruments, producing many damaging effects to offset their potential usefulness. Their formal, ritualistic nature has impeded them in their primary tasks. They have become like show-piece trials, with those being investigated invariably cast in the role of defendants. Their procedures and thoroughness have often left much to be desired, and their propensity to treat witnesses in different ways has led to bitterness. Unsatisfactory inquiries are worse than no inquiry at all. They have tended to over-simplify and over-personalise complex issues and events. They can be protracted, paralysing agencies and individuals. They can give a false impression, relying as they must upon hindsight, powers of recall and evidence extracted under 'trial' conditions. By focusing upon a case in isolation it is difficult to paint a realistic picture of what was happening at the time, the other pressures upon workers and the context in which decisions are made. Inquiries can too easily resort to black or white, right or wrong, ways of looking at actions and judgments rather than teasing out the more subtle shades of grey. (p. 1.)

The report focuses principally upon the structure of inquiries, the criteria that should underpin their procedures and a recommended pattern for their conduct. It emphasizes the relationship between child abuse inquiries and the social background:

society should not shield behind inquiries and the scapegoating which so often accompanies them without looking at these wider dimensions, and in particular at the social and economic policies which fundamentally affect the lives and behaviour of its members. (p. 3.)

10.109. Inquiries into serious child abuse cases are, broadly speaking, of two types:

- (*a*) statutory inquiries instituted under section 26 of the Child Care Act 1980; and
- (*b*) inquiries by a review panel specially appointed by local authority or local agencies.

Both types are to be distinguished from internal case reviews by an individual agency. The BASW report concentrated on proposals for the improvement of the second variety and hoped that if that was achieved it would minimize the need for the first (p. 18). The report stressed the desirability that in future a common structure should be adopted in all parts of the country thus ensuring 'the application of a consistent set of standards'. It proposed an extension of the existing responsibilities of the Area Review Committees to include the institution of inquiries. Their present responsibility is to promote inter-agency co-operation in the control of child abuse. The Committees consist of senior officials of all agencies concerned with child welfare within each local authority area. They were set up under the guidance of a Department of Health and Social Security Circular of April 1974, *Non Accidental Injury to Children* (LASSL (74) 13). The BASW report sees these Committees as 'a local multi-disciplinary body ... in permanent residence' and as such well placed to undertake the proposed responsibility of automatic preliminary examination in all cases of death believed to result from child abuse (p. 16). If such an examination disclosed the need for an inquiry and there was little public concern, the inquiry should be conducted by a subcommittee of the Area Review Committee itself. In cases where there was widespread involvement of local agencies, or the facts or their interpretation were seriously in dispute, or there was considerable public concern, the inquiry should be conducted by a chairman and panel from outside the area concerned appointed by the Area Review Committee after consultation with the Department of Health and Social Security.

10.110. The report proposes detailed criteria for inquiries under the headings of credibility, factual search, agency dimension (that is, the need to consider the context of individual performance), conduct of the inquiry, and report. The report's specific recommendations included:

(*a*) the need to establish an inquiry as soon after the event as possible: 'We do not consider that the commencement of an inquiry need await the conclusion of any criminal proceedings' (p. 24);

(*b*) that hearings should, generally, be held in private (this point is strongly pressed);

(*c*) a flexible and inquisitorial procedure; and

(*d*) the observance of fairness to witnesses by informing them of their rights, treating them as witnesses not as defendants, providing them with an opportunity to comment on criticism of their performance made at the inquiry and access to comments on them in the inquiry report.

The report considered that informal hearings or interviews were more effective than formal sessions and urged that legalistic proceedings and publicity be avoided. Inquiries should not be used for disciplinary purposes and reports of inquiries should not be used in evidence in disciplinary proceedings.

Guidance for child abuse inquiries

10.111. In July 1985 the Department of Health and Social Security issued a consultative paper on the formal guidance to be offered to agencies responsible for the investigation of cases of child abuse other than inquests, criminal proceedings, and care proceedings. Previously, departmental advice on action to be taken in such cases had been of an informal nature. The paper acknowledged the work of both the Marre Committee and the BASW Project Group. The paper discusses two types of investigation: (i) review by management, and (ii) inquiry by a review panel. It emphasizes the need for urgency, impartiality, thoroughness, and confidentiality. Guidance is proposed on the composition of the review panel, its chairmanship and legal expertise, its terms of reference, the necessary documentation, time-tabling, and written information for witnesses. The paper recommends that proceedings should normally be conducted in private (paragraph 4.2).

10.112. The DHSS paper asserts that 'The distinction between the purposes of the inquiry and any action under disciplinary proceeding should be made clear' (paragraph 4.8). Later, in paragraph 4.9(e), the paper observes: 'Any person against whom critical comments are made must be informed in writing of the points which have been made, and given an opportunity to comment on and question them.' We think that the consultative paper tends to minimize and obscure somewhat the critical difficulty that confronts any inquiry where reputations are at stake and we hope that the guidance eventually formulated will not do so. The consultative paper attracted a considerable response and the task of sifting the numerous comments on it has delayed the issue of the formal guidance. Publication of this was expected to be in 1987.

The report of the Jasmine Beckford Inquiry

10.113. Jasmine Beckford died on 5 July 1984 at the age of $4\frac{1}{2}$. On 28 March 1985 the Council of the London Borough of Brent appointed a panel under the chairmanship of Mr Louis Blom-Cooper QC to inquire into the events leading up to and the circumstances surrounding the death of the child. Subsequently the Brent Health Authority became associated as sponsors of the inquiry. The report was comprehensive and its first three chapters contain much that is of general concern. If we discuss its recommendations more fully than those of the Marre Committee or the British Association of Social Workers on child abuse inquiries, that is because it is the most recent of the three and also because the Government has announced that it 'fully supports and welcomes the main themes of the report' (Written Answer of the Secretary of State for Social Services, Hansard, 6 May 1986, vol. 97, c.68–9W). There are, in fact, many points of agreement between the three reports on matters of principle if not of detail. Thus, the Blom-Cooper report, like that of the BASW, favours a standing local body to set up non-statutory inquiries though it would not give that responsibility to the Area Review Committees (for reasons of insufficient perceived independence and lack of funds to finance an inquiry (p. 28)). The BASW argument in favour of private hearings was presented to the Blom-Cooper panel by a member of the Child Abuse Inquiries Project Group which formulated it. The panel also considered the DHSS consultative paper of July 1985 which proposed that 'the inquiry should normally be conducted in private'. For reasons which we find persuasive, however, the panel reached the opposite conclusion, namely, that there should be a presumption in favour of the inquiry being in public. They found support for this not only in the panel's own experience but in the implied preference by Parliament for it indicated in section 98(2) of the Children Act 1975 (which, following the Maria Colwell case, gave power to institute statutory child abuse inquiries, and which has been replaced by section 76 of the Child Care Act, 1980).

10.114. The Blom-Cooper report recognizes that the unavoidable function of an inquiry is 'to find out what, if anything, people have done wrong or omitted; and if anything has been done wrong or omitted . . . Prior disclosure of evidence should, therefore, always be made to witnesses likely to be criticised in consequence of that evidence' (p. 34).

10.115. This reiterates the emphasis of the Salmon Royal Commission on the necessity to inform persons criticized at inquiries of the precise nature of the allegation. The Blom-Cooper inquiry dealt with this requirement itself by sending out 'Salmon letters' to the relevant witnesses warning them of possible criticism ('You should be aware that your conduct may be called into question in the following respects . . .').

10.116. Of the report's conclusions and recommendations the following seem to us particularly important in the context of inquiries:

(*a*) A child abuse inquiry should concentrate on specific aspects of organizational efficiency and effectiveness, on professional competence or responsibility, and on aspects of multidisciplinary approach, without being deflected by the 'moral panic' that pervaded the scene at the time of the death of Maria Colwell in 1973 (p. 12).

(*b*) The preliminary hearing should be arranged well in advance of the opening of the inquiry (p. 31).

(*c*) The procedures of the inquiry should be announced explicitly at the preliminary hearing (p. 30). The report commended the opening statement of Lord Scarman at the preliminary hearing of the Red Lion Square inquiry, 1974 [see Appendix 13].

(*d*) Representation should be limited to those directly affected by the evidence (p. 35).

(*e*) The inquiry panel should not number more than five and should incorporate all the major professional disciplines involved (p. 29).

(*f*) The position of advisers and assessors is ambiguous. It is preferable that whatever input they can supply should be provided instead by a full member of the panel (p. 29).

(g) The costs of parties should be met out of public funds as was done at the instance of Lord Scarman at the inquiry into the Brixton Disorders, 1981 (p. 37).

We consider these recommendations and observations to be sensible and we support them.

10.117. The importance of the role of counsel to the inquiry is stressed in the report with compelling illustrations of the assistance rendered to the inquiry by this means (p. 5). The cost to the local authority of the Jasmine Beckford inquiry has been estimated to be of the order of £250,000. The report suggests that this is an unreasonable burden for local government to be expected to bear and recommends that the Department of Health and Social Security should consider the machinery of financing such inquiries. We agree with these recommendations also.

Inquiries into rule-making

10.118. There have been a few instances where inquiries might be called for by those likely to be affected by legislation as, for example, regulations made under the Factories Act, 1961 and the Offices, Shops and Railway Premises Act, 1963 (though the provision for this was removed from both statutes in 1974 by subordinate legislation; SI 1974/1941 and SI 1974/1943). Generally, however, no inquiries are required by statute or are held in practice as part of the process of producing regulatory subordinate legislation. This is in marked contrast to the position in the United States of America where the Administrative Procedure Act, 1946, establishes a right for interested persons to be heard as part of the process of administrative rule-making. With the privatization of various publicly conducted industries, utilities, and services, and the trend towards strengthening public supervision of other commercial activities, regulation may become a more prominent feature of this country. Sir William Wade has pointed out that the practice of the administration in the United Kingdom to consult the informed public before subordinate legislation is introduced is 'one of the firmest and most carefully observed conventions' (*Administrative Law*, 5th edn., 1982, p. 767). That practice provides only a partial substitute for rule-making hearings. We recommend that consideration should be given to the holding of inquiries, which could be non-statutory, into any proposed rule-making legislation for utilities and services.

Conclusion

10.119. To conclude this chapter we offer some general observations on the public inquiry as an instrument of government. As an administrative process the inquiry is subject to all the requirements for administrative decision-making that have been discussed earlier in this report. Thus, the purpose of the inquiry, its place in the decision-making process, and the framework of policy to which it is subject should be made clear to all concerned at the outset. The hearing should be a fair hearing and should be conducted with a degree of formality and without disruption. Any statutory procedural requirements should be observed and the report of the inquiry should be published without delay. The outcome of the inquiry should be rationally related to (i) the particular circumstances investigated and (ii) relevant policy. But though all this be scrupulously observed the individual, if his expectations are unrealistic, may still be left with a sense of dissatisfaction.

10.120. The end product of an inquiry is not necessarily an impartial decision; inevitably it is influenced by policy, and policy may fluctuate abruptly in response to a number of factors bearing on political responsibility. Thus the indivdiual may be dissatisfied because of his disagreement with the determining policy, or because the superficial resemblance of inquiries to judicial proceedings encourages expectations of a judicial result, or, in the case of a retrospective inquiry, because of some adverse reflection on his reputation contained in the report which he has no means of challenging. But these things are of the nature of inquiries and perhaps the best that can be done to dispel dissatifaction is to make the limitations clear at the outset of the proceedings.

CHAPTER 10. RECOMMENDATIONS

1. Development plans should be flexible, frequently reviewed, and revised when necessary. The process of producing them should be simple, swift, open, and accessible to the public. The occurrence of public participation at the plan-making stage should not be seen as a reason for depriving applicants for planning permission and participants at site-specific inquiries of the ability to question the policy of District development ment plans (paragraph 10.33).

2. An inspector conducting a development plan inquiry should be able to comment on the proposed plan as a whole, not merely on those aspects of it to which objection has been taken (paragraph 10.33).

3. The Government is rightly concerned to achieve simplification, speed, and efficiency in the process of planning appeals. We welcome the detailed examination instituted by the Department of the Environment and the Scottish Development Department of the various processes for the consideration of proposals for development plans and for disposing of planning appeals. But we add a note of caution: the achievement of these objectives should not be at the expense of the quality of the final plan or decision (paragraph 10.37).

4. The possibility of replacing enforcement appeal inquiries by standing Enforcement Tribunals should be examined (paragraph 10.41).

5. Planning inspectors should be more broadly recruited. In the more complex cases two inspectors should hear the case. There should be longer induction training and regular in-service training of inspectors and additional resources for this should be provided (paragraph 10.43).

6. It should be exceptional for a site visit to be unaccompanied (paragraph 10.46).

7. The sentence in paragraph 2.7 of the DoE booklet, *Planning Appeals—A Guide*, which asserts that the outcome of an appeal is unaffected by the choice of procedure, may mislead and should be deleted (paragraph 10.47).

8. The Department's encouragement of the use of the written representations procedure should not be carried to the point where it jeopardizes fairness or sacrifices the quality of the system (paragraph 10.48).

9. Attention should be paid to how more can be done for the appellant who lacks professional assistance (paragraph 10.49).

10. The option of an informal hearing should be fully described in the Department of the Environment booklet, *Planning Appeals—A Guide* (paragraph 10.50).

11. There should be a presumption in favour of the appellant's choice of procedure and if it cannot be satisfied in any particular case, reasons for that should be given (paragraph 10.50).

12. The Scottish practice of allowing the parties to comment, within fourteen days, on the provisional findings of fact for the inquiry report should be adopted experimentally (paragraph 10.56).

13. Where costs at inquiries are thrown away through no fault of the parties, the parties should be reimbursed out of public funds (paragraph 10.60).

14. The statutory appeals to the High Court in planning cases should not be abolished (paragraph 10.61).

15. There should be a right of appeal against the grant of planning permission (paragraph 10.62).

16. The Code of Practice for major inquiries should contain a specific

provision to meet the needs of participants of limited means for information, studies, and research (paragraph 10.68).

17. The possibility of giving the Code of Practice for major inquiries legislative force should be considered in the light of experience. Vigilance will be needed to ensure that the procedure for major inquiries does not invade and unnecessarily complicate the lesser planning inquiries (paragraph 10.69).

18. The appointment of counsel to the inquiry at major inquiries should be the rule rather than the exception (paragraph 10.70).

19. Third-party participation at major inquiries is important and should, where appropriate, be supported financially. The real problem is how to achieve that without unacceptable public expense or discrimination. Where there is to be funding of third parties, its distribution should be the responsibility of the inspector on the basis of relevance. The pound-for-pound approach probably offers the most practical solution (paragraphs 10.72 to 10.74).

20. We support the proposal to give the inspector explicit powers to exclude from inquiries those who indulge in disruptive behaviour (paragraph 10.75).

21. At an inquiry it should be open to a person whose interests may be adversely affected by proposed development to challenge the technical considerations that underlie an adopted policy (paragraph 10.78).

22. There should be reasonable scope for the discussion of need at inquiries (paragraph 10.80).

23. We endorse the recommendations of the Marre Committee for rules of procedure and a code of practice for formal *ad hoc* inquiries. In any guidance offered to *ad hoc* inquiries there should be a reference to the six cardinal principles of the Salmon Royal Commission and to the substance of Lord Scarman's opening statement at the preliminary hearing of the Red Lion Square Inquiry 1974 (paragraph 10.97).

24. The guidance on inquiries offered by the Department of Health and Social Security should not minimize the difficulties of reconciling the demands of natural justice with the essential purpose of the inquiry (paragraph 10.112).

25. We endorse generally the following conclusions and recommendations for the conduct of child abuse inquiries put forward in the Blom-Cooper Panel's report:

    (*a*) child abuse inquiries should concentrate on specific aspects of organizational efficiency and effectiveness, on professional competence and responsibility, and on aspects of multidisciplinary approach;

    (*b*) the preliminary hearing should be arranged well in advance of the opening of the inquiry;

    (*c*) the procedures of the inquiry should be announced explicitly at the preliminary hearing; Lord Scarman's statement at the opening of the Red Lion Square inquiry, 1974 provides an excellent model;

(*d*) representation should be limited to those directly affected by the evidence;

(*e*) the inquiry panel should not number more than five and should, if practicable, incorporate all the major professional disciplines involved;

(*f*) whatever input could be supplied by advisers and assessors is better provided by full members of the inquiry panel;

(*g*) the costs of parties should be met out of public funds

(paragraph 10.116).

26. The burden on local government of some local inquiries is unreasonable. The Secretary of State should consider the machinery for financing them (paragraph 10.117).

27. Consideration should be given to holding inquiries into proposed rule-making legislation for utilities and services (paragraph 10.118).

28. The limitations of inquiries should be made clear at the outset to all who participate in them (paragraph 10.120).

11

Compensation: Financial Loss caused by Administrative Action

SUMMARY OF ARGUMENT. Special provisions apart, the existing law in the United Kingdom stops short of providing for compensation for economic loss caused by invalid administrative action or by excessive delay in arriving at an administrative decision, or by the giving of wrong advice by a public official. It has been suggested that liability for damages is inappropriate in such cases on the principle that it is always open to the person affected to ignore an invalid administrative decision; but we consider that unrealistic. The administration is liable for such of its wrongful conduct as fits into one of the recognized common-law categories such as trespass, nuisance, negligence, or breach of statutory duty. A particular difficulty occurs in the case of allegations of negligence in the exercise of statutory powers by a public body because such powers must necessarily often contain a large element of policy and that is a matter for the public body, not for the courts. But, generally speaking, the law of negligence is capable of dealing satisfactorily with cases of injury caused by negligence of the administration and in our view it should be allowed to develop on a case by case basis.

For the many types of wrongful administrative conduct that do not fit into the recognized common-law categories the court has no power to award damages. 'Wrongful' includes those cases of action or omission by a public authority where a court would find that the conduct or any resulting decision should be declared illegal or be quashed or held void or voidable. For the present, the law takes no account of the fact that the administration is capable of inflicting damage in ways in which a private person cannot.

Reform is clearly needed to provide a remedy for the person injured by wrongful administrative action not involving negligence. In French law there is a principle of general liability for injury caused by malfunctioning of the public service. There is no real likelihood that the common law will develop in that direction and we therefore suggest legislation to provide generally for compensation for material injury caused either by wrongful acts or omissions or by unreasonable or excessive delay of a public body. Decisions of courts and tribunals would be excluded.

In the United Kingdom specific legislation may provide for the award of compensation for injury caused by lawful administration; an example is the Vaccine Damage Payments Act, 1979. But there is in the law of the United Kingdom no recognition of the risk principle on which compensation for such lawful action may be awarded in France and many other countries. The Committee of Ministers of the Council of Europe have adopted a Recommendation (No. R(84)15) aimed at achieving uniformity of the law among member states relating to 'the obligation of public authorities to make good the damage caused by their acts'. But its terms are qualified to such an extent that the Recommendation adds little to what already exists in the law of the United Kingdom.

The law is not the only means by which compensation may be obtained in the United Kingdom for injury caused by administrative action. Maladministration covers a wide range of action or omission (and may involve no unlawful action), and where it is found to have caused injustice the ombudsmen not infrequently recommend the payment of compensation. The ombudsman's decision whether or not to investigate a complaint is discretionary and the payment of compensation by government departments is *ex gratia*, though it is hardly ever refused; the same, unfortunately, cannot be said of local authorities.

The Law Commission exposes the problem

11.1. In 1967 the Law Commission for England and Wales drew attention to a number of deficiencies in administrative law. One of their points related to damages. They said (Working Paper No. 13, paragraph 8):

It has been suggested that we need a body of law which, inter alia, makes the remedy for damages more widely available where administrative acts are found to be unlawful, and which recognises in the field of contract and tort that the administration as a party is different from a private party and, as in a number of other countries, provides special rules of public law accordingly.

This led them to think that a relevant question for a future Law Commission programme might be: 'How far should remedies controlling administrative acts or omissions include the right to damages?' After wide consultation on their Working Paper they reported to the Lord Chancellor in 1969 (Law Com. No. 20, Cmnd. 4059, paragraph 9) that they believed this question should be pursued. They recognized that the administration was as liable as a private person to be sued in tort and that breach of statutory duty could constitute a tort for which damages could be awarded. They added:

But there are many types of administrative conduct which, although wrongful, do not fall within the categories of wrongs for which damages can be awarded against a private person and where there is no right to award damages for breach of a statutory duty; in such cases the courts have at present no power to award damages.

The Law Commission made further glancing references to the topic in 1971 in Working Paper No. 40 (*Remedies in Administrative Law*) and in the Report which followed in 1976 (Law Com. No. 73, Cmnd. 6407, paragraph 9) but Government did not allow them to include it in any programme.

11.2. In our view the Law Commission correctly identified the problem. English law has traditionally taken a narrow approach to the problem of the liability of the administration. Subject to the rather special exceptions referred to below under the heading 'Other liabilities in tort' (paragraph 11.25), resort has been had exclusively to the familiar categories of tort. If what is done by the administration can be made to fit within one of the recognized torts (such as trespass, nuisance, negligence, breach of statutory duty) then liability can be established; but if the wrongful conduct will not fit into one of these pigeon-holes there is no liability. The objection to this approach is that it ignores the fact that wrongful conduct by the administration is capable of inflicting damage in ways in which private persons cannot. The administration has this capacity both by virtue of the enforceable statutory powers with which it is often clothed and through the pressure and influence which it applies.

Terminology—'unlawful', 'illegal', 'invalid', 'void'

11.3. We should point out that there is much discussion in the literature as to the difference between 'unlawful', used in the sense of illegal administrative action, and 'invalid', used in the sense of void administrative action. The distinction was adverted to by the Privy Council in *Dunlop* v. *Woolahra Municipal Council* [1982] AC 158, the authorities having been fully considered in the court below. We find it convenient to use at this stage the term 'wrongful', which we intend to cover all cases of action or omission to act by a public authority which are such that a court would hold that the conduct, or any resulting decision, should be declared illegal, quashed, or held void or voidable.

Arrangement of topics in this chapter

11.4. We proceed now to consider the subject of compensation under the following heads:

> *Part* I. Damages for wrongful administration action
> (*a*) under existing law (paragraphs 11.5–11.32)
> (*b*) the area not covered by existing law (paragraphs 11.33–11.41).

> *Part* II. Compensation for lawful administrative action (paragraphs 11.42–11.51).

> *Part* III. Compensation under the ombudsman system (paragraphs 11.52–11.54).

> *Part* IV. Recommendations for reform (paragraphs 11.55–11.92).

PART I

DAMAGES FOR WRONGFUL ADMINISTRATIVE ACTION:
THE TRADITIONAL APPROACH

(*a*) *Existing law*

11.5. The traditional approach of the courts has been to seek to apply to the liability of public authorities and officials the same rules of liability as apply to private undertakings and individuals. Thus in *Mersey Docks and Harbour Board Trustees* v. *Gibbs* (1866) LR 1 HL 93, the liability of a publicly owned harbour authority was assimilated to that of a privately owned company and the authority was held liable for the negligence of its employees in allowing a mudbank to block the entrance to a dock. The Crown Proceedings Act, 1947, section 2 also expressly provided that the Crown should be subject to the same liabilities in tort or delict in respect of the wrongful acts of its servants as if it were a private person of full age and capacity.

Interpretation of statutory powers

11.6. The courts have sometimes interpreted the conferment of powers by statute as being subject to a duty to avoid the commission of unnecessary wrongful acts, such as acts of nuisance, but in other cases where the powers conferred have been quite explicit the courts have held that there was statutory sanction for the 'nuisance'. As regards the tort of negligence, the courts have adopted the strict line summarized in Lord Blackburn's well-known dictum in *Geddis* v. *Bann Reservoir Proprietors* (1878) 3 App. Cas. 430 at 455:

It is now thoroughly well established that no action will lie for doing that which the legislature has authorised, if it be done without negligence, although it does occasion damage to anyone; but an action does lie for doing what the legislature has authorised, if it be done negligently.

Damages may sometimes be recoverable for breach of statutory duty

11.7. Public authorities and officials who fail to perform a statutory duty may be liable in damages. Whether a particular statutory duty can be enforced in this way is a matter for judicial interpretation and may depend, *inter alia*, on whether the statute provides a particular means of enforcing the duty. The duty must be a ministerial one, that is to say an administrative, duty not involving a judicial function. Thus, breach of the duty imposed on housing authorities to house the homeless created by the Housing (Homeless Persons) Act 1977 (now Part III of the Housing Act 1985) has been held to give rise to liability in damages (*Thornton* v. *Kirklees MBC* [1979] QB 626). By contrast, a statute may exceptionally give special protection or immunity to those in the public services (for instance Mental Health Act, 1983, s. 139), or to those exercising regulatory functions in the public interest (for instance, the Lloyd's Act, 1982, section 14 and the Financial Services Act, 1986, section 187).

11.8. The difficulties of deciding in any given case whether a civil action for damages is available for breach of statutory duty are notorious. The absence of any statutory sanction for breach and the absence of any express statutory remedy are indications in favour of the existence of a civil action (*Cutler* v. *Wandsdworth Stadium Ltd.* [1949] AC 398, 407). In *Garden Cottage Foods Ltd.* v. *Milk Marketing Board* [1984] AC 130, 144 a majority of the House of Lords expressed the firm view (without deciding) that breach of Article 86 of the Treaty of Rome (abuse of dominant position) gives rise to an action for damages, at the suit of the person injured, against the person or enterprise which has abused its dominant position. In the important case of *Bourgoin SA* v. *Ministry of Agriculture* [1985]

3 All ER 585 there was a division of judicial opinion as to whether breach by the United Kingdom Government of Article 30 of the Treaty (prohibition of import restrictions) entitled a trader damaged by such unlawful conduct to bring an action for damages against the Ministry responsible. The trial judge, Mann J., and Oliver LJ in the Court of Appeal answered this question in the affirmative. The majority of the Court of Appeal (Parker and Nourse L JJ) decided in the opposite sense. The whole court, however, decided in the plaintiff's favour on a separate argument based on misfeasance by a public officer.

Public authorities can be held liable for negligent advice or for the negligent discharge of their functions.

11.9. Because the approach of the courts has been to apply to public authorities the same rules of liability as apply to private individuals, developments in the law of negligence are potentially of great importance in this field. One illustration is afforded by the developing law of negligence in relation to erroneous advice. In *Hedley Byrne and Co.* v. *Heller and Partners* [1964] AC 465, the House of Lords had held that in principle there could be liability for financial loss caused through reliance on a negligent misstatement contained in a banker's reference. It was subsequently held that an individual who relied to his detriment on inaccurate statements made to him by a public official in the course of his duties had a remedy in damages against both the official and his employing authority: *Ministry of Housing* v. *Sharp* [1970] 2 QB 223.

11.10. In *Mutual Life and Citizen's Assurance Co. Ltd.* v. *Evatt* [1971] AC 793 the Privy Council in an Australian appeal sought to stem the tide by holding that a 'special duty' of care was demanded only from those whose business or profession it was to give advice in the relevant field and who held themselves out as having special skill and competence to give such advice. But the authority of that case was shaken by the dissent expressed by Lords Reid and Morris and the decision has been much criticized. The High Court of Australia in *Shaddock Pty. Ltd.* v. *Parramatta City Council* (1981) 36 ALR 385 treated *Evatt*'s case as wrongly decided, and held that a city council was liable for negligently supplying to a solicitor a certificate which failed to mention a road widening proposal of which the council was aware.

11.11. Two House of Lords decisions have been particularly influential in the development of the law in relation to the liability in negligence of public authorities. These cases are *Dorset Yacht Co. Ltd.* v. *Home Office* [1970] AC 1004 and *Anns* v. *London Borough of Merton* [1978] AC 728. In the former case, it was held that borstal officers owed a duty of care to the plaintiff to exercise proper supervision of the borstal boys in their charge since it was reasonably foreseeable that damage to the plaintiff's property would be likely to occur if the officers failed to exercise proper control or supervision; there was, moreover, no ground in public policy for granting immunity from liability to the Home Office or its officers. In *Anns* it was held that a local authority owed a duty of care to the eventual owners of houses as to the manner in which it performed its function under the Public Health Act, 1936, of inspecting the foundations of such houses. Breach of this duty could be established if either (*a*) the council's employees had carelessly inspected the foundations, or (*b*) the foundations had not been inspected at all, and the council had failed, in the exercise of a statutory discretion, to take reasonable care to ensure that the relevant by-laws were complied with.

11.12. The *Anns* case contains an analysis by Lord Wilberforce of the tests to be applied in deciding whether liability in negligence can be established. He said ([1978] AC at 751–2) that it was first necessary to ask whether the relationship between the plaintiff and the defendant was such as to give rise to a prima facie duty of care. This depended on the degree of proximity which existed and on whether there was a reasonable contemplation of damage. If this first question was answered in the affirmative it was next necessary to inquire whether there were any considerations which ought to negative or reduce or limit the scope of the duty or the class of person to whom the duty was owed or the damages to which a breach of it might give rise.

11.13. This twofold test has been much cited and for a time it was treated as authoritative. Thus in a later House of Lords case, *Junior Books* v. *Veitchi* [1983] 1 AC 520, the test was used by Lord Roskill, with the concurrence of Lords Fraser and Russell, in deciding that a building owner could recover damages from a specialist flooring subcontractor (with which it had no direct contract) for the defective construction of the floor of a factory. It was held that the subcontractor owed a duty not to inflict economic loss on the building owner and not to install a defective floor. Elsewhere the trend has been in the same direction. By way of illustration we refer to the reception of *Anns* in Scotland (*Hallett* v. *Nicholson* 1979 SC 1) and in the Republic of Ireland (*Siney* v. *Dublin Corporation* [1980] IR 400) and to the group of decisions in the New Zealand Court of Appeal culminating in *Meates* v. *Attorney-General* [1983] NZLR 308, 334, 378, in all of which Lord Wilberforce's test was adopted.

11.14. But more recently there has been a swing against this two-fold test. In England the movement can be traced to the speech of Lord Keith of Kinkel in *Governors of the Peabody Donation Fund* v. *Sir Lindsay Parkinson and Co. Ltd.* [1985] AC 210. In that case a developer claimed against a local authority alleging that the authority was to blame for the fact that a building which the developer had commissioned had not been constructed in accordance with the approved plans. The House of Lords rejected this claim holding that the local authority owed no duty of care to the developer to safeguard it from economic loss resulting from the developer's own failure to comply with the approved plans. The local authority had a statutory power to require the developer to halt work being done in contravention of approved plans and to require it to demolish and re-execute the work correctly. But these powers were not conferred for the purpose of protecting the developer from loss. The purpose of the powers was to safeguard the occupiers of houses built in the local authority's areas and also members of the public generally against danger to their health arising from defective installations.

11.15. In the *Peabody* case Lord Keith, delivering the single judgment of a unanimous House of Lords, said (p. 240) that there had been a tendency to treat Lord Wilberforce's test and an earlier generalizing statement by Lord Reid in the *Dorset Yacht* case as if they were of a definitive character. 'This is a temptation which should be resisted.' He went on to say that the true question in each case was whether the particular defendant owed to the particular plaintiff a duty of care having the scope contended for and whether he was in breach of that duty with consequent loss to the plaintiff. A relationship of proximity had to exist before any duty of care could arise, but the scope of the duty must depend upon all the circumstances of the case. In deciding whether an alleged duty of care should be imposed by law upon a party the court should ask whether it was *just and reasonable* to do so. It was neither reasonable nor just to require the local authority in this case to protect the developer from his own criminal conduct in departing from the approved plans.

11.16. *Peabody* was applied by the Court of Appeal in *Investors in Industry Commercial Properties Ltd.* v. *South Bedfordshire District Council* [1986] 1 All ER 787 where the claim was again by property developers who were themselves in breach of statutory duty in erecting warehouses on inadequate foundations. It was held to be irrelevant that the developers were themselves free from personal blame and had relied exclusively on the advice of professionals. It was not 'just and reasonable' in the circumtances of the case to impose a duty on the local authority to indemnify the developer against loss resulting from its 'disastrous reliance' on its professional advisers (p. 804J).

11.17. It is also significant that in *Council of the Shire of Sutherland* v. *Hayman* (1985) 59 ALJR 564 the High Court of Australia declined to follow *Anns*. The ultimate purchaser of a house failed in his allegation that the Council had negligently approved plans and specifications for the building. The High Court reversed the Court of Appeal of New South Wales which had based its decision on *Anns*. Three members of the High Court held that the Council owed no duty to the plaintiff as a subsequent purchaser. It was not as if the plaintiff, before buying the house, had sought assurances from the Council.

11.18. Brennan J. in the High Court was particularly critical of Lord Wilberforce's twofold test of liability (see paragraph 11.11 above). He thought the first limb went too far and the second (restraining) limb was too imprecise. In Brennan J.'s view the first limb did not deal adequately with omission to act. Foreseeability of injury had not, in his view, ever been applied as an exhaustive test for determining whether there was a prima facie duty to act to prevent injury caused by the acts of another or by circumstances for which the alleged wrongdoer was not responsible. He cited the reference by Deane J. in *Jaensch* v. *Coffey* (1984) 58 ALJR 426, 439 to the biblical story of Dives and Lazarus: 'The common law has neither recognised fault in the conduct of the feasting Dives nor embraced the embarrassing moral perception that he who has failed to feed the man dying from hunger has truly killed him.' In this view of Brennan J. (p. 588) it was preferable that the law should develop novel categories of negligence incrementally and by analogy with established categories, rather than by a massive extension of a prima facie duty of care restrained only by 'indefinable considerations' which (on Lord Wilberforce's approach) ought to negative or reduce or limit the scope of the duty or the class of person to whom it is owed.

11.19. It seems that the result of the cases is now that the High Court of Australia will not impose liability in the *Anns* type of case unless there is a very direct proximity between the plaintiff and the defendant authority. This attitude appears to be out of line with *Anns* itself, with the New Zealand cases already referred to, and with the law in Canada (*City of Kamloops* v. *Nielsen* [1982] 2 SCR 2).

11.20. Meanwhile it is possible to detect in England signs of a swing against any expanding imposition of liability for pure economic loss. The House of Lords decision in *Leigh* v. *Aliakman Shipping Co.* [1986] 2 All ER 145 is symptomatic of the anxieties that have begun to develop; the potential implications of a decision like the *Junior Books* case (referred to in paragraph 11.13 above) are now viewed with concern.

11.21. Considerable problems have arisen in the wake of *Anns* as to the date of the accrual of the cause of action where a purchaser buys a house which many years ago was negligently built by a builder, negligently designed by the architect, or negligently approved or inspected by a local authority inspector. Detailed consideration of the case law on this aspect lies outside the scope of this Report. The problem has now been tackled by the legislature in the Latent Damage Act, 1986.

The distinction between the 'policy' area and the 'operational' area in relation to decisions and actions by public authorities

11.22. Problems arise in distinguishing these concepts in a case in which it is said that a public authority has acted negligently in relation to the exercise of statutory *powers* (as distinct from duties) conferred on it. Such powers must necessarily contain a large 'policy' element and it is for the public body (not the courts) to decide what policy to pursue. Lord Wilberforce said in *Anns* ([1978] AC at 754):

Many statutes also prescribe or at least presuppose the practical execution of policy decisions: a convenient description of this is to say that in addition to the area of policy or discretion there is an operational area. Although this distinction between the policy area and the operational area is convenient, and illuminating, it is probably a distinction of degree: many 'operational' powers or duties have in them some element of 'discretion'. It can safely be said that the more 'operational' a power or duty may be, the easier it is to superimpose on it a common law duty of care.

A similar distinction between the policy area and the operational area had been drawn in the Supreme Court of Canada in *Wellbridge Holdings Ltd.* v. *Metropolitan Corporation of Greater Winnipeg* (1970) 22 DLR (3d) 470 by Laskin J. (at p. 477). He distinguished legislative and quasi-judicial functions on the one hand from administrative, ministerial, or business powers on the other. Liability for negligence could only arise in connection with the exercise of powers in the latter category.

11.23. In *Rigby* v. *Chief Constable of Northamptonshire* [1985] 1 WLR 1242, 1251 it was held by Taylor J. that the defendant's decision to defer the purchase of a CS gas device known as Ferret, use of which did not involve a fire risk, fell within the policy or discretion area. Consequently a claim for negligence could not be founded on the making of this decision.

11.24. An interesting example of a discretionary ministerial decision which was held to be in the 'operational' category is afforded by the New Zealand case of *Takaro Properties Ltd.* v. *Rowling*. This much litigated case has produced three decisions of the Court of Appeal of New Zealand—[1975] 2 NZLR 62, [1978] 2 NZLR 314, and [1986] 1 N2LR 22. The company bought Crown land for the purpose of developing a luxury hunting and fishing lodge in a beautiful landscape. To support the project foreign finance was needed. The Minister of Finance (Mr Rowling) refused to grant permission for a Japanese company to acquire ordinary and preference shares in the plaintiff company. This refusal caused the collapse of the company. The dominating reason for the minister's refusal was that he wanted to make sure that the land reverted to New Zealand interests. It was held by the Court of Appeal on the first appeal that this was an improper reason for refusing. On the second occasion (where the court had to decide whether the case as pleaded disclosed any cause or causes of action), it was held that the minister would be liable if negligence could be established but that a claim could not be founded simply on an invalid administrative act causing damage. On the third occasion, on an appeal which followed the trial, the Court of Appeal held that the minister had been negligent and made an award of damages. The minister should have taken advice as to the scope of his powers. Cooke J. said (p. 68): 'The duty owed, I think, by the Minister to the company at least included a duty to take reasonable care to ensure that he acted within his legal powers.' An appeal against this decision is pending in the Privy Council.

Other liabilities in tort

11.25. We turn from the tort of negligence to two further classes of case where the administration will be held liable in tort to pay damages.

11.26. One such class is where the defendant acts maliciously in the performance of his duty and with the intent of inflicting injury on the plaintiff. An example of this is *David* v. *Abdul Cader* [1963] 1 WLR 834 where it was alleged that a cinema licence had been maliciously refused. The Privy Council held that the pleading disclosed a triable issue. The trial court would have to investigate carefully the malice alleged.

11.27. The second class of case is where the defendant knowingly acts without lawful authority, as where the Prime Minister of Quebec personally directed that the plaintiff's liquor licence be revoked by the State Liquor Commission because the plaintiff had provided bail for Jehovah's Witnesses (*Roncarelli* v. *Duplessis* (1959) 16 DLR (2d.) 689). That case was in terms decided under the Quebec Civil Code, but the common-law provinces of Canada have accepted it as laying down a general rule. In *Gershman* v. *Manitoba Vegetable Products Marketing Board* (1976) 69 DLR (3d.) 114, 123 (Manitoba CA) O'Sullivan JA said: 'Since that case it is clear that a citizen who suffers damages as a result of flagrant abuse of public power aimed at him has the right to an award of damages in a civil action in tort.'

11.28. In the *Bourgoin* case (discussed in paragraph 11.8 above) the plea which was held by all the judges to give rise to an admissible claim was the one which alleged misconduct in the discharge of public duties. The facts which were admitted for the purpose of the preliminary point were that the Minister of Agriculture revoked the plaintiff's licence to import turkeys into the United Kingdom and did so as an anti-competitive measure and in the knowledge that his conduct was in breach of Article 30 of the Treaty of Rome.

11.29. In *The Mihalis* [1984] 2 Lloyds Rep. 525 a Scottish court imposed liability on a like basis in the case of a harbour master who had deliberately refused a harbour berth to an oil tanker until the vessel gave a satisfactory explanation as to oil pollution which had been observed from it at sea. Malice was held to be constituted by the ulterior motive for the exercise of power.

Exemplary damages—generally

11.30. It may be appropriate to mention here that one of the rare categories of cases in which it is legitimate for the court to award exemplary damages is where there has been oppressive, arbitrary, or unconstitutional action by the servants of the Government. This old principle was reaffirmed by the House of Lords in *Rookes* v. *Barnard* [1964] AC 1129, 1223–6 where Lord Devlin spoke of the valuable purpose served by the award of exemplary damages 'in restraining the arbitrary and outrageous use of executive power'. The first case in which an award was made was *Wilkes* v. *Wood* (1763) Lofft 1 where John Wilkes' house had been searched under an illegal general warrant. Modern instances of awards are *A.-G. of St Christopher* v. *Reynolds* [1980] AC 637 (a case of false imprisonment) and two cases where the principle was applied to police officers: *George* v. *Commissioner of Police of the Metropolis* [1984] CLY 1018 (where there was forcible entry by several officers, followed by the ransacking of a house for half an hour and physical assault on the occupier, the mother of a wanted suspect) and *Connor* v. *Chief Constable of Cambridgeshire* [1984] CLY 1017 (an incident involving an unprovoked truncheon assault on an innocent spectator at a football match).

Exemplary damages for violation of rights guaranteed by a constitution

11.31. It is an open question whether a written constitution providing for 'redress' for deprivation, without due process of law, of a basic constitutional right (such as the right to liberty), empowers a court to award exemplary damages—*Maharaj* v. *A.-G. of Trinidad and Tobago (No. 2)* [1979] AC 385, 400. It seems that if the word used in the constitution is 'compensation', exemplary damages are ruled out unless the plaintiff can also assert a common-law claim for a tort such as wrongful imprisonment (*A.-G. of St Christopher* v. *Reynolds* above, at p. 662).

11.32. In Canada the Canadian Charter of Rights and Freedoms, 1982 (which forms Part I of the Constitutional Act, 1982 in

Schedule B of the Canada Act, 1982), provides in section 24(1): 'Anyone whose rights or freedoms, as guaranteed by this Charter, have been infringed or denied may apply to a court of competent jurisdiction to obtain such remedy as the court considers just and appropriate in the circumstances.' It has been held that this provision entitles the court to award both compensation and exemplary damages. The case involved the conduct of a police officer who had failed to afford to the plaintiff his right under section 11 of the Charter right to counsel when charged with an offence (*A. H. Crossman* v. *The Queen* [1984] 1 FC 681). In the Republic of Ireland it has been held that violation of a constitutional right gives rise to a cause of action in damages: *Meskell* v. *Cōras Iompair Eireann* [1973] IR 121.

(b) The area not covered by existing law

Pecuniary loss caused by invalid administrative action

11.33. When a citizen has been adversely affected by administrative action which he considers to be wrong, the primary redress which he seeks will often be the reversal of the offending decision; thus, he will wish to secure the payment of a grant which has been withheld, the repayment of money wrongfully demanded, the abandonment of an excessive claim for tax, the granting of a licence which has been refused, the withdrawal of an order requiring him to discontinue his business activities, and so on. Yet in many cases, the offending administrative act may cause the citizen pecuniary loss before it is reversed; for example, the market-stall holder whose licence is revoked in breach of natural justice may succeed in getting his licence restored by the court, but, on the law as it stands, he cannot recover in respect of the loss of income which he suffered while he had no licence, unless he can prove a tort such as negligence. So if a planning authority imposes a restriction in good faith, but unjustifiably (perhaps under a mistake of law), the person aggrieved can no doubt get the court to set aside the decision but even if he has suffered heavy financial loss he has no remedy for that.

Pecuniary loss caused by delay

11.34. Another situation in which the common law as yet provides no remedy is where a citizen suffers loss because of excessive delay by a public authority in processing an application on which a business transaction depends, for example for exchange control permission or for an important licence. Again, delay in deciding a planning application may cause the developer to incur interest and other charges even to the extent of jeopardizing the budget for the development project, should he later obtain permission for it. But in *Revesz* v. *Commonwealth of Australia* (1951) 51 SR (NSW) 63, the New South Wales Court rejected a claim of this kind as disclosing no cause of action. In the absence of a statutory requirement, there is no duty to act with reasonable expedition, and, even with such a requirement, delay may give rise to a right of appeal but import no right to claim damages.

Pecuniary loss caused by wrong advice

11.35. Where advice is given by a public official which is acted upon, the public authority need not endorse the advice given and will not be estopped from taking a decision contrary to that notified by their official (*Western Fish Products Ltd.* v. *Penwith DC* [1981] 2 All ER 204). This case appears to exclude for all practical purposes the law of estoppel from the exercise of statutory powers (it is considered more fully at paragraph 7.17 above). A claim might, of course, be possible if the official or minister concerned could be shown to have acted negligently in giving the relevant advice or assurance (*Meates* v. *Attorney-General* [1983] NZLR 308 CA).

Rare instances in which public authorities have been held liable for loss

11.36. It is possible to point to isolated decisions where liability appears to have been imposed without proof of malice or any recognized tort and simply on the basis that the defendant authority's conduct was wrongful and caused damage. The Canadian case of *McGillivray* v. *Kimber* (1915) 26 DLR 124 is an example. The revocation of the plaintiff's pilot licence was unjustifiable and the rules of natural justice had been violated. The plaintiff was awarded damages. The English Court of Appeal's decision in *Wood* v. *Blair* (*The Times* 3, 4, 5 July 1957) is a further example. A local authority, fearing the spread of typhoid, ordered a farmer to stop selling milk except under specified conditions. It had no power to issue such an order. The farmer was obliged to throw away a large quantity of milk. There was no malice and no deliberate abuse of power. The trial judge, Hallett J., appears to have held that there was a good cause of action for misfeasance. On appeal, the defendants conceded their liability; the only argument was about the quantum of damages.

Generally liability is not imposed save on proof of a recognized tort

11.37. The above cases are contrary to the modern trend. The fact that an administrative decision may be struck down on grounds of invalidity is not now enough in itself to impose liability on the administration for any resulting economic loss caused thereby (*Takaro Properties Ltd.* v. *Rowling* [1978] 2 NZLR 314). Merely to prove that the minister had invalidly or in an *ultra vires* manner exercised statutory powers was not in itself a sufficient foundation for an action for damages, and this aspect of the claim was struck out. Woodhouse J. made the important statement (at p. 326):

> ... in the present state of the law (although it may well be developing in the area) an invalid administrative act or decision is still incapable, by itself, of supporting a civil law claim for damages. The relevant facts must give rise, independently of the invalidity, to a remedy in damages that is already recognised by the civil law in general.

The Privy Council decision in *Dunlop* v. *Woolahra*

11.38. However, the possibility expressed by Woodhouse J. (that the law might well be developing in this area) has been checked by the decision of the Privy Council in *Dunlop* v. *Woolahra* [1982] AC 158. A local authority, acting on legal advice and in good faith, passed two invalid resolutions affecting the plaintiff's property. One resolution was *ultra vires* as it purported to limit the number of stories that could be built. The other resolution imposed a building line restriction. It was invalid because the plaintiff was not given the opportunity to object. That case firmly established that the invalidity of an administrative decision cannot by itself give rise to a claim for damages. In addition it established that the tort of misfeasance by a public officer in the discharge of his public duties, which some commentators had hoped would be developed to provide a remedy in this area, is limited to cases involving malice or knowledge of invalidity. The Privy Council obviously entertained doubts as to the correctness of a proposition laid down by three members of the High Court of Australia in *Beaudesert Shire Council* v. *Smith* (1966) 120 CLR 145, 156 to the effect that 'independently of trespass, negligence or nuisance but by an action for damages upon the case, a person who suffers harm or loss as the inevitable consequence of unlawful, intentional and positive acts of another is entitled to recover damages from the other'. But the Privy Council were able to hold that the proposition did not apply because resolutions which were null and void were not *unlawful*, that is, illegal, in the sense intended in *Beaudesert*.

11.39. As regards the claim in negligence in the *Dunlop* case, the Privy Council held that the failure by a public authority to give a person an adequate hearing before deciding to exercise a statutory power in a manner which would affect him or his property could not by itself amount to a breach of a duty of care sounding in damages. This decision well illustrates the point which we have already made that the problem in this field is that the courts are trying to fit the liability of public authorities into tort categories created by private law. It may be right to say that 'no duty *of care*' is owed to give a fair hearing, but in public law there is *a duty* to do just that. We believe that it should be open to a court to award damages if loss actually flows from the breach of such a duty. Part of the difficulty here may be caused by the tendency, which we discuss elsewhere, for the courts to become obsessed with the public law terminology, the use of this beguiling langauge leading to the conclusion that there can be no 'private' right to damages for breach of a 'public law' obligation.

11.40. There is a further passage in *Dunlop* on which we must comment. The Privy Council said (p. 172 D–E):

The effect of the failure [sc. to give an adequate hearing before passing the resolution about the building line] is to render the exercise of the power void and the person complaining of the failure is in as good a position as the public authority to know that that is so. He can ignore the purported exercise of the power. It is incapable of affecting his legal rights.

With all respect to their Lordships we cannot understand how someone in the position of Dr Dunlop can be expected to 'ignore' a resolution of the local authority laying down a building line for a property which he is about to develop. When challenged the local authority did not immediately admit that what they had done was void. Indeed they resisted until the trial judge ruled against them. However 'void' in law the resolution may have been, it had practical effects in the real world and was capable of causing damage to the property owner.[1] Serious problems are likely to arise if the doctrine

---

[1] For the conflicting authorities on 'ignoring' invalid decisions see Wade, *Administrative Law*, 5th edn., pp. 308–10.

of ignoring a decision believed to be invalid becomes an established principle.

11.41. Because invalid administrative action which causes loss is not enough in itself to give rise to liability it would seem that a government department is not liable for loss resulting directly from *ultra vires* delegated legislation which it may have made.[2] In the *Bourgoin* case, which we have discussed in paragraphs 11.8 and 11.28 above, all the members of the Court of Appeal were agreed in thinking that (as a matter of domestic English law) a minister who in good faith made a regulation which subsequently turned out to be *ultra vires* could not be sued for damages—see [1985] 3 All ER 585, 618j Oliver LJ and 632c–d Parker LJ.

PART II

COMPENSATION FOR LAWFUL ADMINISTRATIVE ACTION

11.42. Under this heading it is necessary to consider two main classes of conduct which, while being lawful in inception and execution, are capable of causing harm to individuals. One such class of conduct is the enactment of legislation. Bodies possessing legislative power may by the laws which they pass inflict loss on individuals or categories of persons. An obvious example is a law which has confiscatory features. The other class of conduct to consider is action by a public authority carried out without fault which nevertheless causes damage to individuals.

11.43. We consider first legislation. Statutes may authorize acts by public authorities which would otherwise amount to unlawful interference with private rights of property or with the right to liberty. In such cases, whether compensation is payable for the loss or impairment of the individual's rights, and how much, depends on the terms of the statute, though there is a presumption to the effect that Parliament does not intend to take property without paying compensation. Compensation in accordance with the code in the Lands Clauses Acts (now the Compulsory Purchase Act, 1965) is payable for the compulsory taking of land. In other cases, the statute may make no provision for compensation.

---

[2] See *Hoffman La Roche* v. *Secretary of State for Trade* [1975] AC 298.

11.44. Questions have been raised as to whether the United Kingdom's accession to the First Additional Protocol of the European Convention on Human Rights has had the effect of placing severe limitations on the power of Parliament to enact measures of expropriation. Article 1 of the Protocol provides as follows:

Every natural or legal person is entitled to the peaceful enjoyment of his possessions. No one shall be deprived of his possessions except in the public interest and subject to the conditions provided for by law and by the general principles of international law.

The preceding provisions shall not, however, in any way impair the right of a State to enforce such laws as it deems necessary to control the use of property in accordance with the general interest or to secure the payment of taxes or other contributions or penalties.

The European Court of Human Rights has held that the first paragraph of this Article is intended to confer rights on nationals of signatory states and not merely on foreigners within their territory (the *Sporrong and Lonnroth* case—(1983) 5 EHRR 35).

11.45. It has also been decided in a recent judgment of the court, in a case concerning the Duke of Westminster's Belgravia estate and the enfranchisement of the long leaseholds thereon pursuant to the provisions of the Leasehold Reform Act, 1967 (*James and Others* v. *United Kingdom* [1986] 8 EHRR 123), that there is nothing in the Article to prevent a state from depriving a person of property without providing for the payment of full compensation. The court rejected the argument that the words 'except in the public interest' in the first paragraph meant that the property in question had to be taken for a public purpose of benefit to the community and that the expropriation of property so as to confer a private benefit on a citizen did not come within the words. Taking property in pursuance of a policy calculated to enhance social justice within the community was held to fall within these words (judgment, paragraph 41). Moreover, the state was entitled to a wide margin of appreciation as to the nature of the problem and as to the measures necessary to remedy it. There had to be a reasonable relationship of proportionality between the means employed and the aim sought to be realized. In this respect too the state had a wide margin of appreciation as to whether a fair balance had been struck between the demands of the general interest of the community and the requirements of the protection of the individual's fundamental rights. Finally, it was decided that the reference to 'the general principles of international law' in the first paragraph of the Article (importing a reference to the need for prompt, adequate, and effective compensation) was only applicable to a case where the property of a non-national was expropriated. The result seems to be that, as regards nationals, the United Kingdom Parliament is not significantly inhibited by Article 1 from enacting measures of expropriation which it reasonably judges to be necessary. In the absence of manifestly unfair features, the only compensation payable to nationals will be that provided for in the legislation. Non-nationals will, however, be entitled to compensation which satisfies the international law standard.

11.46. It is of interest to note in this context that in France the Conseil d'Etat has the power, albeit used only in exceptional cases, to award compensation to a citizen who has been particularly disadvantage by the enactment of a law. This power can be exercised notwithstanding the absence of any express or implied indication in the law that compensation should be awarded. An example is afforded by *Société La Fleurette* CE 14 Jan. 1938; Rec. 25 where a synthetic cream manufacturer, who was put out of business by legislation prohibiting the use of the word 'cream' in connection with any synthetic product, recovered compensation for special loss.

11.47. We turn now to the second class of conduct by public authorities referred to in paragraph 11.42 above, namely, action carried out in the public interest and without fault which nevertheless causes damage to an individual.

11.48. We can illustrate this second class of conduct by reference to the facts of a Quebec case which was recently decided on appeal by the Supreme Court of Canada. The case is *Lapierre* v. *Attorney-General of the Province of Quebec* [1985] 1 SCR 241. The appellant's daughter had responded to a vigorous programme launched by the Quebec Government with the aim of preventing an epidemic of measles. The girl had been vaccinated against measles and as a result had developed acute viral encephalitis leading to her total disablement. By the time the case reached the Supreme Court it was admitted (a) (by the appellant) that there had been no fault on the part of the Government and (b) (by the respondent) that the vaccination had caused the injuries. The evidence suggested that there was a one in a million chance of such an occurrence.

11.49. The case fell to be decided in accordance with Quebec law.

Arguments based on old rules of law and on a specific provision in the Code having failed, resort was had to the risk (*risque*) principle. Reference was made to principles of French law and to the issue formulated in the well-known textbook by Mazeaud and Tunc (*Traité théorétique et pratique de la responsabilité civile délictuelle et contractuelle*, 6th edn. (1965) para. 339, p. 431): '... il s'agit de savoir si un seul citoyen, la victime, supportera la charge du fonctionnement du service qui l'a lésé, ou si tous les citoyens, représentés par l'État, participeront à cette charge.' It was held that under Quebec law the risk principle in a form which would have permitted recovery had not been adopted. So the appeal failed, though Chouinard J., in giving the judgment of the Supreme Court (and concurring with the Court of Appeal's view on this point), thought that it would be an 'excellent thing' if the law were different from what he held it to be.

11.50. So far as the law of England and Wales is concerned it was recognized in the report of the Pearson Royal Commission on Civil Liability (1978 Cmnd. 7054, paragraphs 1377–1413) that the only possible source of compensation for a child damaged by a vaccine was an action for negligence. A claimant who conceded the absence of fault (as in *Lapierre*'s case above) would necessarily fail in his or her action. The Commission's report led to the enactment of the Vaccine Damage Payments Act, 1979, allowing for the payment of £10,000 (£40,000 since 1 August 1985; *Hansard*, HL, 26 July 1985, cc. 1491–7) on proof of severe disablement (80 per cent or more). This sum is, of course, small in comparison with awards made by the courts in some tort cases where severe disablement is proved.

11.51. We consider in paragraphs 11.56 and following below a proposal for reform which has been made by the Committee of Ministers of the Council of Europe which could be of relevance to the second class of governmental conduct considered above.

PART III

COMPENSATION UNDER THE OMBUDSMAN SYSTEM

11.52. The case-work of both the Parliamentary Commissioner for Administration and the Commissioners for Local Administration demonstrates that acts of maladministration on the part of administrative agencies may cause injustice to an individual for which the appropriate remedy is compensation. Although the ombudsmen have no power to order them to pay compensation, and any payments made are *ex gratia*, they can bring pressure to bear on a department or local authority to pay compensation where, for example, a citizen has suffered financial loss through relying on incorrect advice from an official, or where an official decision has been excessively delayed, or where money has been improperly withheld. Thus, when two boys absconded from an open borstal in a stolen car and during a police chase crashed into a house-owner's garden fence, the PCA secured compensation for her from the Home Office (1st Report of PCA, Session 1973–4, HC 42, page 111). When other borstal boys escaped at night from a summer camp and caused damage to yachts moored nearby, the House of Lords held that the Home Office could be liable for the negligence of the borstal officers in supervising the borstal boys (*Dorset Yacht Co.* v. *Home Office* [1970] AC 1004). This conveniently illustrates the fact that in some situations there are now two distinct means by which the subject may obtain pecuniary compensation: through the courts and through the ombudsman. Under French administrative law those who live in the vicinity of the equivalent of a borstal institution would be able to claim compensation from the administration on the basis of abnormal risk for injury done to them by escaping inmates without having to establish that the negligence of the institution's officers caused the escape (*Thouzellier*, CE 3 February 1956).

11.53. The ombudsmen will recommend the payment of compensation when in their view an act of maladministration has caused injustice to the complainant of such a kind that compensation is an appropriate remedy. Compensation is never automatic and other remedies (such as the substitution of a fresh decision or review) may be considered more appropriate. But there can be no doubt that in at least some of the cases in which the ombudsmen recommend the payment of compensation, the authority could be held legally liable to pay monies due or damages to the complainant if the relevant facts had been established by litigation. It will suffice to quote three cases summarized in the PCA's 1982 Report (pp. 4–5): 'Withholding part of compensation for restoration works. Department's action wrong in law. Full compensation and legal expenses paid together with *ex gratia* payment of £130 . . .'. 'Mishandling of application for regional selective assistance. £57,000 paid as compensation.' 'Pension increases wrongly withheld from U.K. pensioner in Israel. £1,506 arrears paid and 22 other cases reviewed.'

Northern Ireland

11.54. In Northern Ireland there is provision for the courts to assess damages in cases where the Commissioner for Complaints has found injury resulting from maladministration. This provision does not, however, apply to the Parliamentary Commissioner for Northern Ireland, whose concern is with central administration. In chapter 5 we recommend similar powers of enforcement for the recommendations of the Local Commissioners in England, Wales, and Scotland. An application to the court is only necessary when a local authority has failed to comply with a Commissioner's recommendation.

PART IV

RECOMMENDATIONS FOR REFORM

11.55. We have formed clear views of our own as to the ways in which it is desirable to amend the law. Before setting these out, however, we think it appropriate to discuss a major initiative in the direction of reform which was published in 1984.

Council of Europe—Committee of Ministers' 1984 Recommendation

11.56. On 18 September 1984 the Committee of Ministers of the Council of Europe adopted Recommendation No. R(84)15 entitled Public Liability. The term public liability is used in the Recommendation to connote 'the obligation of public authorities to make good the damage caused by their acts'. This document was the end product of a process which began in October 1979 when a Council of Europe colloquy on European Law was held in Madrid, the subject of study being the liability of the state and regional and local authorities for damage caused by their agents and administrative services. As a result of the comparative law analysis that took place on that occasion it was decided to instruct the committee of experts on administrative law to draw up an instrument aimed at achieving uniformity of the law among the member states.

11.57. The published document consists of Recommendation No. R(84)15 adopted by the Committee of Ministers and an explanatory memorandum adopted by the European Committee on Legal Co-operation. The Recommendation contains a number of recitals, two recommendations, and an Appendix which lays down eight principles. The text is reproduced in Appendix 14 to our Report. The recitals include a reference back to Resolution (77) 31 and to Recommendation No. R(80)2 (which we discussed in chapter 2 above). It also recites as follows:

Considering that public authorities intervene in an increasing number of fields, that their activities may affect the rights, liberties and interests of persons and may, sometimes, cause damage;

Considering that, since public authorities are serving the community, the latter should ensure reparation for such damage when it would be inappropriate for the persons concerned to bear it . . .

The first of these recitals contains an echo of the sentiment we expressed in paragraph 11.2 above. The second recital calls to mind the language of Mazeaud and Tunc quoted in paragraph 11.49 above. As might be expected in the light of such recitals, the principles annexed to the Recommendation cover both 'unlawful' action and 'lawful' (that is 'no fault') liability of public servants and administrative bodies.

11.58. The first request in Recommendation No. R(84)15 is that governments of member states should be guided in their law and practice by the principles annexed to the Recommendation. They are recommended, in the second place, to examine the advisability of setting up appropriate machinery to ensure that obligations of public authorities do not remain unsatisfied through lack of funds.

Committee of Ministers' proposals as regards 'unlawful' conduct

11.59. We take the term 'unlawful' from the explanatory memorandum which follows the Recommendation. As will be seen, the term is inexact. Clearly the framers of the principles encountered the same difficulty as we faced in selecting the term 'wrongful' as defined in paragraph 11.3 above. Principle I is expressed as follows:

Reparation should be ensured for damage caused by an act due to a failure of a public authority to conduct itself in a way which can reasonably be expected from it in law in relation to the injured person. Such a failure is presumed in case of transgression of an established legal rule.

11.60. Some of the terms used in Principle I are covered by the definitions in the Appendix. '*Reparation*' covers the making good of damage either by compensation or by any other appropriate means. '*Public authority*' covers both (*a*) 'any entity of public law of any kind or at any level (including state, region, province, municipality, independent public entity)' and (*b*) 'any private person, when exercising prerogatives of official authority'. An example of (*b*) would be the Securities and Investment Board, which is actually a private limited company but which, as the 'designated agency' is discharging transferred ministerial powers and duties under the relevant provisions of the Financial Services Act, 1986, are brought into force.

11.61. The term '*act*' is defined as meaning any action or omission which is of such a nature as to affect directly the rights, liberties, or interests of persons. This broad definition is narrowed by the following language in the section of the Appendix entitled 'scope and definitions':

The acts covered by this Recommendation are the following:
  (*a*) normative acts in the exercise of regulatory authority;
  (*b*) administrative acts which are not regulatory;
  (*c*) physical acts.

It seems that the intention is to exclude from the scope of the Recommendation the exercise of the legislative function. This is certainly so as regards the supreme legislature in a state. What is less clear from the explanatory memorandum is whether all examples where a legislative function is exercised (by, say, a minister or subordinate authority pursuant to a power conferred by primary legislation) are excluded.

11.62. It is not intended to cover the activity of the courts so far as the giving of judgment is concerned. This is made clear by a provision which states that amongst the acts covered are 'those acts carried out in the administration of justice which are not performed in the exercise of a judicial function'. Ministerial acts whether carried out by the judge himself or by court officials would fall within the scope of the Recommendation.

11.63. Reverting to the text of Principle I (see paragraph 11.59

above) it seems to us that there are certain obscurities in the language. Thus:

1. The concept of conduct which is reasonably to be expected of a public authority may prove an uncertain test of liability in damages. It may be close to liability at common law based on negligence, in which case it does not add much to existing heads of liability in the United Kingdom.

2. At first sight the second sentence of Principle I ('Such failure [sc. to conduct itself in a way which can reasonably be expected from it in law] is presumed in case of transgression of an established legal rule') appears to extend the principle further than negligence. But the explanatory memorandum qualifies this in two ways. First, it says that the presumption may be rebutted (paragraph 20). This apparently means that there are some violations of the law which do *not* fall into the category of failure by a public authority to conduct itself in accordance with reasonable expectations. It is not at all clear what types of violation are contemplated by this reservation. Secondly, it is said that the words 'expected from it in law' refer to the established legal rules, being rules that are known at the time when the act was carried out. 'This excludes those rules defined by the courts by means of an overall interpretation of legal provisions after the carrying out of the act that caused the damage' (paragraph 19). To take an example, this would seem to mean that if a public authority were taken to court on an allegation that it had acted in breach of statute or *ultra vires* in revoking a licence, if the issue depended upon the interpretation of a doubtful statutory provision which had not previously been judicially construed, there could be no liability in damages. This does not seem satisfactory to us.

3. It will be noted that Principle I speaks of conduct which can reasonably be expected '*in relation to* the injured person'. This entails, perhaps inevitably, an inquiry into the nexus between the plaintiff and the conduct complained of. In English law terms the question becomes: was the plaintiff a person whom the public authority ought reasonably to have had in contemplation?

4. Principle I has nothing to say about the possibility of exceptions. There is no provision covering the possibility that the state might wish to provide for immunity in certain categories of case (see the final sentence of paragraph 11.7 above).

11.64. Ordinary domestic law rules about causation of damage and contributory negligence would be applicable. The heads of recoverable damage and the form of reparation would also be left to domestic law (Principles III and VII).

11.65. So far as concerns the time-limits for commencing legal proceedings. Principle VII lays down that 'Rules concerning time limits relating to public liability actions and their starting points should not jeopardise the effective exercise of the right of action'. This has a direct bearing on the provision in Order 53 of the Rules of the Supreme Court laying down a standard three-month time-limit for the commencement of proceedings for judicial review. As we explain elsewhere, this time-limit applies to proceedings in which damages are sought for breach of 'public law' obligations; the shortness of the time-limit imposed (although provision is made for exceptional cases) can, in our view, 'jeopardise the effective exercise of the right of action'.

Committee of Ministers' proposals as regards 'lawful' conduct

11.66. Recommendation No. R(84)15 contains the following suggested rule as Principle II:

> 1. Even if the conditions stated in Principle I are not met, reparation should be ensured if it would be manifestly unjust to allow the injured person alone to bear the damages, having regard to the following circumstances: the act is in the general interest, only one person or a limited number of persons have suffered the damage, and the act was exceptional or the damage was an exceptional result of the act.

11.67. This is a formulation based on the risk principle which we discussed in paragraphs 11.47 to 11.49 above and illustrated by reference to the Canadian case of *Lapierre* (permanent injury caused by measles vaccination). The Principle starts from the standpoint that the conduct of the public authority has been perfectly proper and that no breach of duty has taken place. All social activity has some inherent risk attaching and it would be impossible to expect reparation in all cases and for every injury. But (so it is argued in the explanatory memorandum) where the conditions mentioned in Principle II are satisfied it seems unjust to require the individual to bear the damage and to support a burden which is excessive 'in relation to the principle of equality in sharing the consequences of public obligations'.

11.68. It is, however, to be noted that the framers of paragraph 1 of Principle II quoted above proceed to restrict its application and scope in two ways: first, paragraph 2 of Principle II states: 'The application of this principle may be limited to certain categories of acts only'; secondly, Principle V provides that 'reparation under Principle II may be made only in part, on the basis of equitable principles'. This contrasts with the 'full' reparation which is expected for cases falling under Principle I.

11.69. The first of the above limitations seems to have the effect that it is for the legislature of each member state to decide in what classes of case compensation is to be provided on a 'no fault' basis. The Vaccine Damage Payments Act, 1979, referred to in paragraph 11.50, is a perfect illustration of the application of Principle II on a selective basis. The quantum of the permissible award (now £40,000) is also an illustration of reparation 'in part' in accordance with Principle V.

Proposals for reform

11.70. So far as concerns the topics discussed above in the section entitled 'Damages for wrongful administrative action: The traditional approach (*a*) Existing law' (paragraphs 11.5 to 11.32) we have no proposals for reform. We have illustrated the vitality of the law of negligence and noted the interesting resurgence of the tort of misconduct in a public office.

11.71. As regards the liability in negligence of public authorities the law should be left to develop through the cases. The two major problem areas are likely to be the extent to which recovery for economic loss will be permitted and the degree of proximity required between the public authority and the victim.

11.72. In relation to proximity it seems that a plaintiff still has a significantly better chance of success if he can show that the public authority has a direct relationship with him, as where he seeks advice or submits an application or asks for a certificate to be issued to him or in respect of property he proposed to buy. Into this category fall cases such as *Takaro Properties Ltd.* v. *Rowling* [1986] 1 NZLR 22 CA (negligent consideration by minister of application for consent for foreign financing of plaintiff's project); *Neville Nitschke Caravans* v. *McEntee* (1976) 40 LGRA 276, Bray CJ South Australia (negligent consideration of plaintiff's planning development application); and *Shaddock Pty. Ltd.* v. *Parramatta City Council* (1981) 55 ALJR 713, HC of A (negligent issue of misleading certificate in respect of the plaintiff's land).

11.73. The plaintiff will have more difficulty in recovering in cases in which the public authority cannot be expected to have the plaintiff in contemplation or to take account of his particular interests. For example, in a Manitoba case (*Lucas* v. *Taxicab Board* [1985] 2 WWR 681) the defendant authority was sued for its alleged negligence in setting the minimum insurance of taxi cabs at too low a level. The plaintiff had been injured in an accident and could not recover in full for his loss. The claim failed on other grounds but the court was obviously unsympathetic to the suggested basis for liability. Similarly, in a New South Wales case, the plaintiffs failed to make good a claim founded on the theory that they had bought land on the strength of representations contained in a town development plan and that the local authority had acted negligently in preparing and publishing the plan and of failing to warn of its possible abandonment. (*Minister Administering the Environmental Planning and Assessment Act 1979* v. *San Sebastian Pty. Ltd.* [1983] 2 NSWLR 268 CA and (1986) 68 ALR 161 (HC of A).) In the Court of Appeal of New South Wales Hutley JA made the interesting observation:

The plan was a social plan; it was a plan for changing the face of Woolloo-mooloo and involved complex evaluation of the public interest. The pursuit of the public interest involves the disregard or, perhaps, the crushing of other interests. In this situation it is, in my opinion, impossible to impose a duty of care to those who may be affected.

The judgment of four members of the High Court (Gibbs CJ, Mason, Wilson, and Dawson JJ) proceeded on the basis that on a true analysis the development contained no representations or assurances of the definitive binding character relied on by the plaintiffs. Brennan J. held that the circumstances were such that the plaintiffs were not entitled to say that they relied upon the development plan as a representation. He said (p. 183):

When persons chart their conduct in the expectation that a public authority will exercise in accordance with a policy a discretionary power which it is bound to exercise in the public interest, they have no justification for complaint if the public authority, without fraud or breach of contract, alters its policy and disappoints the expectations which the policy engendered, even if the reason for alteration is that the policy was carelessly prepared.

11.74. For the reasons which we have given we see no practical alternative to leaving the law of negligence to develop on a case-by-case approach.

11.75. The question, however, which has to be faced is whether the absence of a remedy in law for the citizen who is injured by wrongful administrative action not involving negligence should be rectified. We think that reform is clearly needed. Some continental systems of law afford the citizen much more extensive rights to damages and compensation in this area. For instance, in France, there is a principle of general liability for injury caused by the malfunctioning of the public service, and claims may be brought before the Conseil d'Etat.

11.76. The law of the European Communities is less generous and applies a rigorous test which it may not be easy to satisfy. Liability to compensate for the effects of invalid regulations may arise if there is a breach of a superior rule of law designed to protect the individual, and 'the institution concerned has manifestly and gravely disregarded the limits on the exercise of its powers': *Bayerische HNL* v. *Council and Commission* [1978] ECR 1209, 1224). Thus though the conditions to be satisfied are severe, and have been criticized as being far too restrictive,[3] Community law can sometimes provide compensation for loss caused by invalid subordinate legislation in circumstances where the law of the United Kingdom does not.

11.77. Lord Wilberforce drew attention to these discrepancies in *Hoffman-la-Roche* v. *Secretary of State for Trade* [1975] AC 295, 358–9 where in his dissenting judgment he said: '. . . underlying most of the reasoning in the Court of Appeal is an unwillingness to accept that a subject should be indemnified for loss sustained by invalid administrative action ... In more developed legal systems this particular difficulty does not arise. Such systems give indemnity to persons injured by illegal acts of the administration . . .' Most of our panel of consultants, and most of the representations we received in response to our Discussion Paper, favoured the principle of general liability in damages for wrongful administrative action, and this is our own conclusion.

11.78. Two arguments are commonly deployed against the reform which we favour. The first is that if there were to exist the potential risk of legal liability for making a mistake of law, for example issuing a regulation which is subsequently held to be *ultra*

---

[3] E.g. Ernst-Werner Fuss, *La responsabilité des Communautés européennes pour le comportement illégal de leurs organes*, (1981) 17 RTDE 1.

vires, public authorities would be unduly inhibited in the discharge of their public responsibilities. The second argument is that the proposed reform would unleash a torrent of claims.

11.79. As regards the fear of inhibiting public authorities, we think this is much exaggerated. Ministers, departments, and other responsible authorities take action in accordance with what they conceive to be the relevant public interest. They take legal advice and in the great mass of cases they get the law right. We do not think that the authorities will fail to act through fear that they may occasionally get the law wrong. We concede that there may be special situations where specific protection from claims is required but generally this should not be so. If one takes a case like *Bourgoin*, discussed in paragraphs 11.8 and 11.28 above, it is legitimate to ask why it was necessary for the plaintiffs to show that the minister acted from an ulterior motive. Precisely the same damage would have been inflicted on the plaintiff if the minister had acted bona fide but under a mistaken view as to the scope of his legal powers.

11.80. The *in terrorem* argument to the effect that 'it will cost too much' does not impress us. We do not think there is much wrongful administrative action which would attract damages in this country; standards of administration are high. The effect of general liability would probably be to reduce still further the extent of illegality.

11.81. So we take the view that where wrongful administrative action injures the citizen he should have a remedy in damages. Already an injured citizen can obtain *ex gratia* compensation for maladministration via the ombudsman in circumstances which may involve no unlawful action. It is anomalous that sometimes he cannot get compensation from the courts where there is plain illegality.

11.82. Although we welcome the development of the tort of negligence in this area which the courts have undertaken in recent years, we have pointed out the difficulties inherent in trying to extend a private law remedy to deal with the malfunctioning of the public service. We do not think there is any real likelihood that the courts can develop the common law to the point of general liability. The decision in *Dunlop* v. *Woolahra* (pararaphs 11.38–11.39 above) seems to have put a full stop to any such prospect. For reasons which we have endeavoured to explain we can see real difficulty in trying to force 'public law' wrongdoing into the mould of 'private law' torts.

Proposed legislative provision

11.83. We have criticized the formulation embodied in Principle I of the Council of Ministers' Recommendation (paragraph 11.63 above) and we do not think that that is the best way in which to proceed. We for our part would recommend legislation which might take some such form as the following:

Subject to such exceptions and immunities as may be specifically provided, compensation in accordance with the provisions of this Act shall be recoverable by any person who sustains loss as a result of either

(a) any act, decision, determination, instrument or order of a public body which materially affects him and which is for any reason wrongful or contrary to law; or

(b) unreasonable or excessive delay on the part of any public body in taking any action, reaching any decision or determination, making any order or carrying out any duty.

The word 'wrongful' and the term 'public body' would need to be carefully defined. The Crown should, of course, be bound by the Act.

11.84. As regards the remedy we propose for delay, what is unreasonable and excessive delay will have to be determined in the light of all the facts. Whilst the factor of excessive delay gives rise to the right, it would still be necessary to establish that loss or damage followed which was directly attributable to the delay.

11.85. It is sometimes suggested that compensation for injury caused by wrongful administrative action should be awarded *ex gratia* by a special compensation board, like the Criminal Injuries Compensation Board. It may well be that this would be more acceptable to the administration, but from the citizen's point of view it is very much a second best solution. We consider that the citizen should have the legal right to compensation which we have recommended.

11.86. Causation is sometimes mentioned as a difficulty in establishing legal liability for invalid administrative acts. We do not see this as a major problem. The courts are very experienced in dealing with causation and we are confident that they will be able to deal with any issues which arise from a general liability for wrongful administrative action. These problems arise and have been dealt with in several continental systems. For instance in French administrative law, where a trading licence is wrongly cancelled a claim lies for any loss of profits caused by the cancellation for the period until the cancellation is revoked and trading can be resumed. Where an original application for a licence is refused and the refusal is held invalid, the court considers whether the authority might validly have refused the licence, and takes that into account in determining damages. Our legislation should, however, make clear that loss may be caused by a void or voidable exercise of power if in all the circumstances it was reasonable for the plaintiff to treat it as valid until set aside (see paragraph 11.40 above).

11.87. We envisage that the ordinary principles of remoteness of damage, measure of damages, mitigation of damages, and contributory negligence would apply to a general liability for wrongful administrative action, and if necessary the legislation should include provisions to this effect.

11.88. Another problem to be considered is the question of restitution. Cases can arise where in consequence of an invalid regulation a trader has made payments to a statutory body. In principle, he should be able to recover these together with interest. But the law says that some payments are 'voluntary' or made under a 'mistake of law' and so are not recoverable: see, for instance, *Twyford* v. *Manchester Corporation* [1946] Ch. 236. We intend that the legislation we are proposing should provide a general right to recover payments made in such circumstances.

11.89. We should make it clear that we are not intending by our proposals to impose liability for a decision taken by a court or tribunal. The New Zealand Public and Administrative Law Reform Committee in its 14th Report, *Damages in Administrative Law*, published in 1980, touched on this question (at pp. 5 and 29) and concluded, correctly in our opinion, that tribunal members should never be personally liable to pay damages (p. 31). We would go further and should make it clear that we are not recommending that any liability should be imposed on any person or body in connection with a decision taken by a court or tribunal exercising judicial powers.

11.90. Fears were expressed in the New Zealand Report mentioned above that the introduction of a general principle such as we advocate could lead to undesirable consequences. The authors of that Report stressed (p. 343) the width of the existing liability in tort of public authorities and they pointed to the 'expanding' tort of negligence. They believed that judge-made law was likely to be better than statute. (This view was, of course, expressed before *Dunlop* v. *Woolahra* cut off the prospect of growth over a wide field.) They also thought that any new statutory remedy would be likely to create as much injustice as it cured. If liability were to follow from any administrative law error, however trivial, there would be no distinction between gross and very minor jurisdictional errors. This would lead to two dangers. First the courts would be much slower than in recent years to strike down decisions if they thought that damages would flow from the quashing of the decision. Second, officials would be much more cautious about arriving at decisions for fear of exposing their department to liability. This would lead to delay and inefficiency.

11.91. We are unmoved by these fears. In our view the controlling factor is that it will always be for the plaintiff to show that his loss was caused by the wrongful conduct complained of. Where this can be shown we see no reason why the courts should be reluctant to grant relief. So far as the administration is concerned, we do not believe that there will be unacceptable delay or inefficiency, or that officials will become over-cautious.

11.92. As regards law reform in the field of 'no fault' liability, we have drawn attention to the Recommendation of the Council of Ministers in this regard (Principle II discussed in paragraphs 11.66–11.69). We have shown that the qualifications imposed on this principle really bring one back to a situation in which the government is recommended to intervene and provide compensation (which may be partial) in those situations in which there is a special need for protection. That is already the practice of the United Kingdom Parliament. We see no case for legislating in this regard.

CHAPTER II. RECOMMENDATIONS

1. The law relating to negligence should be left to develop on a case-by-case basis, untramelled by broad statements of principle (paragraphs 11.14, 11.18, 11.71, and 11.74).
2. A remedy should be available where a person suffers loss as a result of wrongful administrative action not involving negligence (paragraphs 11.75 and 11.81).
3. There should be a remedy where loss is caused by excessive or unreasonable delay in reaching a decision (paragraph 11.83).

4. Consideration should be given to the formula which we propose as a basis for giving effect to Recommendations 2 and 3 above (paragraph 11.83).
5. Ordinary principles of causation, remoteness of damage, measure of damages, mitigation, and contributory negligence should apply to the remedies referred to in Recommendations 2 and 3 above (paragraphs 11.86 and 11.87).
6. Legislation should provide for the possibility of restitutionary claims (paragraph 11.88).
7. Members of courts and tribunals should be exempted from the scope of the new provisions (paragraph 11.89).
8. No change in the law is required as regards 'no fault' cases (paragraph 11.92).

APPENDIX I

The Terms of Reference of the Committee[1]

To examine and report on the reforms that may be considered necessary or desirable in the law and procedure whereby a person may secure effective redress of grievances suffered as a consequence of acts or omissions of the various agencies of government, including Ministers of the Crown, public corporations, and local authorities throughout the United Kingdom. In particular, but without excluding the generality of the foregoing, to consider the following:

1 The changes that may be desirable with regard to the form and procedures of existing judicial remedies;
2 Whether these remedies should be extended in scope so as to provide additional grounds of review or so as to cover acts and omissions of the administration not at present subject to appeal or judicial review, and so as to render such remedies more effective;
3 The desirability of including the right to damages or compensation as a means of redressing grievances;
4 Whether any special, and if so what, principles should be formulated governing contracts made with the administrative agencies, and also the tortious or delictual liability of such agencies;
5 Whether the administrative agencies should be required to observe a code of administrative practice, and if so whether any, and what, remedy or redress should be provided for a breach of such code;
6 What, if any, changes are desirable in the institutions for hearing appeals from or reviewing administrative action; for example:

   (a) whether there should be specialist branches of the superior courts of law in Scotland and Northern Ireland, and in England and Wales an Administrative Division of the High Court;
   (b) whether there should be a separate system of administrative courts;
   (c) whether the present system of tribunals and inquiries could be improved;

[1] See text paragraphs 1.10 and 2.1.

7 To what extent the redress of grievances against the administration is best dealt with by the existing or an improved ombudsman system;

8 Whether the procedure for the scrutiny and review of subordinate legislation and administrative rule-making are adequate in the context of these terms of reference;

9 The impact upon administrative law in the United Kingdom of membership of the European Communities.

The Review Committee will be particularly concerned to consider what practical difficulties would arise in implementing any reforms proposed, and how these might be overcome, and also the availability of legal aid.

APPENDIX 2

Brief History of the JUSTICE–All Souls Review[1]

In 1969 the Law Commission recommended that administrative law in England and Wales should be comprehensively reviewed by a Royal Commission or by a body of comparable status. This advice was endorsed by the Scottish Law Commission and by the Standing Commission on Human Rights in Northern Ireland, and was supported by a substantial body of informed opinion. But the Government discouraged the Law Commission from itself conducting such an examination, though it did instruct the Law Commission to study the matter of remedies, and that led to the adoption of procedural reforms of considerable significance. The failure to adopt a comprehensive approach was in striking contrast to developments in several Commonwealth countries, notably Australia, New Zealand, and Canada as well as in the United States. In the absence of an official initiative the Review Committee was established by JUSTICE and All Souls College, Oxford in 1978. Its task was to devise practical proposals for reform with the aim of giving administrative law clarity, coherence, comprehensiveness, and accessibility. The Committee's terms of reference are given in Appendix [1]; its members are listed on page xi. An Advisory Panel (p. xiii) and a Scottish Working Group (p. xii), under the chairmanship of Professor A. W. Bradley, were established in 1979. The Committee met frequently throughout the period, usually for a full day. Two seminars attended by the Committee, the Advisory Panel and members of the Scottish Working Group, were held at All Souls College. Sir Robin Cooke, President of the Court of Appeal of New Zealand, manifested his outstanding interest in administratrive law by making a special journey from New Zealand to attend the second seminar.

The Chairman and the Vice-Chairman visited Australia and New Zealand in 1980. The Chairman, the Vice-Chairman and the Secretary visited Washington to attend a meeting of the Administrative Conference of the United States in December 1981. A Discussion Paper was published in April 1981. It raised issues in broadly the same order as the present report. Respondents to the Discussion Paper are listed in Appendix [5]. Witnesses and correspondents of the Review are listed in Appendix [4].

---

[1] See text paragraph 1.1.

Generous financial support for the work of the Review came from the Leverhulme Trust Fund and from other sources. These are listed at page xv. A great deal of assistance was received by the Review from many quarters in the course of its work; these are acknowledged in the Preface and elsewhere.

APPENDIX 3

Acknowledgments

Miss L. Applewaite, Office of the High Commissioner for Barbados in the United Kingdom

Mr L. J. Blom-Cooper, QC
Judge Stephen Breyer
Rt Hon. Leon Brittan, QC, MP
Mrs Julia Bruce
Professor P. W. Budge

Professor Enid Campbell
Mrs C. Cosgriff, Department of Justice, New Zealand
Mr Albert Chapman, Institute of Local Government Administration
Mr Paul Craig
Dr B. M. Cromellan
Council of Europe, Directorate of Legal Affairs

The Hon. Sir Ronald Davidson, GBE, CMG
Professor K. Culp Davis
Mr G. R. Drewry
Mr P. Druce
Senator P. D. Durack, QC

David Edwards
The Hon. Mr Justice Else-Mitchell, CMG
Department of the Environment
Mons. Roger Errera

Mr Julian Gardner, Fitzroy Legal Service, Victoria, Australia
Professor Walter Gellhorn
Mr C. N. Geschke, OBE, Director of Consumer Affairs, Victoria, Australia
Mr Percy Grieve, QC

D. S. Hetherington

Dr Raymond Kemp

Mr L. Katz
Rt Hon. Lord Justice Kerr

Sir George Laking, KCMG, Chief Ombudsman, New Zealand

Professor David Lanham
Law Commission of England & Wales
Law Officers' Department
Law Reform Commission of Canada
Law Reform Commission of Western Australia

Messrs Lawford & Co
Miss F. Lucette
Mr Edward Lyons, QC

Mrs Ruth McJannett, Librarian, Administrative Appeals Tribunal, Australia
Messrs. McKenna & Co
Mr R. P. Meagher, QC
Ministry of Justice, Sweden
The Hon. Sir John Minogue, QC, Law Reform Commission, Victoria, Australia

Mr R. D. Nicholson, Secretary-General, Law Council of Australia
National Consumer Council

Mr James T. O'Reilly

Mr David Rose, Royal Town Planning Institute

Mr John R. Salter
Justice Antonin Scalia
The Hon. Mr Justice Speight
Mr K. Smithers, CBE, Ombudsman, New South Wales
Standing Advisory Commission on Human Rights, Northern Ireland
The Hon. Haddon Storey, QC
The Hon. Sir Laurence Whistler Street, KCMG, KStJ

Mr A. Tate
Town & Country Planning Association

Mr J. A. Usher

Lord Wigoder, QC
Mr L. E. Wingrove, Secretary, Mobil Services Co. Ltd
The Hon. J. H. Wootton, Law Reform Commission, New South Wales

The Hon. Sir John McIntosh Young, KCMG

Professor Graham Zellick

APPENDIX 4

Witnesses and Correspondents

WITNESSES

The Association of County Councils (represented by Mr J. R. Lorill, Chairman, Policy; Mr I. D. Coutts, CBE, Chairman, Finance; Mr L. R. Roberts, Deputy Secretary; and Mr Alan Fraser, County Secretary, Cumbria)

Professor T. St John Bates

Mr Mario Bouchard

Sir Cecil Clothier, KCB, QC

Professor A. A. Dashwood

The Hon. Mr Justice Daryl Davies

Mr M. J. Elliott

Sir Basil Hall, KCB, MC, TD

Professor David Harris

Mr Adrian G. T. Kellet

Sir Ian Percival, QC, MP

Rt. Hon. Sam Silkin, QC, MP

Dr G. D. S. Taylor

Mr C. C. Turpin

Professor Harry Whitmore

CORRESPONDENTS

Miss Phyllis R. Bellchambers

Mr A. Gordon Bellingham

Mr R. A. Bennett-Levy

Professor A. W. Bridge

Professor L. Neville Brown

Mr C. Bursell

Commission des Services Juridiques, Quebec

Mr F. P. Cook

Sir Robin Cooke

Mr I. S. Dickinson

Mr J. D. Evans

The Law Society

The Law Society of Scotland
Professor D. Lemieux
Professor J. P. W. B. McAuslan
Mr Charles Morrison, QC
Dr Jagat Narain
Office of Law Reform, Northern Ireland
Sir Ian Percival, QC, MP
Paul Robertshaw
Professor John Whelan
Miss Ethel Wix
Professor D. C. M. Yardley

APPENDIX 5

Respondents to the Discussion Paper

Rodney Austin
G. R. Baldwin
E. M. Barendt
Charles B. Blake
Miss Elizabeth Burns
Paul Burns
Child Poverty Action Group
Dudley Coates
Lawrence Collins
Commission for Local Administration in England
Commission for Local Administration in Scotland
Council on Tribunals
Electricity Consumers' Council
Philip English
Dr M. A. Fazal
David Feldman
J. A. Fletcher
Dr Geoffrey Flick
E. R. Giles
R. E. C. Jewell
Dr Peter Kay
The Hon. Mr Justice Kirby
The Law Society
Law Society Local Government Group
The Law Society of Scotland

Jeremy Lever, QC
Professor Norman Lewis
John Loosemore
Mrs M. W. Lord
V. W. E. Moore
C. D. Morgan
National Society for the Prevention of Cruelty to Children
Mrs Dawn Oliver
Parliamentary Commissioner for Administration
M. L. S. Passey
Professor D. C. Pearce
Colin Reid
J. R. Robinson
Runnymede Trust
Alec Samuels, JP
Konrad Schiemann, QC
M. Scott
Miss Alison Seager
Senate of the Inns of Court and the Bar
Society of County Secretaries
D. R. Thompson, Master of the Crown Office
Barry K. Winetrobe
Professor D. C. M. Yardley

APPENDIX 6

Council of Europe
Committee of Ministers

(*a*) RESOLUTION (77) 31: ON THE PROTECTION OF THE INDIVIDUAL IN RELATION TO THE ACTS OF ADMINISTRATIVE AUTHORITIES (ADOPTED BY THE COMMITTEE OF MINISTERS ON 28 SEPTEMBER 1977, AT THE 275TH MEETING OF THE MINISTERS' DEPUTIES)[1]

The Committee of Ministers,

Considering that the aim of the Council of Europe is to achieve greater unity between its members;

Considering that, in spite of the differences between the administrative and legal systems of the member states, there is a broad consensus concerning the fundamental principles which should guide the administrative procedures and particularly the necessity to ensure fairness in the relations between the individual and administrative authorities;

Considering that it is desirable that acts of administrative authorities should be taken in ways conducive to the achievement of those aims;

Considering that, in view of the increasing co-operation and mutual assistance between member states in administrative matters and the increasing international movement of persons, it is desirable to promote a common standard of protection in all member states,

Recommends the government of member states:

a. to be guided in their law and administrative practice by the principles annexed to this resolution,

b. to inform the Secretary General of the Council of Europe, in due course, of any significant developments in relation to the matters referred to in the present resolution;

Instructs the Secretary General of the Council of Europe to bring the contents of this resolution to the notice of the governments of Finland and Spain.

---

[1] See text paragraph 2.4.

Appendix to Resolution (77) 31

The following principles apply to the protection of persons, whether physical or legal, in administrative procedures with regard to any individual measures or decisions which are taken in the exercise of public authority and which are of such nature as directly to affect their rights, liberties or interests (administrative acts).

In the implementation of these principles the requirements of good and efficient administration, as well as the interests of third parties and major public interests should be duly taken into account. Where these requirements make it necessary to modify or exclude one or more of these principles, either in particular cases or in specific areas of public administration, every endeavour should nevertheless be made, in conformity with the fundamental aims of this resolution, to achieve the highest possible degree of fairness.

I *Right to be heard*

1. In respect of any administrative act of such nature as is likely to affect adversely his rights, liberties or interests, the person concerned may put forward facts and arguments and, in appropriate cases, call evidence which will be taken into account by the administrative authority.

2. In appropriate cases the person concerned is informed, in due time and in a manner appropriate to the case, of the rights stated in the preceding paragraph.

II *Access to information*

At his request, the person concerned is informed, before an administrative act is taken, by appropriate means, of all available factors relevant to the taking of that act.

III *Assistance and representation*

The person concerned may be assisted or represented in the administrative procedure.

IV *Statement of reasons*

Where an administrative act is of such nature as adversely to affect his rights, liberties or interests, the person concerned is informed of the reasons on which it is based. This is done either by stating the reasons in the act, or by communicating them, at his request, to the person concerned in writing within a reasonable time.

V *Indication of remedies*

Where an administrative act which is given in written form adversely affects the rights, liberties or interests of the person concerned, it indicates the normal remedies against it, as well as the time-limits for their utilisation.

(*b*) RECOMMENDATION NO. R (80) 2: CONCERNING THE EXERCISE OF DISCRETIONARY POWERS BY ADMINISTRATIVE AUTHORITIES (ADOPTED BY THE COMMITTEE OF MINISTERS ON 11 MARCH 1980 AT THE 316TH MEETING OF THE MINISTERS' DEPUTIES)[1]

The Committee of Ministers, under the terms of Article 15.*b* of the Statute of the Council of Europe,

Considering that the aim of the Council of Europe is to achieve greater unity between its members:

Considering that administrative authorities are acting in an increasing number of fields, and, in the process, are frequently called upon to exercise discretionary powers;

Considering it is desirable that common principles be laid down in all member states to promote the protection of the rights, liberties and interests of persons whether physical or legal against arbitrariness or any other improper use of a discretionary power, without at the same time impending achievement by the administrative authorities of the purpose for which the power has been conferred;

Recalling the general principles governing the protection of the individual in relation to the acts of administrative authorities as set out in Resolution (77) 31;

Considering that it is desirable that the said Resolution be supplemented when applied to acts taken in the exercise of discretionary powers,

Recommends the governments of member states:

a. to be guided in their law and administrative practice by the principles annexed to this recommendation,

b. to inform the Secretary General of the Council of Europe, in due course, of any significant developments relating to the matters referred to in the present recommendation;

Instructs the Secretary General of the Council of Europe to bring the contents of this recommendation to the notice of the Government of Finland.

---

[1] See text paragraph 2.8.

Appendix to Recommendation No. R (80) 2
Principles applicable to the exercise discretionary powers by administrative
authorities

I *Scope and definitions*

The following principles apply to the protection of the rights, liberties and interests of persons with regard to administrative acts taken in the exercise of discretionary powers.

The term 'administrative acts' means, in accordance with Resolution (77) 31, any individual measure or decision which is taken in the exercise of public authority and which is of such nature as directly affects the rights, liberties or interests of persons whether physical or legal.

The term 'discretionary power' means a power which leaves an administrative authority some degree of latitude as regards the decision to be taken, enabling it to choose from among several legally admissible decisions the one which it finds to be the most appropriate.

In the implementation of these principles the requirements of good and efficient administration, as well as the interests of third parties and major public interests should be duly taken into account. Where these requirements or interests make it necessary to modify or exclude one or more of these principles, either in particular cases or in specific areas of public administration, every endeavour should nevertheless be made to observe the spirit of this recommendation.

II *Basic principles*

An administrative authority, when exercising a discretionary power:

1. does not pursue a purpose other than that for which the power has been conferred;
2. observes objectivity and impartiality, taking into account only the factors relevant to the particular case;
3. observes the principle of equality before the law by avoiding unfair discrimination;
4. maintains a proper balance between any adverse effects which its decision may have on the rights, liberties or interests of persons and the purpose which it pursues;
5. takes its decision within a time which is reasonable having regard to the matter at stake;
6. applies any general administrative guidelines in a consistent manner while at the same time taking account of the particular circumstances of each case.

III *Procedure*

In addition to the principles of fair administrative procedure governing administrative acts in general as set out in Resolution (77) 31, the following principles apply specifically to the taking of administrative acts in the exercise of a discretionary power.

7. Any general administrative guidelines which govern the exercise of a discretionary power are:
   i. made public, or
   ii. communicated in an appropriate manner and to the extent that is necessary to the person concerned, at his request, be it before or after the taking of the act concerning him.
8. Where an administrative authority, in exercising a discretionary power, departs from a general administrative guideline in such a manner as to affect adversely the rights, liberties or interests of a person concerned, the latter is informed of the reasons for this decision.

This is done either by stating the reasons in the act or by communicating them, at his request, to the person concerned in writing within a reasonable time.

IV *Control*

9. An act taken in the exercise of a discretionary power is subject to control of legality by a court or other independent body.

This control does not exclude the possibility of a preliminary control by an administrative authority empowered to decide both on legality and on its merits.

10. Where no time-limit for the taking of a decision in the exercise of a discretionary power has been set by law and the administrative authority does not take its decision within a reasonable time, its failure to do so may be submitted to control by an authority competent for the purpose.
11. A court or other independent body which controls the exercise of a discretionary power has such powers of obtaining information as are necessary for the exercise of its function.

APPENDIX 7

Statement of Principles of Good Administration (*Administration Under Law*, JUSTICE, 1971)[1]

1. Before making any decision, an authority shall take all reasonable steps to ensure that all persons who will be particularly and materially affected by such decision have been informed in sufficient time of its intention to make the decision and shall afford to all such persons a reasonable opportunity of making representations to the authority with respect thereto.

2. No decision shall have retrospective effect unless the decision is taken to relieve particular hardship resulting from an earlier decision.

3. It shall be the duty of an authority in proceeding to a decision to take all reasonable steps to ascertain the facts which are material to the decision.

4. Where a written request is made to any authority for information relating to the discharge of its duties or the exercise of its powers, being information that ought reasonably to be given, it shall be the duty of the authority to take all reasonable steps to ensure that such information is given expeditiously and is accurate.

5. Where an authority receives a request in writing from any person to make a decision in pursuance of a statutory duty which prescribes no time limit for making such decision, it shall be the duty of that authority to make the decision to which the request relates within two months of the date of the receipt of the request by the authority. Provided that where the said period of two months is extended for a further specific period by agreement between the authority and the said person, this sub-paragraph shall have the effect as if for the period of two months there were substituted the period as extended; and provided that where by reason of exceptional circumstances, particulars of which are to be notified, it is impracticable to make a decision within the said period, and the decision is made as soon as the circumstances permit, the authority shall be deemed to have complied with this sub-paragraph.

6. Where an authority receives a request in writing from any person to make a decision in pursuance of any statutory *power or discretion* it shall be the duty of that authority to make the decision to which the request relates

[1] See text paragraph 2.11.

within a reasonable time of the date of the receipt of the request by the authority.

7. An authority shall upon request in writing give a written statement of the reasons justifying any decision it has made.

8. An authority may refuse to give information under paragraph 4 or a statement under paragraph 7 if—

(a) to give such information or statement would be prejudicial to national security: or

(b) the relevant request was made more than two months after the date on which the duty was finally discharged or the power finally exercised or the decision made, as the case may be: or

(c) the relevant request is made under paragraph 7 by a person not particularly and materially affected by the decision and to give a statement of reasons would be contrary to the interests of any person so affected.

9. An authority shall take all reasonable steps to ensure that its decisions are made known to those persons likely to be affected by them.

10. Where by any statute or statutory instrument express provision is or shall hereafter be made in respect of matters referred to in 'The Principles of Good Administration', compliance with the said statute or statutory instrument shall to that extent be presumed to be compliance with 'The Principles of Good Administration'.

Note: 'all reasonable steps' means measures by way of inquiry, verification, deliberation or otherwise as are in all the circumstances of the case necessary according to good administrative practice.

APPENDIX 8

(Australian) Administrative Decisions (Judicial Review) Act, 1977 (as amended 1978 and 1980)—extracts[1]

Interpretation

3.(1) In this Act, unless the contrary intention appears—
'Court' means the Federal Court of Australia;
'decision to which this act applies' means a decision of an administrative character made, proposed to be made, or required to be made, as the case may be (whether in the exercise of discretion or not) under an enactment, other than a decision by the Governor-General, or a decision included in any of the classes of decisions set out in Schedule 1.

.   .   .   .   .

(2) In this Act, a reference to the making of a decision includes a reference to—

(a) making, suspending, revoking or refusing to make an order, award or determination;
(b) giving, suspending, revoking or refusing to give a certificate, direction, approval, consent or permission;
(c) issuing, suspending, revoking or refusing to issue a licence, authority or other instrument;
(d) imposing a condition or restriction;
(e) making a declaration, demand or requirement;
(f) retaining, or refusing to deliver up, an article; or
(g) doing or refusing to do any other act or thing,

and a reference to a failure to make a decision shall be construed accordingly.

[1] See text paragraphs 2.20, 3.92, 3.93, 3.95, 3.96 and 6.33.

(3) Where provision is made by an enactment for the making of a report or recommendation before a decision is made in the exercise of a power under the enactment or under another law, the making of such a report or recommendation shall itself be deemed, for the purpose of this Act, to be the making of a decision.

. . . . .

Applications for review of decisions

5.(1) A person who is aggrieved by a decision to which this Act applies that is made after the commencement of this Act may apply to the Court for an order of review in respect of the decision on any one or more of the following grounds:—

   (a) that a breach of the rules of natural justice occurred in connexion with the making of the decision;

   (b) that procedures that were required by law to be observed in connexion with the making of the decision were not observed;

   (c) that the person who purported to make the decision did not have jurisdiction to make the decision;

   (d) that the decision was not authorized by the enactment in pursuance of which it was purported to be made;

   (e) that the making of the decision was an improper exercise of the power conferred by the enactment in pursuance of which it was purported to be made;

   (f) that the decision involved an error of law, whether or not the error appears on the record of the decision;

   (g) that the decision was induced or affected by fraud;

   (h) that there was no evidence or other material to justify the making of the decision;

   (j) that the decision was otherwise contrary to law.

(2) The reference in paragraph (1)(e) to an improper exercise of a power shall be constructed as including a reference to—

   (a) taking an irrelevant consideration into account in the exercise of a power;

   (b) failing to take a relevant consideration into account in the exercise of a power;

   (c) an exercise of a power for a purpose other than a purpose for which the power is conferred;

   (d) an exercise of a discretionary power in bad faith;

   (e) an exercise of a personal discretionary power at the direction or behest of another person;

(f) an exercise of a discretionary power in accordance with a rule or policy without regard to the merits of the particular case;

(g) an exercise of a power that is so unreasonable that no reasonable person could have so exercised the power;

(h) an exercise of a power in such a way that the result of the exercise of the power is uncertain; and

(j) any other exercise of a power in a way that constitutes abuse of the power

(3) The ground specified in paragraph (1)(h) shall not be taken to be made out unless—

(a) the person who made the decision was required by law to reach that decision only if a particular matter was established, and there was no evidence or other material (including facts of which he was entitled to take notice) from which he could reasonably be satisfied that the matter was established; or

(b) the person who made the decision based the decision on the existence of a particular fact, and that fact did not exist.

Application for review of conduct related to making of decisions

6.(1) Where a person has engaged, is engaging, or proposes to engage, in conduct for the purpose of making a decision to which this Act applies, a person who is aggrieved by the conduct may apply to the Court for an order of review in respect of the conduct on any one or more of the following grounds:—

(a) that a breach of the rules of natural justice has occurred, is occurring, or is likely to occur, in connexion with the conduct;

(b) that procedures that are required by law to be observed in respect of the conduct have not been, are not being, or are likely not to be, observed;

(c) that the person who has engaged, is engaging, or proposes to engage, in the conduct does not have jurisdiction to make the proposed decision;

(d) that the enactment in pursuance of which the decision is proposed to be made does not authorize the making of the proposed decision;

(e) that the making of the proposed decision would be an improper exercise of the power conferred by the enactment in pursuance of which the decision is proposed to be made;

(f) that an error of law has been, is being, or is likely to be, committed in the course of the conduct or is likely to be committed in the making of the proposed decision;

(g) that fraud has taken place, is taking place, or is likely to take place, in the course of the conduct;

(h) that there is no evidence or other material to justify the making of the proposed decision;

(j) that the making of the proposed decision would be otherwise contrary to law.

(2) The reference in paragraph (1)(e) to an improper exercise of a power shall be construed as including a reference to—

(a) taking an irrelevant consideration into account in the exercise of a power;

(b) failing to take a relevant consideration into account in the exercise of a power;

(c) an exercise of a power for a purpose other than a purpose for which the power is conferred;

(d) an exercise of a discretionary power in bad faith;

(e) an exercise of a personal discretionary power at the direction or behest of another person;

(f) an exercise of a discretionary power in accordance with a rule or policy without regard to the merits of the particular case;

(g) an exercise of a power that is so unreasonable that no reasonable person could have so exercised the power;

(h) an exercise of a power in such a way that the result of the exercise of the power is uncertain; and

(j) any other exercise of a power in a way that constitutes abuse of the power.

(3) The ground specified in paragraph (1)(h) shall not be taken to be made out unless

(a) the person who proposes to make the decision is required by law to reach that decision only if a particular matter is established, and there is no evidence or other material (including facts of which he is entitled to take notice) from which he can reasonably be satisfied that the matter is established; or

(b) the person proposes to make the decision on the basis of the existence of a particular fact, and that fact does not exist.

Applications in respect of failures to make decisions

7.(1) Where—

(a) a person has a duty to make a decision to which this Act applies;

(b) there is no law that prescribes a period within which the person is required to make that decision; and

(c) the person has failed to make that decision,

a person who is aggrieved by the failure of the first-mentioned person to make the decision may apply to the Court for an order of review in respect of the failure to make the decision on the ground that there has been unreasonable delay in making the decision.

(2) Where—

(a) a person has a duty to make a decision to which this Act applies;

(b) a law prescribes a period within which the person is required to make that decision; and

(c) the person failed to make that decision before the expiration of that period,

a person who is aggrieved by the failure of the first-mentioned person to make the decision within that period may apply to the Court for an order of review in respect of the failure to make the decision within that period on the ground that the first-mentioned person has a duty to make the decision notwithstanding the expiration of that period.

Jurisdiction of Federal Court of Australia

8. The Court has jurisdiction to hear and determine applications made to the Court under this Act.

.   .   .   .   .

Application to be made a party to a proceeding

12.(1) A person interested in a decision, in conduct that has been, is being, or is proposed to be, engaged in for the purpose of making a decision, or in a failure to make a decision, being a decision, conduct or failure in relation to which an application has been made to the Court under this Act, may apply to the Court to be made a party to the application.

(2) The Court may, in its discretion—

(a) grant the application either unconditionally or subject to such conditions as it thinks fit; or

(b) refuse the application.

Person entitled to apply for review of decision may obtain reasons for decision

13.(1) Where a person makes a decision to which this section applies, any person who is entitled to make an application to the Court under section 5 in relation to the decision may, by notice in writing given to the person who made the decision, request him to furnish a statement in writing setting out the findings on material questions of fact, referring to the evidence or other material on which those findings were based and giving the reasons for the decision.

(2) Where such a request is made, the person who made the decision shall, subject to this section, as soon as practicable, and in any event within

28 days, after receiving the request, prepare the statement and furnish it to the person who made the request.

(3) Where a person to whom a request is made under sub-section (1) is of the opinion that the person who made the request was not entitled to make the request, the first-mentioned person may, within 28 days after receiving the request—

(a) give to the second-mentioned person notice in writing of his opinion; or

(b) apply to the Court under sub-section (4A) for an order declaring that the person who made the request was not entitled to make the request.

(4) Where a person gives a notice under sub-section (3), or applies to the Court under sub-section (4A), with respect to a request, the person is not required to comply with the request unless—

(a) the Court, on an application under sub-section (4A), declares that the person who made the request was entitled to make the request; or

(b) the person who gave the notice under sub-section (3) has applied to the Court under sub-section (4A) for an order declaring that the person who made the request was not entitled to make the request and the Court refuses that application,

and, in either of those cases, the person who gave the notice shall prepare the statement to which the request relates and furnish it to the person who made the request within 28 days after the decision of the Court.

(4A) The Court may, on the application of—

(a) a person to whom a request is made under sub-section (1); or

(b) a person who has received a notice under sub-section (3),

make an order declaring that the person who made the request concerned was, or was not, entitled to make the request.

(5) A person to whom a request for a statement in relation to a decision is made under sub-section (1) may refuse to prepare and furnish the statement if—

(a) in the case of a decision the terms of which were recorded in writing and set out in a document that was furnished to the person who made the request—the request was not made on or before the twenty-eighth day after the day on which that document was so furnished; or

(b) in any other case—the request was not made within a reasonable time after the decision was made,

and in any such case the person to whom the request was made shall give to the person who made the request, within 14 days after receiving the request, notice in writing stating that the statement will not be furnished to him and giving the reason why the statement will not be so furnished.

(6) For the purposes of paragraph (5)(b), a request for a statement in

relation to a decision shall be deemed to have been made within a reasonable time after the decision was made if the Court, on application by the person who made the request, declares that the request was made within a reasonable time after the decision was made.

(7) If the Court, upon application for an order under this sub-section made to it by a person to whom a statement has been furnished in pursuance of a request under sub-section (1), considers that the statement does not contain adequate particulars of findings on material questions of fact, an adequate reference to the evidence or other material on which those findings were based or adequate particulars of the reasons for the decision, the Court may order the person who furnished the statement to furnish to the person who made the request for the statement, within such time as is specified in the order, an additional statement or additional statements containing further and better particulars in relation to matters specified in the order with respect to those findings, that evidence or other material or those reasons.

(8) The regulations may declare a class or classes of decisions to be decisions that are not decisions to which this section applies.

(9) Regulations made under sub-section (8) may specify a class of decisions in any way, whether by reference to the nature or subject matter of the decisions, by reference to the enactment or provision of an enactment under which they are made, by reference to the holder of the office by whom they are made, or otherwise.

(10) A regulation made under sub-section (8) applies only in relation to decisions made after the regulation takes effect.

(11) In this section, 'decision to which this section applies' means a decision that is a decision to which this Act applies, but does not include—

(a) a decision in relation to which section 28 of the *Administrative Appeals Tribunal Act* 1975 applies;

(b) a decision that includes, or is accompanied by a statement setting out, findings of facts, a reference to the evidence or other material on which those findings were based and the reasons for the decision; or

(c) a decision included in any of the classes of decision set out in Schedule 2.

Certain information not required to be disclosed

13A.(1) This section applies in relation to any information to which a request made to a person under sub-section 13(1) relates, being information that—

(a) relates to the personal affairs or business affairs of a person, other than the person making the request; and

(b) is information—

(i) that was supplied in confidence;

(ii) the publication of which would reveal a trade secret;

    (iii) that was furnished in compliance with a duty imposed by an enactment; or

    (iv) the furnishing of which in accordance with the request would be in contravention of an enactment, being an enactment that expressly imposes on the person to whom the request is made a duty not to divulge or communicate to any person, or to any person other than a person included in a prescribed class of persons, or except in prescribed circumstances, information of that kind.

    (2) Where a person has been requested in accordance with sub-section 13(1) to furnish a staement to a person—

(a) the first-mentioned person is not required to include in the statement any information in relation to which this section applies; and

(b) where the statement would be false or misleading if it did not include such information—the first-mentioned person is not required by section 13 to furnish the statement.

    (3) Where, by reason of sub-section (2), information is not included in a statement furnished by a person or a statement is not furnished by a person, the person shall give notice in writing to the person who requested the statement—

(a) in a case where information is not included in a statement—stating that the information is not so included and giving the reason for not including the information; or

(b) in a case where a statement is not furnished—stating that the statement will not be furnished and giving the reason for not furnishing the statement.

    (4) Nothing in this section affects the power of the Court to make an order for the discovery of documents or to require the giving of evidence or the production of documents to the Court.

Certification by Attorney-General concerning the disclosure of information

14.(1) If the Attorney-General certifies, by writing signed by him, that the disclosure of information concerning a specific matter would be contrary to the public interest—

(a) by reason that it would prejudice the security, defence or international relations in Australia;

(b) by reason that it would involve the disclosure of deliberations or decisions of the Cabinet or of a Committee of the Cabinet; or

(c) for any other reason specified in the certificate that could form the basis for a claim in a judicial proceeding that the information should not be disclosed, the following provisions of this section have effect.

(2) Where a person has been requested in accordance with section 13 to furnish a statement to a person—

    (a) the first-mentioned person is not required to include in the statement any information in respect of which the Attorney-General has certified in accordance with sub-section (1) of this section; and

    (b) where the statement would be false or misleading if it did not include such information—the first-mentioned person is not required by that section to furnish the statement.

(3) Where, by reason of sub-section (2), information is not included in a statement furnished by a person or a statement is not furnished by a person, the person shall give notice in writing to the person who requested the statement—

    (a) in a case where information is not included in a statement—stating that the information is not so included and giving the reason for not including the information; or

    (b) in a case where a statement is not furnished—stating that the statement will not be furnished and giving the reason for not furnishing the statement.

(4) Nothing in this section affects the power of the Court to make an order for the discovery of documents or to require the giving of evidence or the production of documents to the Court.

Stay of proceedings

15.(1) The making of an application to the Court under section 5 in relation to a decision does not affect the operation of the decision or prevent the taking of action to implement the decision but—

    (a) the Court or a Judge may, by order, on such conditions (if any) as it or he thinks fit, suspend the operation of the decision; and

    (b) the Court or a Judge may order, on such conditions (if any) as it or he thinks fit, a stay of all or any proceedings under the decision.

(2) The Court or a Judge may make an order under sub-section (1) of its or his own motion or on the application of the person who made the application under section 5.

SCHEDULE I: CLASSES OF DECISIONS THAT ARE NOT DECISIONS TO WHICH THIS ACT APPLIES

    (a) decisions under the *Conciliation and Arbitration Act* 1904, other than decisions of the Director of the Industrial Relations Bureau made on behalf of the Bureau;

(b) decisions under the *Public Service Arbitration Act* 1920;

(c) decisions under the *Coal Industry Act* 1946, other than decisions of the Joint Coal Board;

(d) decisions under any of the following Acts:

   Australian Security Intelligence Organization Act 1956
   Australian Security Intelligence Organization Act 1979
   Telecommunications (Interception) Act 1979
   Telephone Communications (Interception) Act 1960;

(e) decisions making, or forming part of the process of making, or leading up to the making of, assessments or calculations of tax or duty, or decisions disallowing objections to assessments or calculations of tax or duty, or decisions amending, or refusing to amend, assessments or calculations of tax or duty, under any of the following Acts:

   Australian Capital Territory Taxation (Administration) Act 1969
   Coal Excise Act 1949
   Customs Act 1901
   Customs Tariff Act 1966
   Estate Duty Assessment Act 1914
   Excise Act 1901
   Gift Duty Assessment Act 1941
   Income Tax Assessment Act 1936
   Pay-roll Tax Assessment Act 1941
   Pay-roll Tax (Territories) Assessment Act 1971
   Sales Tax Assessment Act (No. 1) 1930
   Sales Tax Assessment Act (No. 2) 1930
   Sales Tax Assessment Act (No. 3) 1930
   Sales Tax Assessment Act (No. 4) 1930
   Sales Tax Assessment Act (No. 5) 1930
   Sales Tax Assessment Act (No. 6) 1930
   Sales Tax Assessment Act (No. 7) 1930
   Sales Tax Assessment Act (No. 8) 1930
   Sales Tax Assessment Act (No. 9) 1930
   States Receipts Duties (Administration) Act 1970
   Wool Tax (Administration) Act 1964;

(f) decisions of Taxation Boards of Review;

(g) decisions under Part IV of the *Taxation Administration Act* 1953;

(h) decisions under the *Foreign Takeovers Act* 1975;

(j) decisions, or decisions included in a class of decisions, under the Banking (Foreign Exchange) Regulations in respect of which the Treasurer has certified, by instrument in writing, that the decision or any decision included in the class, as the case may be, is a decision giving effect to the foreign investment policy of the Commonwealth Government;

(k)   decisions under regulations 7, 11 or 12 of the Passport Regulations, other than decisions relating to Australian passports;

(l)   decisions of the National Labour Consultative Council;

(m)   decisions of the National Companies and Securities Commission made in the performance of a function, or the exercise of a power, conferred, or expressed to be conferred, upon it by any State or a law of the Northern Territory;

(n)   decisions of the Ministerial Council for Companies and Securities established by Part VII of the agreement between the Commonwealth and the States a copy of which is set out in the Schedule to the *National Companies and Securities Commission Act* 1979;

(o)   decisions under naval law, military law or air force law, being—

   (i)   decisions in connection with charges (including decisions made in the course of the investigation of charges and decisions to lay charges);

   (ii)   decisions in connection with the taking of summaries of evidence;

   (iii)   decisions in connection with the convening or ordering of courts-martial;

   (iv)   decisions in connection with the conduct of proceedings before commanding officers or other officers or courts-martial (including decisions making findings);

   (v)   decisions in connection with the awarding of sentences or punishments;

   (vi)   decisions in connection with the confirmation or review of findings or sentences; or

   (vii)   decisions in connection with the remission, commutation or substitution of sentences or punishments.

SCHEDULE 2: CLASSES OF DECISIONS THAT ARE NOT DECISIONS TO WHICH SECTION 13 APPLIES

(a)   decisions in connection with, or made in the course of, redress of grievances, or redress of wrongs, with respect to members of the Defence Force;

(b)   decisions in connection with personal management (including recruitment, training, promotion and organization) with respect to the Defence Force, including decisions relating to particular persons;

(c)   decisions under any of the following Acts:

   Consular Privileges and Immunities Act 1972
   Diplomatic Privileges and Immunities Act 1967
   Extradition (Commonwealth Countries) Act 1966
   Extradition (Foreign States) Act 1966
   International Organization (Privileges and Immunities) Act 1963;

(d) decisions under the *Migration Act* 1958, being—
    (i) decisions under section 6, other than—
        (A) a decision relating to a person who, at the time of the decision, was a person in respect of whom there was in force a visa or return endorsement under that Act; or
        (B) a decision relating to a person who, having entered Australia within the meaning of that Act, was in Australia at the time of the decision;
    (ii) decisions in connection with the issue or cancellation of visas;
    (iii) decisions under section 8 relating to whether a person has diplomatic or consular status; or
    (iv) decisions relating to a person who, having entered Australia, within the meaning of that Act, as a diplomatic or consular representative of another country, a member of the staff of such a representative or the spouse or a dependent relative of such a representative, was in Australia at the time of the decision;

(e) decisions relating to the adminisration of criminal justice, and, in particular—
    (i) decisions in connection with the investigation or prosecution of persons for any offences against a law of the Commonwealth or of a Territory;
    (ii) decisions in connection with the appointment of investigators or inspectors for the purposes of such investigations;
    (iii) decisions in connection with the issue of search warrants under a law of the Commonwealth or of a Territory;
    (iv) decisions in connection with the issue of Writs of Assistance, or Customs Warrants, under the *Customs Act* 1901; and
    (v) decisions under a law of the Commonwealth or of a Territory requiring the production of documents, the giving of information or the summoning of persons as witnesses;

(f) decisions in connection with the instutition or conduct of proceedings in civil court, including decisions that relate to, or may result in, the bringing of such proceedings for the recovery of pecuniary penalties arising from contraventions of enactments, and, in particular—
    (i) decisions in connection with the investigation of persons for such contraventions;
    (ii) decisions in connection with the appointment of investigators or inspectors for the purposes of such investigations;
    (iii) decisions in connection with the issue of search warrants, Writs of Assistance or Customs Warrants under enactments; and
    (iv) decisions under enactments requiring the production of documents, the giving of information or the summoning of persons as witnesses;

(g) decisions of the Minister for Finance to issue sums out of the Consolidated Revenue Fund under an Act to appropriate moneys out of that Fund for the service of, or for expenditure in respect of, any year;

(h) decisions under section 32 or 36A of the *Audit Act* 1901;

(i) decisions of the Commonwealth Grants Commission relating to the allocation of funds;

(j) decisions of any of the following Tribunals:
Academic Salaries Tribunal
Federal Police Arbitral Tribunal
Remuneration Tribunal;

(k) decisions of any of the following authorities in respect of their commercial activities:
Australian Canned Fruits Corporation
Australian Dairy Corporation
Australian Egg Board
Australian Honey Board
Australian Industry Development Corporation
Australian Meat and Livestock Corporation
Australian National Airlines Commission
Australian National Railways Commission
Australian Shipping Commission
Australian Wheat Board
Australian Wool Corporation
Canberra Commercial Development Authority
Christmas Island Phosphate Commission
Commonwealth Banking Corporation
Commonwealth Development Bank of Australia
Commonwealth Savings Bank of Australia
Commonwealth Serum Laboratories Commission
Commonwealth Trading Bank of Australia
Health Insurance Commission
Housing Loans Insurance Corporation;

(l) decisions of the Reserve Bank in connection with its banking operations (including individual open market operations and foreign exchange dealings);

(m) decisions in connection with the enforcement of judgments or orders for the recovery of moneys by the Commonwealth or by an officer of the Commonwealth;

(n) decisions of Distribution Commissioners under the *Commonwealth Electoral Act* 1918;

(o) decisions of the National Director of the Commonwealth Employment Service made on behalf of that Service to refer, or not to refer, particular clients to particular employers;

(p) decisions under the *Air Navigation Act* 1920 that—
    (i) relate to aircraft decision, the construction or maintenance of aircraft or the safe operation of aircraft or otherwise relate to aviation safety; and
    (ii) arise out of findings on material questions of fact based on evidence, or other material—
        (A) that was supplied in confidence; or
        (B) the publication of which would reveal information that is a trade secret;

(q) decisions in connection with personnel management (including recruitment, training, promotion and organization) with respect to the Australian Public Service or any other Service established by an enactment or the staff of a Commonwealth authority, other than a decision relating to, and having regard to the particular characteristics of, or other circumstances relating to, a particular person;

(r) decisions made before the expiration of a period of 12 months, or such longer period as is prescribed, commencing on the date of commencement of this Act that relate to promotions, transfers (being transfers that are subject to appeal) or appeals against promotions or transfers, of individual members of the Australian Public Service or of any other Service established by an enactment or of the staff of a Commonwealth authority;

(s) decisions relating to promotions in accordance with sections 53B or 53c of the *Public Service Act* 1922;

(t) decisions relating to—

    (i) the making of appointments in the Australian Public Service or any other Service established by an enactment or to the staff of a Commonwealth authority;
    (ii) the engagement of persons as employees under the *Public Service Act* 1922 or under any other enactment that establishes a Service or by a Commonwealth authority; or
    (iii) the making of appointments under an enactment or to an office established by, or under, an enactment;

(u) decisions in connection with the prevention or settlement of industrial disputes, or otherwise relating to industrial matters, in respect of the Australian Public Service or any other Service established by an enactment or the staff of a Commonwealth authority.

APPENDIX 9

Administrative Justice Act, 1980 of Barbados (in force as from 7 July 1983)—extract[1]

Application for judicial review

3.(1) An application to the Court for relief against an administrative act or omission may be made by way of an application for judicial review in accordance with this Act and with rules of court.

(2) Where the Court is of opinion that a person or body against whom an application for judicial review is made is not an authority of the Government of Barbados, the Court may allow the proceedings to continue, with any necessary amendment, as proceedings not governed by this Act and not seeking any remedy by way of certiorari, prohibition or mandamus.

Grounds for relief

4. The grounds upon which the Court may grant relief by way of the remedies mentioned in this Act are

(a) that an administrative act or omission was in any way unauthorised or contrary to law;
(b) excess of jurisdiction;
(c) failure to satisfy or observe conditions or procedures required by law;
(d) breach of the principles of natural justice;
(e) unreasonable or irregular or improper exercise of discretion;
(f) abuse of power;
(g) fraud, bad faith, improper purposes or irrelevant considerations;
(h) acting on instructions from an unauthorised person;
(i) conflict with the policy of an Act of Parliament;
(j) error of law, whether or not apparent on the face of the record;
(k) absence of evidence on which a finding or assumption of fact could reasonably be based; and
(l) breach of or omission to perform a duty.

[1] See text paragraphs 2.20 and 6.33.

APPENDIX 10

(Australian) Administrative Appeals Tribunal Act, 1975–1979—extracts[1]

PART V—ADMINISTRATIVE REVIEW COUNCIL

Interpretation

47.(1) In this Part, unless the contrary intention appears—
'appointed member' means a member referred to in paragraph 49(1)(d);
'Council' means the Administrative Review Council;
'member' means a member of the Council.

(2) A reference in this Part to an administrative decision or an administrative discretion includes a reference to an administrative decision made, or administrative discretion exercised, otherwise than under an enactment.

Establishment of Council

49.(1) The Council shall consist of—

(*a*) the President;
(*b*) the Commonwealth Ombudsman holding office under the *Ombudsman Act* 1976;
(*c*) the Chairman of the Law Reform Commission established by the *Law Reform Commission Act* 1973; and
(*d*) not less than 3 nor more than 10 other members.

(2) The members referred to in paragraph (1)(d) shall be appointed by the Governor-General and shall be appointed as part-time members.

(2a) The Governor-General shall appoint one of the members to be the Chairman of the Council

Qualifications for appointment

50. A person shall not be appointed as a member referred to in paragraph 49(1)(d) unless he has had extensive experience at a high level in industry, commerce, public administration, industrial relations, the practice of a

[1] See text paragraph 4.3.

profession or the service of a government or of an authority of a government or has an extensive knowledge of administrative law or public administration.

Functions and powers of Council

51.(1) The functions of the Council are—

(a) to ascertain, and keep under review, the classes of administrative decisions that are not the subject of review by a court, tribunal or other body;

(b) to make recommendations to the Minister as to whether any of those classes of decisions should be the subject of review by a court, tribunal or other body and, if so, as to the appropriate court, tribunal or other body to make that review;

(c) to inquire into the adequacy of the law and practice relating to the review by courts of administrative decisions and to make recommendations to the minister as to any improvements that might be made in that law or practice;

(d) to inquiry into the adequacy of the procedures in use by tribunals or other bodies engaged in the review of administrative decisions and to make recommendations to the Minister as to any improvements that might be made in those procedures;

(e) to make recommendations to the Minister as to the manner in which tribunals engaged in the review of administrative decisions should be constituted;

(f) to make recommendations to the Minister as to the desirability of administrative decisions that are the subject of review by tribunals other than the Administrative Appeals Tribunal being made the subject of review by the Administrative Appeals Tribunal; and

(g) to make recommendations to the Minister as to ways and means of improving the procedures for the exercise of administrative discretions for the purpose of ensuring that those discretions are exercised in a just and equitable manner.

(2) The Council may do all things necessary or convenient to be done for or in connexion with the performance of its functions.

APPENDIX II

Commissioner for Complaints Act (Northern Ireland), 1969—extracts[1]

1969. CHAPTER 25

An Act to make provision for the appointment and functions of a Commissioner to investigate complaints alleged to arise from administrative acts for which certain local or public bodies are responsible and for purposes connected therewith. [25th November 1969]

. . . . .

Provisions relating to complaints

6.—(1) A complaint under this Act may be made by any person aggrieved, not being—

(*a*) a government department or a local body or other authority or body constituted for purposes of public service or of local government or for the purposes of carrying on under national or public ownership any industry or undertaking or part of an industry or undertaking;

(*b*) any other authority or body the majority of whose members are appointed by Her Majesty or the Governor or any Minister of the Crown or Minister of Northern Ireland or department of the government of the United Kingdom or of the government of Northern Ireland, or whose revenues consist wholly or mainly of moneys provided by Parliament or by the Parliament of the United Kingdom; or

(*c*) a member, at the time of the action complained of, of the local or public body against whom the complaint is made.

(2) Where the person by whom a complaint might have been made under the foregoing provisions of this Act has died or is for any reason unable to act for himself, the complaint may be made by his personal representative or by a member of his family or other individual suitable to represent him; but except as aforesaid a complaint shall not be entertained under this Act unless made by the person aggrieved himself.

---

[1] See text paragraph 5.77.

(3) A complaint shall not be entertained under this Act unless made in such form containing such particulars as may be prescribed and a separate complaint shall be mde out in respect of each separate injustice alleged to have been sustained by the person aggrieved.

(4) A complaint shall not be entertained under this Act unless it is made to the Commissioner before a day falling not later than two months from the time when the person aggrieved first had knowledge, or might reasonably be deemed to have had knowledge, of the action complained of or not later than six months of the action complained of whichever of those days shall first occur but the Commissioner may conduct an investigation of a complaint not made within the time required by this subsection where he considers that there are special circumstances which make it proper to do so and where the action complained of did not occur earlier than one year before the passing of this Act.

(5) A complaint shall not be entertained under this Act unless the person aggrieved is resident in Northern Ireland (or, if he is dead, was so resident at the time of his death) or the complaint relates to action taken in relation to him while he was present in Northern Ireland or in relation to rights or obligations which accrued or arose in Northern Ireland.

Purpose of investigation and provisions for giving effect to recommendations made thereon

7.—(1) The purposes of the investigation by the Commissioner shall be—

(a) to ascertain if the matters alleged in the complaint (i) may properly warrant investigation by him under this Act, (ii) are in substance, true and (iii) disclose any maladministration by or on behalf of the body against whom the complaint is made; and, where it appears to him to be desirable.

(b) to effect a settlement of the matter complained of or, if that is not possible, to state what action should in his opinion be taken by the body against whom the complaint is made to effect a fair settlement thereof or by that body or by the person aggrieved to remove, or have removed, the cause of complaint.

(2) Where on an investigation made by him under this Act the Commissioner reports that a person aggrieved has sustained injustice in consequence of maladministration, the county court may on an application made to it by that person, in accordance with county court rules and upon notice to the body against whom the complaint investigated was made, by order award that person such damages as the court may think just in all the circumstances to compensate him for any loss or injury which he may have suffered on account of—

(*a*) expenses reasonably incurred by him in connection with the subject matter of the maladministration on which his complaint was founded; and

(*b*) his loss of opportunity of acquiring the benefit which he might reasonably be expected to have had but for such maladministration: subject, however, to the application of the same rule concerning the duty of a person to mitigate his loss as applies in relation to damages recoverable at common law.

(3) Where on application made to it under subsection (2) it appears to the county court that justice could only be done to the person aggrieved by directing the body against whom his complaint was made to take, or to refrain from taking, any particular action, the court may, if satisfied that in all the circumstances it is reasonable so to do, make an order containing such a direction and—

(i) for the purposes of such an order the county court shall have the like jurisdiction as the High Court to grant any mandatory or other injunction; and

(ii) disobedience to any such order by any body on whom notice of the making thereof was duly served or by any member or officer of that body may be treated as a contempt of court to which section 141 of the County Courts Act (Northern Ireland) 1959 applies.

(4) Without prejudice to sections 2 and 7 of the County Courts Appeals Act (Northern Ireland) 1964, any local or public body or any person aggrieved who is dissatisfied with an order of a county court under subsection (2) or subsection (3) may appeal from that order as if it had been made in the exercise of the jurisdiction conferred by Part III of the County Courts Act (Northern Ireland) 1959 and the appeal were brought under section 1 of the said Act of 1964.

(5) Where on an investigation made by him under this Act the Commissioner reports that a person aggrieved has sustained injustice in consequence of maladministration and it appears to the Commissioner (whether or not so stated in his report) that—

(*a*) the local or public body against whom the investigation was made had previously engaged in conduct which was of the same kind as, or of a similar kind to, that which amounted to such maladministration; and

(*b*) such body is likely, unless restrained by order of the High Court under this subsection, to engage in future in such conduct;

the Attorney-General may, at the request of the Commissioner, apply to the High Court for the grant of such mandatory or other injunction, or such declaration or other relief as appears to the High Court to be proper in all the circumstances, including an injunction restraining that local or public body or any member or officer of that body from engaging in, or causing or permitting others to engage in, conduct of the same kind as that which amounted to such maladministration or conduct of any similar kind specified in an order of the High Court and, where any such application is made to it, the High Court, if satisfied as to the matters mentioned in paragraphs (a) and (b), may grant such mandatory or other injunction, or such declaration or other relief.

(6) The jurisdiction conferred by subsection (5) shall be exercisable by a single judge of the High Court without a jury, and for all purposes of or incidental to the exercise of that jurisdiction and the execution and enforcement of any orders under that subsection a judge of the High Court may exercise all the power, authority and jurisdiction vested in or capable of being exercised by the High Court in relation to the hearing or determination of any civil cause or matter within the jurisdiction of the Court.

(7) The High Court may, in determining for the purposes of an application made to it under subsection (5) whether or not a local or public body has engaged in a course of conduct, take into account not only the action investigated by the Commissioner on complaint of the person aggrieved but also any other action whether or not the subject of an investigation by the Commissioner which may appear to the High Court to be relevant.

(8) For the purposes of any proceedings authorised by this section, a recommendation of the Commissioner and any report of the Commissioner relating to the complaint in connection with which the recommendation is made shall, unless the contrary is proved, be accepted as evidence of the facts stated therein and in any such proceedings the authenticity of any such recommendation or report may be proved by production of a certificate of its authenticity signed by the Commissioner or an officer of the Commissioner.

(9) The powers conferred on a county court under subsections (2) and (3) may be exercised by that court notwithstanding anything to the contrary in any transferred provision which imposes limitations on its jurisdiction by reference to an amount claimed or to the value of property.

(10) Nothing in this section shall affect the right to bring any proceedings, whether civil or criminal, which might have been brought if this section had not been passed.

APPENDIX 12

The Application for Judicial Review[1]

(*a*) SUPREME COURT ACT, 1981

Injunctions to restrain persons from acting in offices in which they are not entitled to act

30.—(1) Where a person not entitled to do so acts in an office to which this section applies, the High Court may—

(*a*) grant an injunction restraining him from so acting; and

(*b*) if the case so requires, declare the office to be vacant.

(2) This section applies to any substantive office of a public nature and permanent character which is held under the Crown or which has been created by any statutory provision or royal charter.

Application for judicial review

31.—(1) An application to the High Court for one or more of the following forms of relief, namely—

(*a*) an order of mandamus, prohibition or certiorari;

(*b*) a declaration or injunction under subsection (2); or

(*c*) an injunction under section 30 restraining a person not entitled to do so from acting in an office to which that section applies,

shall be made in accordance with rules of court by a procedure to be known as an application for judicial review.

(2) A declaration may be made or an injunction granted under this subsection in any case where an application for judicial review, seeking that relief, has been made and the High Court considers that, having regard to—

(*a*) the nature of the matters in respect of which relief may be granted by orders of mandamus, prohibition or certiorari;

(*b*) the nature of the persons and bodies against whom relief may be granted by such orders; and

(*c*) all the circumstances of the case,

---

[1] See text paragraphs 6.9 and 6.28.

it would be just and convenient for the declaration to be made or the injunction to be granted, as the case may be.

(3) No application for judicial review shall be made unless the leave of the High Court has been obtained in accordance with rules of court; and the court shall not grant leave to make such an application unless it considers that the applicant has a sufficient interest in the matter to which the application relates.

(4) On an application for judicial review the High Court may award damages to the applicant if—

(a) he has joined with his application a claim for damages arising from any matter to which the application relates; and

(b) the court is satisfied that, if the claim had been made in an action begun by the applicant at the time of making his application, he would have been awarded damages.

(5) If, on an application for judicial review seeking an order of certiorari, the High Court quashes the decision to which the application relates, the High Court may remit the matter to the court, tribunal or authority concerned, with a direction to reconsider it and reach a decision in accordance with the findings of the High Court.

(6) Where the High Court considers that there has been undue delay in making an application for judicial review, the court may refuse or grant—

(a) leave for the making of the application; or

(b) any relief sought on the application,

if it considers that the granting of the relief sought would be likely to cause substantial hardship to, or substantially prejudice the rights of, any person or would be detrimental to good administration.

(7) Subsection (6) is without prejudice to any enactment or rule of court which has the effect of limiting the time within which an application for judicial review may be made.

(b) ORDER 53 OF THE RULES OF THE SUPREME COURT (SI 1977 NO. 155, 1980 NO. 200 (L.31) AND 1982 NO. 1111)

Applications for Judicial Review

Cases appropriate for application for judicial review

1.—(1) An application for—

(a) an order of mandamus, prohibition or certiorari, or

(b) an injunction under section 30 of the Act restraining a person from acting in any office in which he is not entitled to act, shall be made by way of an application for judicial review in accordance with the provisions of this Order.

(2) An application for a declaration or an injunction (not being an injunction mentioned in paragraph (1)(*b*)) may be made by way of an application for judicial review, and on such an application the Court may grant the declaration or injunction claimed if it considers that, having regard to—

(*a*) the nature of the matters in respect of which relief may be granted by way of an order of mandamus, prohibition or certiorari,

(*b*) the nature of the persons and bodies against whom relief may be granted by way of such an order, and

(*c*) all the circumstances of the case,

it would be just and convenient for the declaration or injunction to be granted on an application for judicial review.

Joinder of claims for relief

2. On an application for judicial review any relief mentioned in rule 1(1) or (2) may be claimed as an alternative or in addition to any other relief so mentioned if it arises out of or relates to or is connected with the same matter.

Grant of leave to apply for judicial review

3.—(1) No application for judicial review shall be made unless the leave of the Court has been obtained in accordance with this rule.

(2) An application for leave must be made *ex parte* to a judge by filing in the Crown Office—

(*a*) a notice in Form No. 86A containing a statement of

(i) the name and description of the applicant,

(ii) the relief sought and the grounds upon which it is sought,

(iii) the name and address of the applicant's solicitors (if any) and

(iv) the applicant's address for service; and

(b) an affidavit which verifies the facts relied on.

(3) The judge may determine the application without a hearing, unless a hearing is requested in the notice of application, and need not sit in open court; in any case, the Crown Office shall serve a copy of the judge's order on the applicant.

(4) Where the application for leave is refused by the judge, or is granted on terms, the applicant may renew it by applying—

(*a*) in any criminal cause or matter, to a Divisional Court of the Queen's Bench Division;

(*b*) in any other case, to a single judge sitting in open court or, if the Court so directs, to a Divisional Court of the Queen's Bench Division:

Provided that no application for leave may be renewed in any non-criminal cause or matter in which the judge has refused leave under paragraph (3) after a hearing.

(5) In order to renew his application for leave the applicant must, within 10 days of being served with notice of the judge's refusal, lodge in the Crown Office notice of his intention in Form No. 86B.

(6) Without prejudice to its powers under Order 20, rule 8, the Court hearing an application for leave may allow the applicant's statement to be amended, whether by specifying different or additional grounds or relief or otherwise, on such terms, if any, as it thinks fit.

(7) The Court shall not grant leave unless it considers that the applicant has a sufficient interest in the matter to which the application relates.

(8) Where leave is sought to apply for an order of certiorari to remove for the purpose of its being quashed any judgment, order, conviction or other proceedings which is subject to appeal and a time is limited for the bringing of the appeal, the Court may adjourn the application for leave until the appeal is determined or the time for appealing has expired.

(9) If the Court grants leave, it may impose such terms as to costs and as to giving security as it thinks fit.

(10) Where leave to apply for judicial review is granted, then—

(a) if the relief sought is an order of prohibition or certiorari and the Court so directs, the grant shall operate as a stay of the proceedings to which the application relates until the determination of the application or until the Court otherwise orders;

(b) if any other relief is sought, the Court may at any time grant in the proceedings such interim relief as could be granted in an action begun by writ.

Delay in applying for relief

4.—(1) An application for judicial review shall be made promptly and in any event within three months from the date when grounds for the application first arose unless the Court considers that there is good reason for extending the period within which the application shall be made.

(2) Where the relief sought is an order of certiorari in respect of any judgment, order, conviction or other proceeding, the date when grounds for the application first arose shall be taken to be the date of that judgment, order, conviction or proceeding.

(3) The preceding paragraphs are without prejudice to any statutory provision which has the effect of limiting the time within which an application for judicial review may be made.

Mode of applying for judicial review

5.—(1) In any criminal cause or matter, where leave has been granted to make an application for judicial review, the application shall be made by originating motion to a Divisional Court of the Queen's Bench Division.

(2) In any other such cause or matter, the application shall be made by originating motion to a judge sitting in open court, unless the Court directs that it shall be made—

(a) by originating summons to a judge in chambers; or
(b) by originating motion to a Divisional Court of the Queen's Bench Division.

Any direction under sub-paragraph (a) shall be without prejudice to the judge's powers under Order 32, rule 13.

(3) The notice of motion or summons must be served on all persons directly affected and where it relates to any proceedings in or before a court and the object of the application is either to compel the court or an officer of the court to do any act in relation to the proceedings or to quash them or any order made therein, the notice or summons must also be served on the clerk or registrar of the court and where, any objection to the conduct of the judge is to be made, on the judge.

(4) Unless the Court granting leave has otherwise directed, there must be at least 10 days between the service of the notice of motion or summons and the hearing.

(5) A motion must be entered for hearing within 14 days after the grant of leave.

(6) An affidavit giving the names and addresses of, and the places and dates of service on, all persons who have been served with the notice of motion or summons must be filed before the motion or summons is entered for hearing and, if any person who ought to be served under this rule has not been served, the affidavit must state that fact and the reason for it; and the affidavit shall be before the Court on the hearing of the motion or summons.

(7) If on the hearing of the motion or summons the Court is of opinion that any person who ought, whether under this rule or otherwise, to have been served has not been served, the Court may adjourn the hearing on such terms (if any) as it may direct in order that the notice or summons may be served on that person.

Statements and affidavits

6.—(1) Copies of the statement in support of an application for leave under rule 3 must be served with the notice of motion or summons and, subject to paragraph (2) no grounds shall be relied upon or any relief sought at the hearing except the grounds and relief set out in the statement.

(2) The Court may on the hearing of the motion or summons allow the

applicant to amend his statement, whether by specifying different or additional grounds or relief or otherwise, on such terms, if any, as it thinks fit and may allow further affidavits to be used if they deal with new matters arising out of an affidavit of any other party to the application.

(3) Where the applicant intends to ask to be allowed to amend his statement or to use further affidavits, he shall give notice of his intention and of any proposed amendment to every other party.

(4) Any respondent who intends to use an affidavit at the hearing shall file it in the Crown Office as soon as practicable and in any event, unless the Court otherwise directs, within 21 days after service upon him of the documents required to be served by paragraph (1).

(5) Each party to the application must supply to every other party on demand and on payment of the proper charges copies of every affidavit which he proposes to use at the hearing, including, in the case of the application, the affidavit in support of the application for leave under rule 3.

Claim for damages

7.—(1) On an application for judicial review the Court may, subject to paragraph (2) award damages to the applicant if—

(*a*) he has included in the statement in support of his application for leave under rule 3 a claim for damages arising from any matter to which the application relates, and

(*b*) the Court is satisfied that, if the claim had been made in an action begun by the applicant at the time of making his application, he could have been awarded damages.

(2) Order 18, rule 12, shall apply to a statement relating to a claim for damages as it applies to a pleading.

Application for discovery, interrogatories, cross-examination, etc.

8.—(1) Unless the Court otherwise directs, any interlocutory application in proceedings on an application for judicial review may be made to any judge or a master of the Queen's Bench Division, notwithstanding that the application for judicial review has been made by motion and is to be heard by a Divisional Court.

In this paragraph 'interlocutory application' includes an application for an order under Order 24 or 25 or Order 38, rule 2(3) or for an order dismissing the proceedings by consent of the parties.

(2) In relation to an order made by a master pursuant to paragraph (1) Order 58, rule 1, shall, where the application for judicial review is to be heard by a Divisional Court, have effect as if a reference to that Court were substituted for the reference to a judge in chambers.

(3) This rule is without prejudice to any statutory provision or rule of law restricting the making of an order against the Crown.

Hearing of application for judicial review

9.—(1) On the hearing of any motion or summons under rule 5, any person who desires to be heard in opposition to the motion or summons, and appears to the Court to be a proper person to be heard, shall be heard, notwithstanding that he has not been served with notice of the motion or the summons.

(2) Where the relief sought is or includes an order of certiorari to remove any proceedings for the purpose of quashing them, the applicant may not question the validity of any order, warrant, commitment, conviction, inquisition or record unless before the hearing of the motion or summons he has lodged in the Crown Office a copy thereof verified by affidavit or accounts for his failure to do so to the satisfaction of the Court hearing the motion or summons.

(3) Where an order for certiorari is made in any such case as is referred to in paragraph (2) the order shall, subject to paragraph (4) direct that the proceedings shall be quashed forthwith on their removal into the Queen's Bench Division.

(4) Where the relief sought is an order of certiorari and the Court is satisfied that there are grounds for quashing the decision to which the application relates, the Court may, in addition to quashing it, remit the matter to the court, tribunal or authority concerned with a direction to reconsider it and reach a decision in accordance with the findings of the Court.

(5) Where the relief sought is a declaration, an injunction or damages and the Court considers that it should not be granted on an application for judicial review but might have been granted if it had been sought in an action begun by writ by the application at the time of making his application, the Court may, instead of refusing the application, order the proceedings to continue as if they had been begun by writ; and Order 28, rule 8, shall apply as if, in the case of an application made by motion, it had been made by summons.

Saving for person acting in obedience to mandamus

10. No action or proceeding shall be begun or prosecuted against any person in respect of anything done in obedience to an order of mandamus.

Proceedings for disqualification of member of local authority

11.—(1) Proceedings under section 92 of the Local Government Act 1972 must be begun by originating motion to a Division Court of the Queen's Bench Division, and, unless otherwise directed, there must be at least 10 days between the service of the notice of motion and the hearing.

(2) Without prejudice to Order 8, rule 3, the notice of motion must set out the name and description of the applicant, the relief sought and the grounds

on which it is sought, and must be supported by affidavit verifying the facts relied on.

(3) Copies of every supporting affidavit must be lodged in the Crown Office before the motion is entered for hearing and must be supplied to any other party on demand and on payment of the proper charges.

(4) The provisions of rules 5, 6 and 9(1) as to the persons on whom the notice is to be served and as to the proceedings at the hearing shall apply, with the necessary modifications, to proceedings under the said section 92 as they apply to an application for judicial review.

Consolidation of applications

12. Where there is more than one application pending under section 30 of the Act, or section 92 of the Local Government Act 1972, against several persons in respect of the same office, and on the same grounds, the Court may order the applications to be consolidated.

Appeal from judge's order

13. No appeal shall lie from an order made under paragraph (3) of rule 3 on an application for leave which may be renewed under paragraph (4) of that rule.

Meaning of 'Court'

14. In relation to thè hearing by a judge of an application for leave under rule 3 or of an application for judicial review, any reference in this Order to 'the Court' shall, unless the context otherwise requires, be construed as a reference to the judge.

APPENDIX 13

The Red Lion Square Inquiry, 1974[1]—opening statement of Lord Scarman at the preliminary hearing[2]—extracts[3]

I shall refer briefly both to the character of the Inquiry that it is my duty to hold and also to the terms of reference. First of all—and I stress it—this is an Inquiry not a piece of litigation. It is not the sort of adversary-type confrontation between parties with which we English lawyers are familiar in the criminal and civil trials of our country. This Inquiry is to be conducted—and I stress it—by myself. This means that all the decisions have to be taken by me. Let me indicate now so that there need be no misunderstanding, what are the implications of what I have just said. First of all, it is I, and I alone, who will decide what witnesses will be called. I also decide to what matters their evidence will be directed. There is, in an Inquiry of this sort, no legal right to cross-examination, but I propose, within limits, to allow cross-examination of witnesses to the extent that I think it helpful to the forwarding of the Inquiry, but no further, I also have to determine how witnesses will be examined, bearing in mind the inquisitorial rather than the adversarial nature of the Inquiry. All witnesses will first be examined by Tribunal Counsel. An opportunity will then be afforded to those persons who have been granted representation to cross-examine the witnesses called. The cross-examination will be subject, of course, to the limits that I impose, and it should be directed to eliciting matters that affect those who are represented. No witness will be called to give evidence unless he or she has first given to the Tribunal a written statement of evidence. It is from the written statements of evidence submitted to the Tribunal that I shall make my selection as to the witnesses to be called. The only criterion that I propose to observe in exercising this power of selection will be the extent to which, in my judgment, the witness can help the Inquiry.

.   .   .   .   .   .

---

[1] Held under section 32 of the Police Act, 1964.
[2] Printed by courtesy of the Treasury Solicitor.
[3] See paragraphs 10.97 and 10.116(c).

Looking for a moment at the first phase again, the review of events and actions which led to the disorder, it is no part of this Inquiry to conduct a criminal investigation. It is not the object of this Inquiry to label people as offenders against the criminal law. This Inquiry is concerned with more general matters. It is concerned, of course, fundamentally, because the Act of Parliament says so, with the policing of the Metropolis—i.e. the area of the Metropolis. It is concerned with the course of events and actions which led to disorder rather than with the identification of this, that or the other individual. Of course, it is obvious that one cannot consider the events and actions which led to the disorder without also considering the persons who took part in it. There is bound to be, therefore, an overlap between the broad purpose of this Inquiry and the rights and obligations of individual persons. Nevertheless, the emphasis in this Inquiry will be on the course of events not on particular individuals who took part in those events.

APPENDIX 14

Council of Europe
Committee of Ministers[1]

RECOMMENDATION NO. R (84) 15 RELATING TO PUBLIC LIABILITY
(ADOPTED BY THE COMMITTEE OF MINISTERS ON 18 SEPTEMBER 1984 AT THE
375TH MEETING OF THE MINISTERS' DEPUTIES[2])

The Committee of Ministers, under the terms of Article 15.*b* of the Statute of the Council of Europe,

Considering that the aim of the Council of Europe is to achieve a greater unity between its members;

Considering that public authorities intervene in an increasing number of fields, that their activities may affect the rights, liberties and interests of person and may, sometimes, cause damage;

Considering that, since public authorities are serving the community, the latter should ensure reparation for such damage when it would be inappropriate for the persons concerned to bear it;

Recalling the general principles governing the protection of the individual in relation to the acts of administrative authorities as set out in Resolution (77) 31 and the principles concerning the exercise of discretionary powers by administrative authorities set out in Recommendation No. R (80)[3];

Considering that it is desirable to protect persons in the field of public liability.

Recommends the governments of member states:

a. to be guided in their law and practice by the principles annexed to this Recommendation.

---

[1] See text paragraph 11.57.

[2] When this Recommendation was adopted, and in application of Article 10.2.*c* of the Rules of Procedure for the meetings of the Ministers' Deputies, the Representative of Sweden reserved the right of his Government to comply with it or not and the Representatives of Denmark and Norway reserved the right of their Governments to comply or not with Principle II thereof.

[3] See Appendix 6.

b. to examine the advisability of setting up in their internal order, where necessary, appropriate machinery for preventing obligations of public authorities in the field of public liability from being unsatisfied through lack of funds.

Appendix: Scope and definitions

1. This Recommendation applies to public liability, that is to say the obligation of public authorities to make good the damage caused by their acts, either by compensation or by any other appropriate means (hereinafter referred to as 'reparation').

2. The term 'public authority' means:

   a. any entity of public law of any kind or at any level (including state; region; province; municipality; independent public entity); and

   b. any private person, when exercising prerogatives of official authority.

3. The term 'act' means any action or omission which is of such a nature as to affect directly the rights, liberties or interests of persons.

4. The acts covered by this Recommendation are the following:

   a. normative acts in the exercise of regulatory authority;

   b. administrative acts which are not regulatory;

   c. physical acts.

5. Amongst the acts covered by paragraph 4 are included those acts carried out in the administration of justice which are not performed in the exercise of a judicial function.

6. The term 'victim' means the injured person or any other person entitled to claim reparation.

Principles

I

Reparation should be ensured for damage caused by an act due to a failure of a public authority to conduct itself in a way which can reasonably be expected from it in law in relation to the injured person. Such a failure is presumed in case of transgression of an established legal rule.

II

1. Even if the conditions stated in Principle I are not met, reparation should be ensured if it would be manifestly unjust to allow the injured person alone to bear the damage, having regard to the following circumstances: the act is in the general interest, only one person or a limited number of persons have suffered the damage and the act was exceptional or the damage was an exceptional result of the act.

2. The application of this principle may be limited to certain categories of acts only.

III

If the victim has, by his own fault or by his failure to use legal remedies, contributed to the damage, the reparation of the damage may be reduced accordingly or disallowed.

The same should apply if a person, for whom the victim is responsible under national law, has contributed to the damage.

IV

The right to bring an action against a public authority should not be subject to the obligation to act first against its agent.

If there is an administrative conciliation system prior to judicial proceedings, recourse to such system should not jeopardise access to judicial proceedings.

V

Reparation under Principle I should be made in full, it being understood that the determination of the heads of damage, of the nature and of the form of reparation falls within the competence of national law.

Reparation under Principle II may be made only in part, on the basis of equitable principles.

VI

Decisions granting reparation should be implemented as quickly as possible. This should be ensured by appropriate budgetary or other measures.

If, under domestic law, a system for special implementation procedure is provided for, it should be easily accessible and expeditious.

VII

Rules concerning time limits relating to public liability actions and their starting points should not jeopardise the effective exercise of the right of action.

VIII

The nationality of the victim should not give rise to any discrimination in the field of public liability.

Final provisions

This Recommendation should not be interpreted as:

a. limiting the possibility for a member state to apply the principles above to categories of acts other than those covered by the Recommendation or to adopt provisions granting a wider measure of protection to victims;

b. affecting any special system of liability laid down by international treaties;

c. affecting special national systems of liability in the fields of postal and telecommunications services and of transportation as well as special systems of liability which are internal to the armed forces, provided that adequate reparation is granted to victims having regard to all the circumstances;

d. affecting special national systems of liability which apply equally to public authorities and private persons.

Index

unjustifiable action causing loss, for 345
unlawful conduct, for 354
violation of rights guaranteed by a constitution, for 343
where defendant knowingly acts without lawful authority 342
Public participation, *see* Inquiries
Public policy 149
Public/private law boundary, rejection of hard and fast 185–6
Public service, malfunctioning of 360

Quain, Mr Justice 33
Quebec
Prime Minister
risk principle not adopted by law of 351
quo warranto 191

Reading, Lord, Lord Chief Justice 191
Reasonableness, *see* Scope of review
Reasons (Chapter 3)
Summary of Argument 24
Recommendations 72–4
Reasons
absence of, reaction of UK reviewing court 24–5
absence of obligation to give, serious effect on English administrative law 71
adequate, purpose of 62
arguments against giving 70
arguments for giving 70
Australia
Administrative Appeals Tribunal, 1975, ss. 28 and 27, interpretation of 60, 61
general duty to give reasons recommended by Kerr, Ellicott & Bland Committees 54, 57, 58
legislation for obligation to give 57, 58, 59, 60, 387–91
exceptions 59, 391–6
traditional common law view generally prevails in, 53, 55
Osmond case 61–5
tax cases, reasons required in 56
traditional approach illustrated 55
Canada
desirability of reasons recognized 51
Law Reform Commission of

Canada compromise on reasons 53
natural justice and 52
Nova Scotia Court of Appeal holds legal duty to give 51–2
traditional common law view upheld 50
court's circumvention of general rule, examples 32–6
Craig, Paul 26
de Smith, S. A., Professor 26
Denning, Lord 27
Donoughmore Committee 26
EEC, Treaty of Rome, Article 190 68–9
effect of failure to give, or to give inadequate, 36–7, 43
exemptions and exceptions 24
failure to give, denial of justice 37
not *per se* a ground for allowing appeal 44
failure to provide adequately for, common law 26, 71–2
findings, and 45
formulation of, Australian model 23
France
Conseil d'Etat 65
Loi No.79–587 (11 July 1979) 66
Franks Committee Recommendations (22), (23), (80), (84) 38, 40
general rule of law requiring, none in England and Wales or Scotland 24, 26, 27
illustrations of 27
dissatisfaction with operation of 32
historical origins of 29
inquiries 38–43 *passim*
Israel
Administrative Procedure Amendment (Decisions and Statement of Reasons) Law, 1958 67, 68
public servant's duty to give in writing with decision 67
JUSTICE, *Administration under Law* (1971) 71
mandatory, when 73
natural justice, and 26
obligation to give, formulation of 72
on demand, statutory requirement of 72
on request 72
perfunctory statement of, accepted by Court of Appeal 42